Techniques of Value Analysis and Engineering

Techniques of Value Analysis and Engineering

LAWRENCE D. MILES

Second Edition

McGRAW-HILL BOOK COMPANY
New York   St. Louis   San Francisco   Düsseldorf   Johannesburg
Kuala Lumpur   London   Mexico   Montreal   New Delhi
Panama   Rio de Janeiro   Singapore   Sydney   Toronto

To my wife Eleanor. A few times each century the random forces of heredity and environment create a masterwork in the form of a woman—a wife—who nourishes the soul, spirit, emotions, mind, and body of her husband—morning, noon, and night—every day. She enjoys her life and enlarges his. She adds sparkle, zest, accomplishment, joy. One is mine—my wife Eleanor.

To W. A. SREDENSCHEK, *pioneer in management understanding and support, whose effective management actions provided opportunities, guidance, and essential resources for high achievement.*

Contents

Preface to the Second Edition

My son Robert, while 150 feet high on the magnificent four-mile-long Bay Bridge at Annapolis, looked down upon two dozen assorted craft in the water below. Some carried pile drivers, some cement mixers, some steel handlers, and some assorted materials—all working at building a parallel span. He said, "I can't conceive of men being able to build such a bridge," and then added, "And the men who get the job done are no smarter than you and I." Then his next comment struck home to me: "It's the system that does it."

How often, when observing the startling results in ending costs that have brought no benefits, accomplished by people using the value analysis system, have I thought, "Truly the results from fully using the right system at the right time almost transcend understanding!" Such accomplishments accrue from effective use of the techniques of value analysis taught in this text. Thousands upon thousands of cases from actual practice, from small businesses and large, from mass-production and job shop, from product redesign and product research and development, from government entities such as city, state, and Federal, from social-service groups such as hospitals, schools, and churches, from administrative services groups such as banks and other businesses, verify this, as the examples cited throughout the book will indicate.

Created for one specific purpose—the identification of unnecessary costs—value analysis is a system, a complete set of techniques, properly arranged, for the sole purpose of efficiently identifying unnecessary cost before, during, or after the fact. Some of the techniques are familiar, some modified, some new. The effectiveness in utilizing this system depends upon the understanding, training, and skill of the users, as well as the understanding of all business people in the environment in which it operates.

It is a disciplined action system, attuned to one specific need: accomplishing the functions that the customer needs and wants, whether these functions are accomplished by hardware, service, a group of people, professional skills, administrative procedures, or other at the lowest cost. In its disciplined thinking, value analysis is comprised of specific mind-setting, problem-setting, and problem-solving systems. These systems will assist anyone who has the task of providing more of what the customer wants for less cost.

Some have called it "coaching for champions." All golfers can drive and chip and putt, but when it is important to win, the professional gets coaching that gives him a little better drive, chip, or putt. He learns very effective techniques for doing each well and uses them all at the right times. He wins. Similarly, when it is really important to the business or organization to identify and remove unnecessary cost in the most effective, prompt, efficient, and economical manner, the specific system of techniques for that task is learned and always used.

In achieving better value, there are two separate opportunity areas:

1. The identification of costs as unnecessary
2. The decision making which will eliminate the identified unnecessary cost

The techniques in this text apply extensively in area 1, identification. They are applicable in the predesign stage, the design-concept stage, the design stage, the procurement stage, and the manufacturing stage, as well as in later cost-improvement stages.

Success in marketing a product or service is, to an important extent, dependent upon its degree of (1) performance equality or leadership and (2) cost equality or leadership when compared at any time with its competition. Industry generally has rather well developed and successful techniques and procedures through which improvements in performance are planned, researched, developed, and incorporated into the product or service. In contrast, additions to value, i.e., identifying and eliminating unnecessary cost, proceed on a "do as well as we can" and "when we must" basis.

The objective of the concepts and techniques of value analysis is to make possible a degree of effectiveness in identifying and removing unnecessary cost that approaches the effectiveness of identifying performance improvements for the product or service and incorporating them into it. *Value analysis* is the name applied to this disciplined, step-by-step thinking system, with its specific approaches for mind setting, problem setting, and problem solving. *Value engineering* is often the name correctly used by qualified engineers in engineering work.

This book is arranged as a step-by-step teaching text. The student will first understand and master the approaches and techniques of Chapter 1, then of Chapter 2, etc., to Chapter 11. Thereafter follows essential guidance in matters of organization, administration, and measurement. Finally, for the experienced user, chapters on work in the construction industry and advanced techniques are included.

Lawrence D. Miles

MIND SETTING

One day, through the primeval wood,
    A calf walked home as good calves should;
But made a trail all bent askew,
    A crooked trail as all calves do.

Since then two hundred years have fled,
    And, I infer, the calf is dead.
But still he left behind his trail,
    And thereby hangs my moral tale.

The trail was taken up next day
    By a lone dog that passed that way;
And then a wise bell-wether sheep
    Pursued the trail o'er vale and steep,
And drew the flock behind him too
    As good bell-wethers always do.

And from that day, o'er hill and glade,
    Through those old woods a path was made.
And thus, before men were aware,
    A city's crowded thoroughfare.
And soon, the central street was this,
    Of a renowned metropolis.

And men two centuries and a half
    Trod in the footsteps of that calf.
Each day a hundred thousand route
    Followed this calf about.
And on his crooked journey went
    The traffic of a continent.

A hundred thousand men were led
    By a calf near three centuries dead.
They followed still his crooked way
    And lost one hundred years each day.

For thus such reverence is lent
    To well established precedent.

Excerpts from *The Path of the Calf*, Samuel Foss, 1858–1911

chapter 1

Concepts and Approaches
of Value Analysis
and Engineering

Near the beginning of man's history, he survived mainly by the use of brawn. As centuries passed, this survival changed. It depended upon the combination of brawn with brain. Today this trend toward the dependence upon the contribution of brain continues, perhaps at an accelerated pace. Into this reality comes the need, not only for development of the brain, but also for using it more effectively.

This challenge produced the efficient problem-solving system taught in this book. This system organizes the essential elements of the problem and the diversified capabilities of the brain into one plan that promotes the solution of difficult problems.

One of the problems that seemed to demand priority as competition for goods and services increased was that of securing lower costs. Responsive to that need, as the problem-solving system was developed, it was filled with a wide array of specific techniques, approaches, and methods for achieving what the user or customer wants at lower costs.

1-1 Coaching of Champions Concept

In competitive endeavor, it is often essential to win. If a business does not "win" its share of sales, jobs are lost. Life's earnings are lost. Jobs must end, with great uncertainty and often stress. Families must be relocated. Those people who become jobless no longer have opportunities to use their abilities and skills in an organized way to contribute to progress. In contrast, if the business "wins" its share in the competitive market, great benefits are brought to great numbers of deserving people.

When "costs are too high" is an actual or potential reason for losing competitive business, some direct action is in order—not discharging the "team" and getting another with its uncertainties, but providing some precise "coaching" in a few meaningful areas.

Every champion prizefighter knows how to fight. However, he would never expect to win if he *didn't* have coaching. The best champions know how to play a very skillful game of golf. If they didn't, they wouldn't be there. Yet, none would expect to win continuously if he didn't have coaching. Of course, the "pro" cannot achieve an overall score as good as the champion. If he could, he would be the champion. Of course, the prizefighter could knock out the coach in an overall fight, but the coach improves specific skills of the champion, which count. The champion develops a little better timing, a delayed punch, a harder punch, or a deceptive punch. He develops a little surer stance, a little surer swing, or a little better "out" from a bad lie.

The small difference between being the winner and being second is of great importance. The difference between getting the order and bidding close is all important. It is not suggested that value analysis techniques can change a poor organization into a good one. It is self-evident that a coach cannot change a poor fighter into a champion. It is presented that when "costs are too high" is the problem, value analysis "coaching" is specific to the need. The fact that a company is in business and can nearly win its share of the orders indicates that it is a good company and that its essential work is almost competitively done.

Value analysis approaches and techniques will help the persons involved to obtain a better answer to their problems that determine costs; in competitive business, this difference can change the organization from being just "good" to being the "winner."

1-2   *Problem-solving System*

The name *value analysis,* or *value engineering,* has been applied to this problem-solving system with the field of knowledge and supporting techniques for the achievement of lower costs.

Case Study

THE RED POINTER AND RED INK

On an appliance knob, a strip of bright metal containing a red pointer was mounted. Its function was to snap on over the screw which held the knob, thus concealing the screw and providing the appearance which the customer wished.

A value audit of the product showed that $20,000 was spent each year on the production of 1 million. This stylist was apprised of it and asked for guiding suggestions which were followed in developing alternatives. A polished stainless-steel part was one alternative which would accomplish the function as well, providing the customer liked it. There were, of course, other alternatives.

The industrial stylist asked, "Why does the red pointer increase the cost so much?" The answer was that it caused the small part to become a "name plate," which imposed certain costs and restrictions on its manufacture and procurement. Some of the other alternatives, such as the polished stainless steel, were merely small stampings not using name plate technology and not limited to the sources of supply who provide name plates.

The stylist promptly issued instructions to take out the red pointer and use polished stainless steel. He said that the red arrow was not good, that it caused the product to look more like a toy and less the mature, reliable product that it was, that he never had liked the red color in it very well but had never had another alternative in view. The change was made, both improving the customer appearance value of the product and eliminating $15,000 of unnecessary cost.

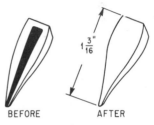

BEFORE   AFTER

Fig. 1-1   The pointer.

Although the answer, once developed, and the thinking process seem simple, $15,000 cash each year ($1,250 each month) for the design life of three to four years shows the benefits of an optimum problem-solving system for simple as well as involved matters.

Value analysis is a problem-solving system implemented by the use of a specific set of techniques, a body of knowledge, and a group of learned skills. It is an organized creative approach that has for its purpose the efficient identification of unnecessary cost, i.e., cost that provides neither quality nor use nor life nor appearance nor customer features.

When applied to products, this approach assists in the orderly utilization of better approaches, alternative materials, newer processes, and abilities of specialized suppliers. It focuses engineering, manufacturing, and purchasing attention on one objective—equivalent performance for lower cost. Having this focus, it provides step-by-step procedures for accomplishing its objectives efficiently and with assurance.

When applied to services, this approach assists in the more precise determination of "What are we trying to do?" in the form of solvable problems, a thorough collection and penetrating analysis of information and assumptions surrounding the service, viable alternatives from the creative mental processes, with skillful sorting and development of better approaches from the "judgment" and "development" parts of the problem-solving system.

Value analysis approaches may assist all branches of an enterprise—engineering, manufacturing, procurement, marketing, and management—by securing better answers to their specific problems in supplying what the customer wants at lower production costs. Quite commonly, 15 to 25 per cent and very often much more of manufacturing costs can be made unnecessary without any reduction in customer values by the use of this problem-solving system in the significant decision areas.

Four Separate Kinds of Thinking

As this problem-solving system is illustrated, it will include four separate kinds of thinking preceded by "mind tuning," which directs all thinking toward a common objective, and followed by a development and refinement activity, which puts the results of the thinking processes into use.

1. Exhaustive accumulation of *information* and identification and improvement of *assumptions*.

2. Penetrating *analysis*. With what senses of direction does this information provide us? What specific problems will, when solved, bring important cost benefits?

3. *Creative mental activity,* in which all judgment is temporarily deferred to form the roots of a variety of different solutions to each of the specific problems developed in the preceding analysis.

4. *Judgment-type mental activity,* in which the results of creative thought are searched for *idea roots* in order to minimize disadvantages and maximize advantages sufficiently to meet the need for cost and/or operation improvement.

Procedures to Locate Unestablished Problems

The problem-solving system must have procedures that locate the often unsuspected areas of real cost-improvement opportunity. It must contain techniques that will identify the *stoppers,* also usually unsuspected, in the work toward lower costs and deal effectively with them.

1-3   What Is Value?

A product or service is generally considered to have good value if that product or service has appropriate performance and cost. Or, by reverse definition, a product is considered not to have good value if it lacks either appropriate performance or cost. It can almost truthfully be said that, by this definition, value can be increased by either increasing the performance or decreasing the cost. More precisely:

1. Value is always increased by decreasing costs (while, of course, maintaining performance).

2. Value is increased by increasing performance *if the customer needs, wants, and is willing to pay for more performance.*

Maximum Value

Maximum value is probably never achieved. The degree of value in any product depends on the effectiveness with which every usable idea, process, material, and approach to the problem have been identified, studied, and utilized. The purpose of the special techniques and special knowledge of value analysis is to bring, with less expenditure of time and money, more of the better value combinations into focus.

Normal Degree of Value

In normal usage, value is considered good if the product contains somewhat better combinations of ideas, processes, materials, and functions, costwise, than competition; it is considered bad if, because the opposite is true, lost sales volume results. This method of determining the degree of value often comes too late and has serious limitations.

Selected typical products have been given a concentrated and over-normal amount of attention in order to determine more nearly the amount of unnecessary cost they contain when compared, not with competition, but with the optimum combination of available ideas, processes, materials, and design concepts. Such studies have shown that unnecessary cost which can be so identified varies between 25 and 75 per cent of the product cost.

We all recognize that these unnecessary costs are not hanging like pears from a tree for those who wish to pluck. Identification and removal are the reward for a well-organized effort using effective value-oriented tools and involve appropriate use of money and competence.

1-4 Importance of Value

In a free enterprise system, with competition at full play, success in business over the long term hinges on continually offering the customer the best value for the price asked. Competition, in other words, determines in what direction one must go in setting the value content in order for a product or a service to be competitive. *This best value is determined by two considerations: performance and cost.*

Over the years, it has been generally recognized that an acceptable product must serve the customer's needs and wishes to the degree that he expects; that is to say, the product must have *performance* capability. In recent years, it has also come into clearer focus that the cost of producing must be such that the customer can buy the product at competitive prices while leaving adequate difference between customer's cost (selling price) and production cost to assure a continuing healthy business. Keeping appropriate performance while securing appropriate cost introduces the *value concept.*

Although the reader might infer that since the word *value* has so many meanings in common usage its use in this book inhibits rather than promotes communication, such is not the intent. Whenever the words *value work, value-oriented work, value-oriented resources,* or similar terms are used, they mean men trained in and skilled in the task of *keeping performance and achieving lower costs,* thus improving value.

Case Study

CONDUCT ELECTRIC CURRENT IN STEEL?

In a control device it was noted that costly nonferrous materials were used for certain parts which could be very economically made from ferrous materials. In a function evaluation, it was discovered that there were, in general, two functions involved: the mechanical function plus the function of conducting electric current. The amount of current was small, and the engineer applying value-analysis techniques to evaluate functions collected information to determine if there was any basic reason why steel could not be used for these parts. He was told, "It is poor practice to conduct electric current through steel. We never do it. For current conduction we use nonferrous metals." He questioned this "design" premise on the basis of the numerous common applications in which electric current is conducted through steel, for example, in the track rails of an electric railway system. On the basis of the comparative conductivity of the nonferrous materials and of the steel which would provide the lower-cost alternative, he made specific suggestions. In finishing this work, he noted that steel was used for one important current-conducting member, and naturally he inquired, "Why, since you have advised me that you believe it is not good practice to conduct electric current in steel?" He was told that in the particular application in which steel was used the temperature was so high that a nonferrous metal would not hold its temper and shape, and it was necessary to use steel in order to properly accomplish the function at all.

Clearly focused, what the statement meant was, "We are using copper-based materials for the easy conducting jobs, but where such materials will not perform, we use steel." The suggested change to conduction of the current through steel was made, and the product was greatly simplified. Besides, costs were reduced, and because of the new and greater simplicity, reliability was increased. *Habits often lead astray.*

1-5 *Why Now?—Better Solutions to Value (Cost) Problems*

Cycle of the History of a Product

In general, the production of a product involves three stages. First is the *research and development stage* in which knowledge is extended toward innovation to create new functions, to provide additional functions, and to accomplish existing functions more reliably or efficiently. This is the stage in which ways and means are sought to fill new needs, to execute new functions, and to improve functions already being performed in one way or another. The resultant products are awaited with anticipation, and if successful, they are sold in sufficient numbers to support continued performance studies.

Then comes the second stage, the *growth stage.* The product, having proved that it fills a need, gains in customer demand, and competition enters the field. In this stage, it becomes evident that the product must be produced at lower costs in order to sell it competitively in sufficient quantities.

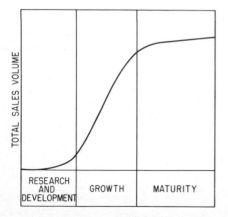

Fig. 1-2 Product research, growth, and maturity cycle.

The third stage, the *maturity stage,* is reached when the product has matured fully. Research and development are no longer making large contributions to the efficiency with which functions are accomplished, to the life of the product, or to the addition of new functions. Thus the prime task of the manufacturer becomes one of tackling the other part

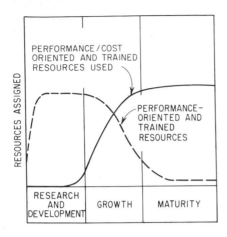

Fig. 1-3 Optimum change in use of performance engineering and value engineering skills as product matures.

of the value job so that product leadership will be maintained by having performance equality and value leadership. This means that more dollars must be committed to identifying unnecessary costs and arranging for their removal and that more competence must be assigned to work on value.

Whether a business continues to increase in profitable sales volume or starts to decrease and then drops out of the field is normally governed by the degree to which it recognizes this broadening from *performance* to *value* (performance with good costs) emphasis at the right time and by the effectiveness with which it shifts its use of resources and competence, as compared with its competitors.

EXAMPLE: Kitchen waste is an unavoidable derivative of food preparation and consumption in the normal household. In the early days of civilized living, it was quite common to dispose of this waste by feeding it to pigs, by burying it in the ground, or by employing

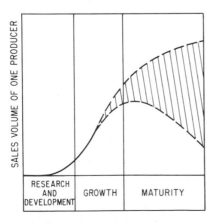

Fig. 1-4 Effect of timing and degree of change from performance-oriented skills to value-oriented skills on sales volume of any one producer. Shaded area shows extent to which producer's sales are controlled by his decision in this matter.

other simple methods. As the mode of living progressed toward town and city settlements, the problem was solved by organized provisions for garbage collection and removal. Less than half a century ago, an awareness developed that there was a need for a better and more sanitary way of handling kitchen waste. Research and development were implemented to solve the problem, and the goal soon became one of reducing the waste at the source to a form in which it could be directly disposed of.

This effort, which included experimentation with chemicals, with combustion, etc., culminated in the process of grinding the waste into a pulp that could be disposed of in a sewage system. Thus the research and development stage brought forth today's household garbage disposer.

The original product gained users' acceptance, and in the growth stage that followed, refinements were made to performance and the cost was brought down to a level at which the demand was sufficient for profitable production. The number of producers of garbage disposers rose from the original one to more than a dozen. The maturity stage was reached, and profitable production of the appliance hinged largely on maintaining the performance effectiveness while eliminating unnecessary costs. (Costs are considered "necessary" until another means is known to keep the performance factors without them—then they become "unnecessary.")

1-6   *Value-oriented Work*

It is seen, then, that the importance of *value work*—effort to keep established performance and secure better costs—increases as the product cycle advances but that it always follows after the period in which the emphasis is on *performance work*—concentration to assure performance. New problems come into the picture because men have been hired, trained, and equipped with performance-oriented tools but the job has become value oriented. A look at the list of all products which occupy human endeavor shows that there are large areas, such as the military, in which performance-oriented work is of the greatest vitality. But, year by year, there is also an expanding list of matured products, and so value work has become of great importance for the successful operation of most businesses.

Use of Value Resources

Performance-oriented work is basically centered on using resources to accomplish new functions which are desired or needed by man. Value-oriented work is aimed at accomplishing these preestablished functions using less of the resources of materials and time. In reality, cost is a measure of the amount of resources expended. Value work, as a study of the use of resources to better advantage, helps to supply more needs of human beings per integer of resources. As such, it is a means of prolonging the prosperity of people by using resources more efficiently.

In performance-oriented work, test results may cause abrupt changes in the attack in that unexpected directions totally contrary to the initial "feelings" of the researcher or designer may be indicated. In value-oriented work, on the other hand, the absence of test results allows feelings to continue to be a large factor in choosing the engineering and manufacturing alternatives which will establish the value level of the product.

Value Work Expands Markets and Jobs

In the case of many products, the usage, and hence the volume in demand, increases in direct proportion to the lowering of cost; to say it another way, as customers find that they can exchange less of their effort for a particular product, larger and larger numbers will find it practical to do so. For instance, if the minimum cost for the rather complicated device known as the television set were around $1,000, the market would be much more limited than it is. At its present lower cost, more pleasure is provided for more people, and employment opportunities are multiplied.

The overall results of the economic endeavor are promoted by the increase in volume that follows with lower cost. Entire industries have been built because very much lower costs have been successively established. Take, for example, the electric clocks which today appear in many rooms of the home or the small electric motors which are now found in dozens of products for the home but which, a few years back, were rarities in private surroundings. These developments certainly could not have occurred on the basis of improvement in performance alone. The value has been improved, i.e., unnecessary costs have been eliminated, and the market has expanded, as have the jobs concerned with the production.

Elimination of Human Toil

In the area that includes the needs and services which people require and want for necessary daily tasks, much human toil must still be expended. Most of this work, however, can be accomplished by machines if only the limitation of their high cost can be eliminated. Effective value-oriented work in sufficient magnitude will bring the cost down, and equipment that eliminates tedious and difficult tasks will come into much greater use. A good example is the home laundry machine, which has been such a boon to millions.

Adequate Defense for Lower Cost

Adequate defense of a nation relies heavily on research and development to provide new functions more efficiently. This has been long recognized. But now it is becoming equally apparent that it also relies on effective and efficient value-oriented practices to identify and remove unnecessary costs so that adequate weapons will be available at less than bankrupting cost. An essential defense weapon eliminated by high cost lowers the country's military capacity, and the matter of reducing costs is one of national importance.

1-7   Considerations for Improving Value

As the twofold job of providing the performance the customer wants and of doing so at an appropriate cost makes progress through the product cycle from the research and development stage into the maturity stage, a number of factors are responsible for continued inclusion of unnecessary cost in the product. Some of these will be evident in the discussion which follows.

Effect of Time Shortage

It seems the way of life that time is short. This is particularly true in the cycle of a product. Until a particular need appears, at least in an undeveloped form, people in the sales area have no way of sensing their customers' requirements. Then when a need arises, there is a rush to provide a proposal to satisfy the need and to do so effectively as quickly as possible, before competition has a chance to gain a hold on it. As the product then moves into the design-engineering area, deadlines must often be met which definitely do not permit complete searching, testing, and securing and utilizing information which would result in accomplishing customer needs at the lowest cost. The same situation exists in purchasing, in manufacturing, and in all other areas of the business. Thus a shortage of time, by the very nature of the problem, is the cause of inclusion of unnecessary costs.

Lack of Measurement in Value Work

Decision making in performance-oriented work can usually be based upon tests and measurements. In contrast, the effectiveness of value-oriented work at each stage of the product design and manufacturing cycle cannot be accurately measured. Therefore, after what the individual considers a reasonable effort using the cost skills and the time and information he has, decisions are made with respect to the manufacturing and engineering alternatives. Again it is seen that, if any of these decisions bring about poor performance, tests will show it. If, on the other hand, they bring poor value, there is no immediate way of making that evident. Consequently, performance-oriented work is normally more efficiently and effectively accomplished than value-oriented work.

Case Study

DEALING WITH TIME AND VALUE

A control, consisting of a cube of 8 inches of electrical and mechanical equipment actuated by some knobs and operating levers, was in the process of manufacture on an order for 400. Time schedules were so short that, although the engineers and others attempted to provide as much value as they could take in stride during the stages of design, tooling, and buying of materials, nothing could be allowed to interrupt or delay production. The question was raised, "Should value analysis techniques be applied to this job now that it is under way?"

One of the engineers involved said, "Let's try the value analysis techniques on it and see what they provide." Another said, "This is a 'dead horse.' We may never make another one. Let's not waste time on it." Still another said, "This is like a post-mortem. But let's not forget that the purpose of the post-mortem which is performed on the dead is to gain information which will provide better life to the living." This viewpoint prevailed, and a value engineer was assigned to work with the design engineers to test the value analysis problem-solving system for its effectiveness under these circumstances.

The various assemblies, subassemblies, and parts were studied to determine precisely the function they contributed to the overall product and to develop alternatives which would accomplish the functions at better costs. The results of the post-mortem were startling. The function of the assembly and of part after part could be provided for one-fifth to one-tenth of actual costs. Some of the *before* and *after* costs for the various assemblies and parts were:

Before	After
$4.54	$0.46
0.42	0.07
2.14	0.57
0.53	0.02
1.85	0.28

In most cases, where parts were involved, the costs applied to practically identical parts. In others, it was a matter of using functional components which were found to be available rather than using custom-built items. For instance:

A small metal knob costing $2.25 operated a miniature potentiometer. In standard catalogues, a knob was found, which performed the total function slightly better for 25 cents each.

A rather large assembly supporting an emergency control lever cost $20.33. Its functions were provided for $8.12.

This was one method of dealing with time and value. There are other methods, some before-the-fact, which are often applicable.

Interestingly enough, a subsequent order was received for this type of control. Since it was a military product, it was quite naturally modified in some respects. Just the same, the engineers were able to take the report on the post-mortem study page for page and to include in the new design the benefits of thirty of the forty-five specific value alternatives suggested. Of course, one considerable gain was accomplished in the new design because it could be "built in" prior to original tooling. *Post-mortems can be direction indicators.*

Human Factors

Lack of sufficient communication, misunderstandings, and normal frictions between human beings become increasingly responsible for unnecessary costs in the more complicated products and systems. With no intent to underrate the good work of average people (and certainly in that category we include ourselves), it must be recognized that the average job is accomplished by an average man and therefore will, in general, be of average grade. The average man can accomplish his job more effectively if he is supplied with special tools which are designed for him. It is, therefore, basic to the philosophy of value analysis that vastly improved tools should be provided, which provide much additional potential to the average man. It is well to remember also that the most skillful golfer also wants precisely the best club available for the particular shot he is making.

Impact of New Processes, Products, and Materials

The constant and accelerating flow of new ideas, new processes, new products, and new materials can, when properly applied, aid in establishing the desired customer values at a lower cost. This leads to the conclusion that when a product is designed and tooled and is on the market, it is already advancing toward becoming obsolete, valuewise. Better tools for value-oriented work will help to incorporate more of such new information sooner and thus minimize the value-obsolescence problem.

Timing for Value Work

Functions can be clearly identified nearly as well before actual design of the product as after design. Alternatives can be nearly as creatively developed from blueprints as from actual models. Therefore, much value work can be done before original design and before purchase of original tooling.

This statement should not in the slightest degree detract from the importance of realizing that after design and after various product parts and assemblies have been proved by actual usage it will be profitable to use the value analysis approach again. Periodically during product life, important cost elements should be identified with the functions which they perform, and further engineering and manufacturing alternatives should be developed with the aid of value analysis knowledge and techniques. This will make possible, in many instances, changes that will eliminate large amounts of unnecessary cost which, for various reasons, eluded the first round of value decision making.

1-8   *System Must Locate Unsuspected Areas Responsible for the Higher Costs*

The fighter does not know that his balance is a little off or he would correct it. The champion golfer does not know that his grip is a little too tight. Any system of aid for champions must include means for locating unexpected areas of needed improvement.

The approaches of the problem-solving system must identify which of the areas holds the solution to each specific integer of unnecessary cost. The necessary knowledge, creativity, and initiative can then be used exclusively where needed to end the cost problem. Some areas are as follows:

1. *Management Organization*

If the organization is not best suited to the task to be performed, it can only produce poorer performance in the product or extra cost. If poorer performance results, tests will normally follow and it will be promptly corrected. If, however, higher costs result, they often continue.

2. *Marketing Concept—Customer Functional Understanding*

The customer purchases a product to accomplish certain functions. These are exclusively *use* and aesthetic functions. To the extent that the customer has not clearly understood and communicated exactly the functions he wants and is willing to pay for, and to the extent that this information is not basic to the engineering and manufacturing processes, extra cost remains in the system, product, or service.

3. Engineering Concept or Approach

After the functions that are to be provided to the customer are determined, the effectiveness used in establishing the engineering concept that will be detailed and implemented introduces either positive or negative factors in the cost area, which remain regardless of actions of any others. Much unnecessary cost is often allowed to remain because the work in the engineering-concept stage was not optimum.

4. Engineering Detail

After the concept, that is, the basic approach for accomplishing the functions, is established, it must be implemented by choice of materials, shapes, assemblies, methods, functions, tolerances, etc. Appropriate cost can also be lost in this work area.

5. Manufacturing Concept or Approach

How much or how little automation? How much to make? How much to buy? What machines and factory layout? If this manufacturing conceptual and planning work is not competitively done, appropriate cost can be lost.

6. Manufacturing Operation

That appropriate cost will be lost in a factory that is less efficiently operated than its competitors is so obvious that it needs no elaboration.

7. Purchasing or Materials Procurement Work

A significant amount of cost is normally spent by purchasing. To the extent that purchasing recognizes its potential to contribute to profits, staffs itself with competent buyers and negotiators, buys function as nearly as practicable, and assumes a major role in getting a wide variety of solutions for the needs of the engineer from the available supplier market, it is eliminating the possibility that significant unnecessary costs are lost in this area.

EXAMPLE: A typical simple example of the latter statement is the case of an electrical control. It worked very well indeed, but its cost was too high. Sales had dropped off. The makers brought the control in for value analysis with a statement which said, "We give you this with tongue in cheek; we don't think that another penny can be taken out of the cost, but we're desperate."

In applying the value analysis approach to the device, one of the first parts to come up for review was a wire clip which held the cover on. It was made of phosphor bronze and cost $7,000 a year. The value specialist asked, "What is the function? How does phosphor bronze contribute to that function? It is a material that is commonly used when a part has to flex millions of times. But this clip is flexed only when the cover is removed for servicing—an average of six times in the life of the product." By changing to spring brass, the same job could be done for $3,000 a year, that is, for less than half.

The cover itself cost 4 cents, an expenditure of $40,000 a year. Its function was to keep extraneous material out of the small mechanism. The entire control was mounted inside another enclosure. Using a plain piece of laminated plastic reduced the cost from 4 cents to 1.5 cents each, and out went $25,000. Many similar findings were made as the analysis of the complete device proceeded.

The new approach, applied after conventional cost-reduction treatment, eliminated obvious, but hidden, amounts of unnecessary costs. No essential function was impaired, no "cheapening" was effected. The product was modified to represent better value.

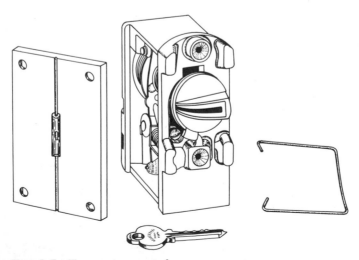

Fig. 1-5   Temperature control.

No Reduction in Quality, Safety, Features, or Attractiveness

Inherent in the philosophy of value analysis is full retention for the customer of the usefulness and aesthetic features of the product. Identifying and removing unnecessary cost, and thus improving value, must be done without reducing in the slightest degree quality, safety, life, reliability, dependability, and the features and attractiveness that the customer wants. Too often in the past, an endeavor to remove cost without the use of professional tools for accomplishing the project has resulted in a lowering of quality. Therefore, it must be clearly understood from the start that accomplishing better value does not mean reducing quality to a point where it is lower but may just get by. No reduction whatever in needed quality is tolerated in the professional grade of value work.

Experience shows that quality is frequently increased as the result of developing alternatives for the accomplishment of the use and aesthetic functions.

1-9   System Must Locate and Deal with Unsuspected Stoppers

Experienced men have learned to expect to confront immediately a whole family of *stoppers,* or *roadblocks,* when considering testing, or using a new approach. The definite and proper treatment of stoppers is just as vital as the proper treatment of the technical factors involved. One stopper, or roadblock, anywhere in the entire process can greatly reduce or end the possibility of results. These stoppers, or roadblocks, may appear in securing an understanding of the problem, securing information, learning what the customer really wants, learning how to bring the best out of specific materials or processes, or obtaining good creative ideation, samples, tests, or interpretations of test material.

Roadblocks that stop small, individual steps are just as damaging as roadblocks that stop approval. Each stopper must be recognized and dealt with in a manner that ends or minimizes its destructive potential. Some common stoppers, or roadblocks, include the following:

The injection of generalities

The absence of meaningful cost

The acceptance of answers from sources that are not the best

Lack of ability to locate industry specialists, vendors' functional products, vendors with specialized skills, vendors with specialty processes needed, and standard products

If a good degree of value work is to be done, effectiveness in overcoming every one of these and dozens of other stoppers must be developed.

Application of the technique of "identifying and overcoming roadblocks" is of the greatest vitality and importance. Experience has shown that in three-quarters of the cases occurring in practice, the development of effective value alternatives is stopped by failure to use this technique. It has also proved that when this technique does apply and is used costs of the order of one-half or less usually result.

Further, it will be understood that this technique is commonly useful in dealing with situations that may be developed by a number of the other value analysis approaches and, in addition, uncovers wide areas of "stoppers" that are not otherwise identified.

1-10   The Approach (Oversimplified) to Prepare the Mind for the Value Analysis Technique

The value analysis approach requires, first of all, that valid and complete answers be developed for the following five questions:

1. What is the item or service?
2. What does it cost?
3. What does it do?
4. What else would do the job?
5. What would that alternative cost?

These basic questions serve the end of uncovering needed pertinent facts. With the establishment of answers to them, the foundation is laid for developing objective data for presentation to the decision makers. Hence the importance of understanding and effectively using these questions cannot be overemphasized.

What is the item or service? This question is usually quite readily determined from objective data.

What does it cost? Here the answer is often obtainable from effective and meaningful cost data, but sometimes such costs are difficult to obtain. This will be further developed in technique 2 of the *more results* techniques presented in Chapter 8.

What does it do? For the moment, all else except precisely the question, "What does it do?" must be disregarded. This means that we put aside such questions as:

What machines does the factory have?
What processes does the factory customarily use?
What special skills do the factory people have?
What special skills are available in the drafting and planning organizations?

What equipment must be liquidated?
What buildings must work be provided for?
What people in what areas must be kept busy?

Admittedly, all these additional questions embrace considerations that will enter into decision making, but at this stage of value analysis, the establishment of sound criteria for decision making is handicapped if any of these questions are allowed to interfere with the effective generation of objective data such as, "It conducts current," "It excludes dust," "It supports the operator," "It separates dials," "It mounts the motor," "It mounts the control."

What else would do the job? This is not a superficial question; it is a penetrating one. The comprehensiveness of the answer to that simple question governs, to a high degree, the effectiveness and the grade of value work being done. No matter how skilled the searcher and no matter how diligent and creative his search, there will always remain alternatives which he did not bring into focus, many of which would have accomplished the total performance reliably at very much lower cost. To ensure good value content, many of the special techniques and much of the special knowledge of value analysis must be used in getting substantial answers to this question. The approach here is to search intensively for alternatives by:

Studying handbooks
Perusing trade literature
Telephoning people who might have pertinent information
Writing to specialists and to companies who might know of effective alternatives
Focusing intense creativity sharply on the precise task to be accomplished
Refining the results of these creative sessions and searching further for additional information

Unless this phase of the work is effectively and penetratingly done, it cannot be hoped that the product will have more than an average degree of value.

What would that alternative cost? Handbooks are full of information on the properties of various products and materials and suggested uses for them. Notably absent from most of these is cost. This is quite understandable. Costs vary from time to time while the properties of materials and their functions are relatively stable. Furthermore, as our civilization has developed, it has been a basic necessity to find materials which, within the appropriate size and weight range, accomplished the necessary functions. Therefore, the handbooks contain the information needed for these pursuits. When value is the objective, it becomes vital to have meaningful costs for decision making. Hence the question of the cost of alternatives must be effectively and objectively answered.

Meaningful costs may be obtained from a variety of sources or from a combination of sources:

The cost department
Cost analyses
Catalogues
Suppliers of products or materials
Special cost studies

But since, in many instances of good value work, materials, products, and processes will be utilized in different ways, really meaningful costs often must be worked up for the job. This does not mean that it is necessary to have perfection in cost data at this stage in the cycle. Costs within a range of plus or minus 5 per cent will usually be sufficient, and often, costs within a range of plus or minus 10 per cent will help to determine whether the particular value alternatives are of sufficient interest to warrant more exact cost determination and further study.

At the risk of appearing too emphatic about this important point, the value specialist must not be too concerned about the comment, "Beware of the situation in which precise costs are not provided." His concern must rather center on statements such as, "Tools are too costly; it is not even worthwhile to provide an estimate on them" or "The quantities are so small that we know the process will not be practicable; therefore we will not provide an estimate" or "We have studied this a number of times and always found it impracticable; it is therefore not worthwhile to prepare an estimate on it now." Such beliefs and habits of the past often lock in large amounts of unsuspected and unnecessary costs.

Case Study

VALUE ANALYSIS TECHNIQUES CERTAINLY
CANNOT IMPROVE THE VALUE OF 10,000 BOLTS!

This was the challenge put forth by a manager whose department used ten thousand ½-inch steel bolts, 12 inches long, with a square head on one end and a square nut on the other, produced by totally standard processes. It is typical of the normal action by the normal person when confronted with a different approach to any situation with which he already has a certain measure of experience. The tendency is to examine what is wrong with it. Experience has taught us not to accept different solutions without careful examination unless we are prepared to be embarrassed by the unsuspected shortcomings of the proposed change.

The challenge was an interesting one for the application of the value analysis approach, which developed the following:

The bolts were used for making cable reels. The ends of the cable reels were wood disks, 3 feet in diameter. Several of these bolts, with washers under the heads and under the nuts, were used on each cable reel.

One of the best suppliers of this type of material was approached and given an appropriate understanding of value analysis. He was advised of the use and function of these bolts, and he, in turn, expressed the feeling that there were benefits to be gained. He was anxious to develop them in detail for this particular bolt. He then provided two interesting suggestions.

First, since one end of the bolt was the same as the other in use (both going through similar ends of a wood spool), an alternative was a threaded stud with two nuts rather than a bolt with one nut. The supplier advised that such studs could be provided with a short thread on one end and with the nut already chased on to the end of this thread, so that from the user's viewpoint, it would be very much the same as starting with a bolt. He stated that the cost would be approximately 15 per cent less.

As a second alternative, he could readjust the machine slightly to provide a substantial flash of metal under the head which would perform the washer function. Obviously, the flash would not be as neatly round as a punched washer, but it could be provided with appropriate area and thickness so that the complete purpose of the washer for this function could be well served. He stated that, if this alternative was used, the necessary adjustment of the machine for the relatively short run of 10,000 bolts would add a little cost which would be offset by the elimination of the normal trimming operation, and they would be able to sell the bolts for the same price as the standard product. The benefit to the user, then, would be in the elimination of the cost of the washer on one end as well as in the complete elimination of the bolt and washer assembly work.

Either alternative would have been good, but in this particular case, the first alternative was immediately chosen because there was need for short delivery on the particular order and the suppliers' upsetters, which would coin the head, had a heavy future schedule. The result was that the supplier was able to provide the needed threaded studs with the nut on one end almost instantly and at a 15 per cent reduction as compared with the cost of the normal bolt.

The value analysis approach had proved its profitability.

The Planned Approach

Value analysis presupposes the use of a planned approach for intensive and effective utilization of every applicable technique to overcome "stoppers." This requires the development of sufficient skill in the application of enough techniques to bring into clear view a liberal number of value alternatives.

The soundness of this statement may be illustrated by a look at the following case involving a strip hinge.

What is the item? A metal strip hinge about 8 inches long has holes in the flattened portion for fastening it on a door and has one edge rolled so that a hinge pin can be inserted. It is made by stamping and forming, by a manufacturer who has proved his reliability in the field of hardware, in quantities of 500,000 per year.

What does it do? The item mounts a door on an appliance; the requirements are that it must be rugged and reliable, must be made uniformly enough to permit ready and reliable assembly, and must come from proven source. Lack of the hinge would stop the entire appliance production line with resulting work delays for thousands of people and large amounts of unexpected cost for the manufacturer.

What else would do the job?

1. Use other manufacturers' hinges. This solution was thought to be not too promising because purchasing had already secured quotations from others and had made a selection of the lowest-cost reliable supplier. His facilities and his ability to meet schedules had been examined. He had proven himself. To study the value of this item again was judged by many to be ill-advised.

2. Make it of a different material—plastics, for example. Great resistance existed against even an investigation of this approach because, during the developing technology in the plastics field, many of the wrong plastics had been misapplied and none with appropriate properties for this hinge had come sharply into the view of the decision makers. There were fears of loss of customer confidence and of costly replacements. All of these and other considerations tended to prevent a thorough investigation of modern or available plastics which might accomplish the job.

3. Cast the hinge strip. Admittedly the quantities were satisfactory to make this or almost any other high-volume process practicable. Those experienced in the art of casting pointed out that the hinge strip comprised relatively thin sections over large areas; basically, this is not a design type in which castings excel. It was also pointed out that the need for the long hole would mean a very long and tricky coring or an equally difficult long-hole drilling operation for the hinge pin. Experience in the past caused casting specialists to believe that it would not be worthwhile to develop alternatives for these parts made as castings, and that was the stand they took when asked for specific information.

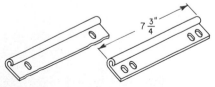

Fig. 1-6   Hinge.

4. Make as a forging. Here the problem of drilling the long, relatively straight hole for the hinge pin discouraged effective work in providing alternatives in the form of forgings.

5. Weld a strip of metal edgewise to a piece of tubing. Here, hardware and hinge engineers were concerned about the quality of the weld, the amount of flash, the deformation that would take place at welding, and the appearance of the finished job. Costs by usual welding processes would work out to be too high. To develop it and plan it through with special jigs and equipment would require time and study, and welding men believed that this was not the way to do the job anyhow. Therefore, it was very difficult, if not impossible, to get a useful estimate of the cost of tooling and of the finished parts. The estimate, to be useful, should be correct to within plus or minus 5 or 10 per cent.

6. Pass a strip of steel through continuous rolls and roll on the edge of the strip the section that would accommodate the hinge pin. Hardware engineers were concerned with the "springback," the variations in tolerance and dimension, and the burrs which would result as the continuous strip was cut into short segments. Then there was the possible necessity for additional operations to bore out, or ream out, the hinge-pin hole and to punch holes in the flat section. Maintenance of the roll equipment was another foreseen problem, as was the question of whether steel of the thickness required could be properly rolled. All these considerations tended to retard or prevent the preparation of any objective proposals showing the approximate costs of a strip made by this method.

Numerous other alternatives can be brought into view and they all must satisfy similar objections before one can proceed with a useful evaluation study. It will be readily seen from the foregoing that the value specialist's problem is to:

Understand and apply each applicable step of an orderly planned approach.

Expect that, when requesting the development of new value alternatives, men who customarily make decisions in their own field and accordingly are not used to seeing the materials or processes used differently will feel that the approach is wrong. Hence they will be very hesitant about investing their important time in serious considerations for the preparation of objective value alternatives.

In value analysis, however, it is essential that this sort of normal negative not be allowed to stop the development of appropriate information. Numerous are the examples in which large improvements have been made promptly after overcoming this type of reluctance and actually securing meaningful value alternatives.

What would that alternative cost? In the case of the hinge, continuing steadfast and effective development of the suggested alternatives brought into focus information which proved the last alternative very practical. The result was a 10-cent reduction in the cost of each hinge, and thus the payoff was $50,000.

SUMMARY

Value analysis or engineering is a complete system for identifying and dealing with the factors that cause uncontributing cost or effort in products, processes, or services. This system uses all existing technologies, knowledge, and skills to efficiently identify costs or efforts that do not contribute to the customer's needs and wants. Its effect is to help the "good" achieve even "better."

The value analysis problem-solving system contains four distinctly different types of thinking, each of which is thoroughly completed before the next is begun. These are:

1. Information and assumption searching
2. Analysis
3. Creative thinking
4. Judgment thinking (minimizing disadvantages and maximizing advantages)

This problem-solving system is needed only when competition makes it desirable or mandatory to achieve lower costs, better problem solutions than the normal good practices in any successful competing business or service are obtaining, or more services than the available dollars will provide by present means.

This system must and does contain approaches that will locate and identify uncontributing costs from unexpected as well as expected business or service areas. In a manufacturing company, for instance, the decisions that "lock in" uncontributing costs may come in the normal operation of management, marketing beliefs (including full understanding of customer-wanted functions), engineering concepts and approaches, engineering details, manufacturing concepts and approaches, manufacturing operations, or purchasing and materials procurement.

Stoppers, or *roadblocks,* always inhibit change, yet change is usually essential to avoid a dying business. The system provides some means for identifying and some help in dealing with the action and decision stoppers.

The chapters immediately following will show how the factors of controlling importance are identified, how the really vital problems are established, or "set," and how the problem-solving system works.

chapter 2

All Cost Is for Function

To help achieve better solutions to problems sooner, some different *building blocks* are needed. These must cut to the heart of the basic problem and keep penetrating thinking in the heart area. This is vital, or side issues, which are apparent, will draw action from the main issue.

2-1 *Customer Wants Use and Aesthetic Functions*

The heart of the situation is "the customer wants a *function*." He wants something done. He wants someone, perhaps himself, pleased. He wants something enclosed, held, moved, separated, cleaned, heated, cooled, or whatever under certain conditions and within certain limits; and/or he wants a shape, a color, an aroma, a texture, a sound, a "precious" (costly) material, or whatever to bring pleasure to himself or others he wishes to please. That is *all* he wants. That is *all* he cares about.

Thus, the language of function is the language of the heart of the problem. The customer wants two and only two types of functions in varying degrees in different products or services. *Use functions* and *aesthetic functions* serve his needs. *Use functions* entail some *action* that he wants performed, and *aesthetic functions* please him or someone he wants to have pleased.

Many products and services require both use and aesthetic functions. Some require only use while some require only aesthetic functions. The refrigerator, automobile, dress, shoe, pipe, and flower vase all require both use and aesthetic functions in varying ratios. The nail within the walls of the building, the concealed wire in the motor, and the oil in the automobile require only use functions. The "Rembrandt," the diamond, and the perfume have only aesthetic functions.

Intense concentration, even what appears to be overconcentration of mental work on these functions, forms the basis for unexpected steps of advancement of value in the product or service.

2-2   *Identify, Clarify, and Name Functions*

The process includes:

Identifying
Clarifying
Naming

What, really, is the function that the customer or user wants?

Case Study

$50,000 FOR CONCRETE—WHAT IS THE FUNCTION?

A new laboratory under installation was to contain very powerful X-ray equipment for deeply searching large forgings and castings for hidden defects. Providing for the protection of adjacent areas from radiation was required. For this, the drawings included a concrete wall, 7 feet thick and 14 feet high, in the shape of a horseshoe outside of the building. The best bid on this wall was approximately $50,000. The contract was taken to the works manager for his initialing. Recognizing his responsibility for the area, he told the manager of the laboratory that he would approve the contract. However, he said, "If you decide to move the laboratory, you will take this concrete away with you and get it out of our way." This was an unexpected condition to which the laboratory manager was unprepared to subscribe. He called in a construction supervisor and asked him what he could do to work out the problem. The construction engineer, who had not worked with problems of radiation, was astonished to see in the plans an enormous amount of concrete, seemingly idle and carrying no load. Inquiring into the function of the concrete, he was advised that it was to stop radiation.

Having studied value analysis function-based techniques, he thought in terms of "what else would stop radiation." He asked whether dirt would stop it and was advised that it would if it was provided in sufficient quantity, which was found to be a mound 14 feet high and 14 feet thick. Bids on it showed that it could be installed for $5,000; of course, the works manager immediately approved. The use, at the proper time, of the function-based value analysis techniques resulted in a superior product, namely, a grassed-over earth mound, at one-tenth of the cost of a solid concrete wall.

State the function in exact sentences. Examine the sentences.

Is that exactly what it does for the customer?
Is that exactly what the customer wants it to do?
Is that exactly what the customer believes he's paying for?

Improve and clarify the sentences until they say exactly what the function really is. Describe what the function does and name it with a verb and a noun, for example, support contact, enclose housing, control current, radiate heat, etc.

	Some verbs		*Some nouns*	
Contain	Secure	Piston	Vibration
Move	Locate	Contacts	Volume
Shorten	Space	Torque	
Support	Rotate	Switch	
Protect	Fasten	Volume	
Prevent	Close	Current	
Actuate	Insulate	Dust	
Time (as a verb)	Ignite	Panel	
Control	Filter	Paint	
Reduce	Mount	Rust	
Modulate	Limit	Noise	

While the naming of functions may appear simple, the exact opposite is the rule. In fact, naming them articulately is so difficult and requires such precision in thinking that real care must be taken to prevent the abandonment of the task before it is accomplished.

2-3   *Quantify Functions When Practicable*

To provide more benefits, functions are named whenever possible using a verb and noun that have measurable parameters. For example *support timer* may also be defined as *support weight*, and *interrupt circuit* may be defined as *interrupt current*. This approach, in many cases, allows and promotes measurement of the appropriate cost for a specified function in more specific terms. Some examples follow:

Conduct current	Conduct heat
Transmit torque	Transmit flux
Enclose volume	Communicate intelligence
Insulate voltage	Amplify voltage
Dampen vibration	

When this naming system is used, the next essential step stands out clearly. How much current? Under what conditions? How much torque? Under what conditions? How much volume? Under what conditions?

2-4   *Unify the Function and Its Specifications*

Thus is evolved the *function and its specification,* or the *function and its constraints,* as it is sometimes called, which open wide possibilities for predetermining the approximate *worth,* or *appropriate cost,* of any function under any specific constraints or specifications.

The framework has been established in which the worth, or appropriate cost, of a specified function under specified conditions can be compared to the worth, or appropriate cost, of the same function under different specified conditions. Likewise the conditions can be held constant and the worth of varying amounts of the specified function can be compared.

2-5   *Analyze Aesthetic Functions*

Naming of the aesthetic functions follows different patterns because the values placed by the customer on aesthetic functions are almost completely subjective. The realistic name that seems to apply to all aesthetic functions is *please customer.* Spelling out just what will please the customer is much more difficult than spelling out what use functions the customer wants and is willing to pay for. However, often, in the difficult lies the largest opportunity. The task is to solve the problems a little better and to get better answers than the best competitor (who, of course, has the same difficult problems).

More specific function names in the aesthetic area often promote some better solutions. Some typical names are:

Provide appearance	Reduce noise
Provide shape	Reduce size
Provide color	Reduce thickness
Provide features	Reduce time required
Provide convenience	Reduce skill required

The aesthetic functions are fully identified and clarified, as are the use functions. Each must then be similarly provided with its exact specifications or constraints.

Cost accepted in use functions is not more wisely used than cost in aesthetic function areas. Sometimes costs accepted in the aesthetic area bring the best return. It depends entirely upon what the customer wants and is willing to pay for and what the product or service now lacks that is desired.

2-6   *Classify Functions As Either Basic or Secondary*

After functions are identified, clarified, understood, and named, the thinking surrounding them is further deepened by classifying them as either *basic* or *secondary* functions. *Basic functions* are those functions for which the customer buys the device or service. The basic function of a refrigerator is to preserve food, that of a lawn mower to cut grass, and that of a bicycle to "move weight," etc.

Secondary functions are those functions required to cause or allow the designer's choice of means for accomplishing the basic functions to do so effectively. If a refrigerator has electric contacts that open and close to regulate its cycle of operation, then the function of mounting and protecting the contacts is required. If the refrigerator has solid-state control equipment with no moving parts to control its operating cycle, then a very different function—different in design and different in cost—may be needed to cause or allow it to accomplish its task.

It is often startling, when this information is developed, to learn what high percentages of the cost are consumed by secondary functions. This pinpoints for the designer areas relatively unrelated to the basic function where his different choices may have large effects upon costs.

SUMMARY

Function

The basic purpose of each expenditure, whether it be for hardware, the work of a group of men, a procedure, or whatever, is to accomplish a function. It is necessary to establish the language of function and stay within this language.

Types of Functions

In the search for basic objective thinking, functions are divided into two types. Either or both may cause the buyer or the user to buy the product. One type is the use function, and the other is the aesthetic function. Each is important. Any costs other than those that provide the amount of each of these two functions that the user or buyer wants are unnecessary costs.

Use Function

The cost that is expended to cause the product to perform a use that the buyer wants and is willing to pay for is called the use function cost.

Aesthetic Function

The cost that is expended for the purpose of pleasing the buyer through color or shape or feature, causing him to buy, is typed as the aesthetic function cost.

Basic Function

The basic function is that function for which the user or buyer buys the product.

Secondary Functions

Secondary functions are those functions that become necessary in order to allow the designer's choice for means of accomplishing the basic function to do so effectively. As is readily seen, the customer is extremely interested in the basic function, but he does not care about the secondary functions. Large amounts of cost are contained in secondary functions and become the immediate target for high-grade value engineering work.

chapter 3

Evaluate the Function

When functions have been identified, clarified, understood, and specified, the greatest help would come from the answer to the questions "How much, under our conditions of quantities, manufacture, etc., is the lowest cost that would provide that function?" and "What approach and method would secure it for that cost?"

The great danger now comes in the form of a proper and practical-sounding question: "How have we accomplished it in the past and what did that cost?" Without new thinking, new searching, and new creating, the old answers come forth, and they point to the broad well-trodden pathway. Too often, too many "feel" that previous costs and methods are "about" optimum. However, this is the pathway to business suicide in competitive business. New approaches for accomplishing the function may be evolving that will cost only a small fraction of the previous amount. A new *appropriate cost,* or *value,* for the function is needed, which is based upon not only new, current, information but also new thinking. To fill this need, the system of *evaluating the function* was developed.

3-1 Evaluation of Function

Since the purpose of value analysis is to achieve the total function for lowest overall cost, effective measures of the value of function are necessary. Techniques are provided for evaluating functions by comparison. However, this evaluation must not be made by comparison with the past. These values are established by other valid comparisons and are then used as a guide to the achievement of the individual function or groups of functions for that value or cost.

To assign a "value" (lowest cost that would fully provide it) to a function, it must be determined what the lowest cost to a competitor who has keen mental resources and good physical resources would be. The process of evaluating functions typically is as follows:

1. Individualize separate functions.
2. Understand them completely.
3. Creatively establish other unobvious means for accomplishing each function. Concentrate intense energies on means that are likely to be much lower in cost. Think searchingly, penetratingly, and courageously.
4. Assign approximate cost.
5. Add the values of the various required functions to arrive at a value for the larger overall functions. Where functions are not interacting, add arithmetically. Where they are interacting, combine them by using plus or minus cost factors for the areas of interaction.

In this preliminary evaluation of the function *do not* strive for arithmetic or technical exactness. Instead search for areas of promise, approximate benefits to be gained by further study, and general directions for precise thinking and work. The result is now the tentative *value of the function,* based not upon the habits and practices of the past, but rather upon such new and different factors as the state of the art now provides and the skill and creativity of the thinking can relate.

3-2   *Evaluation of Functions by Comparison*

Tentative and extremely useful values for functions can usually be made by objective comparisons. How else might an important portion of the function be accomplished, and what approximately would that cost? Such comparisons avoid the dangerous trap of judging and planning the future from the past.

Case Study

EVALUATE A SINGLE FUNCTION

The function of gasoline tanks for Navy landing craft is to reliably contain 200 gallons of gasoline. The noncombat life is eight years. The thinking process used to evaluate this function was:

- What is the appropriate cost for housing 200 gallons of gasoline?
- Using four 50-gallon standard drums $25
- Using one standard 250-gallon oil tank made for domestic use $30

However, some environmental treatment and perhaps some extra connections would be required. Therefore, adding $25, we arrive at a tentative $50 evaluation on the gasoline-containing function.

As a result of applying this technique, $80 gasoline containers were adopted to replace the $520 special-alloy tank previously designed and used. Because at this time the mechanism of evaluating the function proceeded before other decisions were made, the saving to the taxpayers on the 1,000 tanks was $440,000—the difference between $520,000 and $80,000.

Consider now the hours of design time used on the tank used previously in selecting costly noncorrosive material, designing irregular shapes that would be welded together, and specifying welding methods, standards, costs, etc., only to arrive at a "performance" design costing $520.

Case Study

EVALUATE THREE FUNCTIONS

The part is a steel spacer stud used in quantities of 200,000 per year to fasten a timer to an appliance. When the part was made on the automatic screw machines, the cost was 8 cents each or $16,000 per year. Part of the stud also separated two parts of the timer. What are the functions?

1. Hold the 2-pound timer to the appliance.
2. Hold a small timer part to the stud.
3. Space two parts of the timer.

What is the value of the functions? In each case assume (for the moment of first evaluation) that there are no interacting functions. Value must be determined for each function separately by comparison. The No. 1 holding function could be reliably accomplished by a steel screw, for example, which costs ½ cent. Therefore, the value of this holding function is not over ½ cent.

Holding function No. 1   ½¢
Holding function No. 2 would be accomplished by a smaller steel screw   ¼¢
The spacing function (No. 3) could, in general, be accomplished by a cutoff
    length of tubing or a rolled spacer, which would cost about   ¼¢

Adding, the value for all functions is   1.0¢

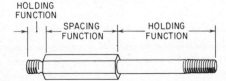

HOLDING
FUNCTION

SPACING
FUNCTION

HOLDING
FUNCTION

Fig. 3-1   Spacer stud showing functions.

Work from now on is directed in several respects:

1. Time will not be expended in developing the details of any approach that will not accomplish this entire function for a cost on the order of 1 cent.

2. Sufficient ideas, information, and appropriate design concepts will be acquired so that a material, design, and product will be provided that will accomplish the functions reliably and within the specified area of cost.

An important question here is "Don't the holding functions interact with the spacing function sufficiently so that it is invalid to directly add the values of the functions?" The answer is "Probably not." The interaction is so simple that it might deduct from the total cost rather than add to it. Hence the approximate value for the functions of the 8-cent stud was placed at 1 cent. The function value had provided a degree of "measurement" that indicated that real mental work should bring tangible results.

This case study was concluded using some value engineering approaches that will be discussed later; however, the example will be finished here. We knew we could not use the present automatic-screw-machine approach because it was necessary to arrive at costs approximately one-tenth of those which would result. Much help was found in the specific value analysis techniques. The one that formed a mechanism for this item was *blast-create-refine*. Thinking started with an eightpenny nail, which was approximately the appropriate size, contained a head, and cost $\frac{1}{10}$ cent.

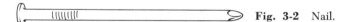

Fig. 3-2   Nail.

Creating and refining, the answers were developed. What must be done to the nail so that it will accomplish the three functions reliably, and what will be the added cost of each added operation?

1. The head must be moved down slightly on the shank.
2. The head must be made hexagonal.
3. Another head must be made in the middle of the nail to provide the necessary spacing action.
4. Threads must be rolled on each end of the modified nail.

Fig. 3-3   Spacer stud—different approach.

Suppliers in this type of business said they could make these changes and, in fact, did so. The modified design is shown in Figure 3-3.

The cost became $\frac{8}{10}$ cent, with a reduction in cost of $7\frac{2}{10}$ cents each or $14,400 per year, for an interchangeable item performing the identical use functions. There were no aesthetic functions.

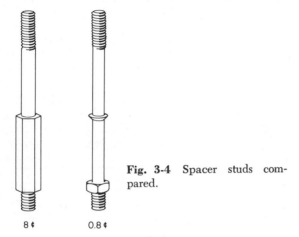

Fig. 3-4 Spacer studs compared.

8 ¢   0.8 ¢

3-3   *Evaluation of Interacting Functions*

Often the evaluation of single functions will cause the search and thought required to make good improvement of value. Usually, however, there are several functions involved—some independent and some interacting functions.

Usually the procedure outlined here will handle the interacting functions:

1. Arrange the functions in suitable order for evaluation. This arrangement will be such that means for accomplishing each succeeding function can be varied without nullifying the work done on previous functions.

2. Evaluate the function at the top of the list as though it were a single function.

3. Evaluate the second function of the arrangement. For this task, temporarily assume that the solution to the first function is a part of the given conditions under which the second function will be evaluated. Do not hesitate, during the evaluation, to alter the design and method thinking previously done on the first function, provided the new methods accomplish both function No. 1 and function No. 2.

4. Proceed through the list, using the same approach. When completed, there will be nothing in the final evaluation of any function that is not compatible with all others.

Case Study

INTERACTING FUNCTIONS

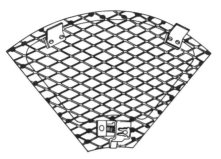

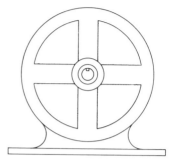

Fig. 3-5   Screen for large electric motor. Made by cutting suitable metal frame approximately 7 inches on each of the radii, welding expanded metal over opening, and riveting in easy-opener lock; $\frac{1}{16}$-inch-thick steel; 4,500 per year; $6 each. Four screens fill end of 18-inch diameter motor opening.

Fig. 3-6   Diagram of motor without protective screens (viewed from shaft end).

The functions were determined to be:

Allow ventilation.
Facilitate maintenance.
Exclude substance.
Please customer.

Had an attempt been made to evaluate the functions in the order of this unarranged list, the work would have been futile for the following reasons: Taking the first function, what must be added to the motor to allow ventilation? Nothing. It is already open. Cost would be 0 cents. Likewise, what must be added to the motor to facilitate maintenance? Again, nothing. Cost would be 0 cents. What must be added to the motor to exclude substance? A cover of some kind. Would this interfere with the accomplishment of the first two functions, which were already evaluated? Probably. Hence no useful benefit has been accomplished.

However, the functions were arranged as follows:

1. Exclude substance.
2. Allow ventilation.
3. Facilitate maintenance.
4. Please customer.

Then the functions were evaluated by creative comparisons in the order of the above list. Much abbreviated, the results were as shown in the following table:

Function 1. Exclude substance (sheet metal)	$0.15 ea.
Function 2. Allow ventilation (open up and modify sheet metal), added cost	0.15
Function 3. Facilitate maintenance (spring clip operated by one-half turn of screwdriver)	0.10
Function 4. Please customer (appearance paint)	0.10
Total value of all functions accomplished	$0.50

Work was motivated and guided by this evaluation of functions presently costing $6 at 50 cents. Costs immediately realized were:

Exclude substance (sheet metal)	$0.25
Allow ventilation (open up and modify sheet metal)	0.30
Facilitate maintenance (Marketing men decided that the costly fastener, which could be removed with the fingers, should be used rather than the screwdriver-actuated spring clip recommended in the evaluation. They judged that it was an aesthetic item that pleased the customer, attracting enough added buyers to justify the extra cost.)	0.60
Please the customer (suitable painting)	0.10
New cost	$1.25

Even keeping the 50-cent aesthetic-function cost, the cost was reduced $4.75 each or $21,000 annually for the design life of the product.

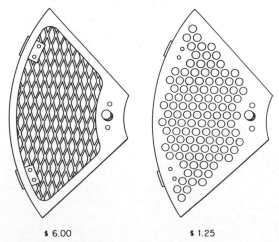

$ 6.00 $ 1.25

Fig. 3-7 Motor screens producing identical functions but differing in cost by more than 4 to 1.

3-4   *Evaluation of Functions*
(from Available Data)

In order to achieve costs that are low enough to equal those of the best competitor, function-cost relationships are exceedingly helpful. Ideally, if the designer knew the lowest cost for which each of the product functions could be provided and had a practical system for adding the values of interacting functions, he could proceed with his design work within the established parameters with confidence that, when completed, his product would not, for a time, experience cost difficulties in competition.

Surprisingly, much basic function-cost information can be produced from published data. Equally surprising, as of this date, tabulations of it have not been generally prepared and are not available to the designer. However, *function-property* relationships are well published, e.g., ratio of current to conductivity. Also, *property-material* relationships are well published, e.g., relationships of conductivity to copper. Finally, *material-cost* relationships are published in catalogues. Therefore, at any one time with a known material cost, the relationship of function to cost is readily determinable.

At all times, when material cost has changed enough to affect the decisions made, it is only necessary to modify the cost factor to have accurate data again. At the present time, each manufacturer, who prepares this data for his specific jobs, understandably considers it proprietary, with the result that, as yet, each must prepare his own.

Some of the types of functions that can be evaluated by published data are:

Insulate voltage. (How much voltage? What area?)
Transmit torque.
Conduct current.
Conduct flux.

Case Study

**PUBLISHED DATA USED TO EVALUATE
THE FUNCTION**

A switchblade was used in a safety-switch assembly enclosed in a space about $2 \times 2 \times 2$ feet. The general type of assembly is shown in Figure

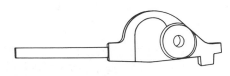

Fig. 3-8 Switchblade. Made by sand-casting and milling the body, then brazing strip of brass $\frac{3}{8} \times \frac{3}{32}$ inch thick and 4 inches long into body; overall length, 7 inches; 600 per year; $3 each. Mounted in enclosed electric switch gear.

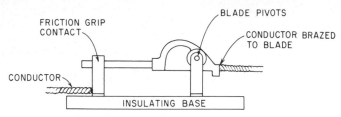

Fig. 3-9   Safety switchblade in use.

3-9. The switch was used a few times each year whenever it was necessary to make adjustments in the switch-gear equipment or in the electrical equipment that was controlled by the switch gear. At such times, the electrician would open a circuit breaker in the circuit preceding the switch-gear equipment, open the equipment, manually open the safety switch, and then, if desired, reclose the preceding circuit breaker. Work could then proceed in 100 per cent safety.

The following functions of the switchblade were named:

1. Conduct current: 50 amperes, 4 inches.
2. Accommodate circuit opening (manually under conditions of no voltage).

It was noted that the first function would lend itself to evaluation from published data while the second must be evaluated by creative searches and comparisons.

Evaluation of function No. 1:
  The amount of copper in standard commercial form
  required to conduct the 50 amperes: 4 inches $0.10
Evaluation of function No. 2:
  Several comparisons were creatively made.
  The construction for the basis of this evaluation was:
    Use bar, not round copper   0.02
    Add an inch to its length   0.03
    Flatten a portion still more at the pivot end   0.05
    Drill or pierce a hole for the pivot   0.05
                                                       ──────
    Total $0.15

The combined value of the two functions then became

1. Conduct current $0.10
2. Accommodate opening   0.15
                             ──────
   Total $0.25

The arithmetic sum of the two function values became the valid value of the combined functions because they were evaluated according to the system for handling interacting functions previously explained.

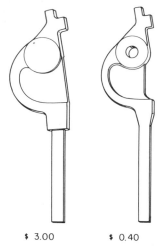

$ 3.00 $ 0.40

Fig. 3-10 Switchblades producing identical function but differing in cost by more than 7 to 1.

Now, with a value of 25 cents on the functions that were costing $3, the men working on the project were motivated and guided to take some actions. One member of this study team was a purchasing man. He obtained quotations on a switchblade made as a one-piece brass forging. With a moderate die cost, its cost became 40 cents. Although more extensive change could probably have developed a good construction at nearer the evaluated cost of 25 cents, the men responsible elected to make the change to the forged switchblade at once since it saved $2.60 each, provided a totally interchangeable part that could be used in maintenance of equipment already installed, and allowed them to use their time on other areas of the equipment.

3-5 *Evaluate All Functions by Comparison*

Value being a relative rather than an absolute measure, the comparison approach must be used in evaluating functions. The basic question, "Is the function accomplished reliably at the best cost?" can be answered only by comparison.

The larger and more complicated the object undergoing analysis, the greater the number of comparisons necessary to make the analysis sufficiently comprehensive to establish the best value for each included function. This means analyzing a series of basic functions, each discovered by breaking the assembly down into its subunits, components, and parts. In this way the problem becomes perhaps one of comparing the use of one material with that of another, the style of one part with that of an equivalent, the application of one process of manufacture with that of another, and so on. It may be a matter of comparing metal with plastics, screw-machined parts with lathe-machined equivalents, or stamping with spinning to determine how the needed function can be obtained reliably at the lowest cost.

It can be said almost without fear of contradiction that, if there is no comparison, there is no evaluation. All evaluation results from comparison of some kind: in some instances, comparison with standards; in other instances, comparison with similar items; and in still others, comparison with partially similar items. If, in the pursuit of better value, functions have not been identified and these functions have not been evaluated by comparison, then the process has not been value analysis but merely cost analysis.

This vitally important step, "evaluate the function by comparison," is perhaps best recognized by looking at a few illustrative examples.

EXAMPLE 1:   *Knowing value of function promotes and guides effort*

The step of identifying the function is the value analyst's initial tool. In some cases, just the clear use of this step prompts ideas and information which result in better value. For example, a round bronze casting 3 inches in diameter and ¼ inch thick, with a center-drilled and splined hole, was found to cost $16. What was its function? It fitted on a valve stem, and its function was to facilitate opening and closing a valve by hand. In other words, $16 was expended on providing a handle to open and close a valve. Nearly everyone has seen valves with suitable handles and realizes that whole valves can be bought for $2 or $3, so one is motivated at once to "do something about it," namely, to look to valve experts for a better answer. By just this step, a similar valve handle of equal effectiveness, readily available, was produced for a cost of 60 cents.

EXAMPLE 2:   *Where use value is of prime importance*

What is the value in dollars of a nail? We find, by comparison, that answers to such questions as: What precisely are the functions with respect to use, convenience, life, etc., which are needed from the nail? Then, what alternative ways are there of accomplishing all those functions with the same reliability? And finally, what is the cost by these alternative methods? The value of the nail cannot exceed the cost of the least expensive alternative method of accomplishing all its functions with equal reliability, as established by comparison.

What is the value of a brass screw? First, all functions of use, of appearance, of convenience, of endurance, etc., must be clearly established. Next, other combinations of materials, processes, and products which will reliably accomplish the total purpose are compared. When the costs of these alternatives have been developed, the cost of the least expensive alternative that will reliably accomplish the total function establishes the maximum value of the screw. And, indeed, the screw must be available for that cost, or informed consumers will buy other products and discontinue the use of the screw.

What is the value of an electric switch? Again, with the total functions of the electric switch in clear view, a search should be made for other means of reliably interrupting a circuit under the same conditions. Some of these alternatives may be more costly and some less costly. If some less costly are found, then the makers of the switch may well expect marketing problems because the shortcoming of their switch is established by comparison.

EXAMPLE 3: *Where aesthetic value is of prime importance*

Total dollar values are normally established by comparisons which include both the use factors and the aesthetic factors in function. In most products for industrial applications—from the nail up—the use function holds primary importance. A great variety of other products, of which the electric clock is one, must, besides accomplishing their use functions reliably, have appearance, attractiveness, and perhaps other interest factors which cause customers to buy them; these we may group broadly under the term *aesthetic*. Consider here an item such as a suit of clothes. The use value derives essentially from the functions providing warmth and comfort, while the aesthetic values consist substantially of the functions yielding appearance, attractiveness, and conformity to social custom. Also, these values can be established by comparison. A thorough search would probably identify means for securing the warmth and comfort functions of a $50 suit of clothes for $10 or $15. This can be developed by comparing all alternative means of securing the same warmth and comfort. To then arrive at the total value of $50 for the suit, we must add the $35 or $40 which represents aesthetic value. Here too we are concerned with comparison. If there are better ways of providing at lower cost all of the attractiveness, appearance, conformity to custom, etc., which are contained in the suit, then the suit does not represent good value at $50; only lack of knowledge on the part of the customer causes him to buy it. An informed user will change to the alternative choice which has been developed by comparison.

Evaluation, then, is seen to be a result of the comparison involved.

3-6   Value of Function Becomes a Guide or Measure

Values of functions, or *measures* of approximate appropriate cost, can be prepared by either those responsible for the work and decision making or an assisting specialist who is skilled in using the value analysis system.

Some questions asked by specialists, while in training, and the answers are included to deepen understanding of this vital technique.

1. *What is measure?* After a function (or a group of functions) is fully understood and described and after intensive and effective work has been completed—using all of the techniques that are appicable—the lowest cost that seems likely to accomplish all of the use and/or aesthetic functions that the customer wants, considering probable manufacturing quantities, is the *measurement*.

2. *Must it be proved?* Yes, a few times. In preparing the measure,

thinking processes, searches, analyses, and comparisons play a significant part. These must be available to show the reasonableness of the conclusions. Sometimes it will be desirable to carry the study further in specific cases. Sometimes a measure is based upon the expected outcome of a test of a minor "unknown" that is expected to work out but does not; then more work should be done to establish a valid measurement. (To be 100 per cent sure of anything, engineering tests must be completed. This is engineering work, not measurement work.)

The great value in the measurement comes from the specific intense searches, analyses, creativity, and thinking, some of which would not have occurred otherwise. As a result, about 95 per cent of the measurements will be about 95 per cent right, and they form excellent guides.

3. *Should explanations be given?* Yes, to the extent that the increased understanding is needed to develop confidence of the user or to the extent that the information and thinking involved will help in the manufacturing, engineering, or other work that will follow in the use of the measurement.

No, when neither of these criteria apply.

4. *When do we go into the creative step?* When we have gathered enough information, analyzed for meaning and direction and made into specific solvable-type problems, creativity for a variety of specific purposes is often a next step.

5. *When is a real and final measure established?* When the conditions in question 1 have been met and the total of the measures meets the needs of the business, they are considered final until a change occurs— either in the needs of the business or in the validity of the measure.

6. *How do we get people to place confidence in the measurements?* By giving them understanding, experience with them, and results from them.

7. *How do we, as specialists in value analysis, divide the work so that our associates will not think that we are taking some of their work from them?* Each associate naturally expects you to do what he has seen you doing in the past. Associates must be shown, usually in orientation meetings, that a new need to meet more severe competition exists and that this method is being used to help. Their managers must discuss the method with them, showing them how they will be affected by it, how they will contribute to it, and how they will benefit from it. Care must be taken in discussing the new method to prevent causing any embarrassment.

8. *Must this method be well known to be used?* Yes, it must become well known and well respected, as with any other important work.

9. *Will this method be so difficult to use with many products that only a "superman" can do it?* No, this work has approaches and techniques quite different than the technology of any one technical field. It may be

recalled that less-than-average knowledge in the precise field of the product or service is adequate.

10. *How will we motivate men to use the measurements we make?* Basically, you won't. No one uses a meter stick just because it is around; neither do people use an engineer or a lawyer just because he is around. Motivation is from business need, and it appears that competitive need is increasing. It is a case of need, availability, orientation, and understanding.

11. *To whom will I present my results?* As marketing people and others determine requirements of performance, selling prices, etc., for the needs of the business for all who need to use them, so you will determine measurements to meet the business need for all who need to use them.

12. *If we provide guides to decision making, won't it be considered troublesome by the men who now advise the managers on decision making?* To the timber appraiser who has always estimated the height and diameter of trees by his experience and skillful intuition, the unexpected appearance of an effective measurement device that readily provides more accurate measurements faster would be troublesome and perhaps embarrassing and injuring. However, if he knew that this device was coming in advance, if he was among the first to understand and use it, and if it helped him to do his job better, the opposite might be true.

When men in the business find that here are measurements that help each one make his cost-affecting decisions, they will like using them, as they like obtaining and using meaningful accounting data or any other useful information.

SUMMARY

Establishing a "value" of a function is one of the new techniques offered by the value analysis system. In this context "value" means the lowest cost that would provide a function with the qualities and specifications with which the customer wants it to operate. This value in dollars and cents then becomes a guide and measure. It indicates the approximate maximum cost that should be accepted for the function in decision making.

Function values are usually prepared from comparisons. They must not be prepared from past practices. Sometimes they may be prepared from engineering data.

When interacting functions are evaluated, they must be arranged in appropriate order and the solution to each must be considered as a part of the situation in evaluating succeeding functions.

In the preliminary evaluation of functions, do not strive for technical exactness. That will follow. Instead, provide a reasonable guide and approximate measurement that is based upon new current information and intense, objective, basic, new thinking.

chapter 4

Problem-setting System

"A problem solvably stated is half solved."

The request "Remove one-fourth of the cost of this refrigerator without reducing any of its quality" is of the same nature as the statement "Improve this stew without decreasing its nutriment." Both statements help to *choose* the problem, but neither helps to *solve* it. They tell us that the cost is to be removed from the refrigerator, not the dishwasher, and improvement made in the stew, not the coffee. When the request becomes "Improve the texture, color, and spicing of the stew," a first essential step has been taken toward improvement. By following procedures described in this chapter, problems in products and services likewise may be stated in more *solvable* forms.

4-1　Step 1: Identify Functions

Precisely what function or functions does the customer need or want to pay for? Precisely what function does each element or group of elements accomplish? Precisely what degree of this function is wanted by the customer? Precisely what degree is being accomplished? Name the functions. Study the limits under which each function must operate.

Every problem must be solved on the basis of its facts and assumptions. There are always assumptions. Great effort has often been made through tests and study of experience to minimize assumptions. Often data that are used as facts are in some part, small or large, assumptions. By incisive questioning and penetrating analysis, separate assumptions from facts. Determine, if possible, some cases in which more information or data can be found that will change some assumptions to the appropriate facts and that will modify some of the remaining assumptions to be more in harmony with the real situation.

4-2   Step 2: Separate Functions

Start with the total function that the customer wants and is willing to pay for. Make the total function precisely clear and understood, with critically reliable assumptions clear and sharp, and then divide it into the major groups of subfunctions, that is, functions that must be accomplished in order to achieve the total, or main, function. Proceed to identify each of these subfunctions with the same precision and clarity used in identifying the overall function. Next subdivide these subfunctions into functions that are necessary to accomplish each subfunction. Identify each of these sharply, question each, identify its real task, and improve its information and assumptions. Further divide, continuing the process until it reaches individual parts.

This process has not, as yet, established, or "set," the problem in a form that will most readily yield a good solution, but it provides information and thinking essential to good problem setting.

> EXAMPLE: Consider the function for which a customer pays certain initial costs and then a stipulated monthly or annual amount. A customer wants and is willing to pay for electric lighting and power service. The functions might be named:
>
> *Use*:   Provide light.
>   Provide power or energy.
> *Aesthetic*:   Provide suitable appearance.
>   Provide convenience (of use).
>   Provide absence of noise.

Several subfunctions are required:

1. Provide energy.
2. Distribute current.
3. Control current.

Each function and subfunction must be performed within its established limits and constraints.

Further examining subfunction No. 3, "control current," it is found that the customer's wants are for

Something to turn the lights off and on (a "use" function)
Acceptable "feel," appearance, and sound ("aesthetic" functions)

The use function might be named *open circuit* or *close circuit*. To accomplish this customer-wanted function, several more subfunctions are required:

1. Accept wires (of electric circuit).
2. Conduct current.
3. Resist disintegration (caused by sparking).
4. Provide movement (to open contacts).
5. Transmit suitable movement (from the thumb).
6. Mount parts.

Dividing subfunction No. 1, "accept wires," further would mean essentially naming materials and parts that perform it by the means we now have in mind: "screws," or "terminal," or "spring." Dividing subfunction No. 2, "conduct current," further would essentially mean supplying material, part, and operation names, not function names: "conductor material," "contact material," "braze," or "weld." Thus, customer-wanted functions have now been so effectively divided that names of parts or materials are being designated.

It is at once seen that this depth penetration of function subdivision in itself has *not* "set" the problem. It has prepared the way for the problem to be set by suitable grouping. When considering *function grouping* on the wall switch, it would be helpful for the reader to group the functions and name the function groups in a manner that will cause other good solutions to come into view, such as the mercury bubble switch.

4-3 *Step 3: Group Functions*

Of course, some benefits may come from suitable study of parts and materials but do not study individual parts and totally separate functions too long, but rather group them into functional groups, or assemblies, each with a specific, well-defined, and well-understood purpose. Group in different ways to provide the necessary supporting functions and finally the total function required. Get the whole task into "mind-sized" pieces. The individual must have the "pieces" that are "his size," that he can solve one at a time, and that will take him to his objective. Each step must be made on the basis of basic, objective material.

By now the overall problem has been broken into a number of specific problems. It is becoming apparent precisely which problem must be solved in order to unlock great opportunities in the larger problem. Furthermore, the information and essentials have been tightly screened and improved so that the next stage of the work will be on the "right" problem.

Case Study

PROBLEM SETTING

The refrigerator is a well-developed, high-quality product that is in the "mature" part of the normal industrial cycle. To maintain its high quality, keep or even add customer features, sell it competitively and provide sufficient earnings to assure the continuity of the business are requirements that make it a useful example for the application of value engineering approaches. In this case study, with only enough changes to avoid disclosing confidential data of the manufacturer, management assigned the task of designing a refrigerator at a cost of $100 for use in the line to replace one costing $125.

The team assigned to this task consisted of the design engineer, the manufacturing engineer, the buyer, and the value analyst. Their first task was to pool their knowledge and decide what would make the most *solvable problem*. The steps in "making the problem solvable" were determined as follows:

Functions that must be performed*	Present cost	Required cost
1. Contain..............................	$ 23	$ 19
2. Cool.................................	65	50
3. Insulate.............................	8	5
4. Control..............................	9	6
5. Please...............................	20	20
Total cost.........................	$125	$100

* Note that in this study (1) all cost is assigned to functions and none to "parts" and (2) function names are abbreviated, consisting of verbs only rather than nouns and verbs as in previous studies.

The team determined that if the task were set up as shown above, each of the steps would be of about the same difficulty of achievement and when they were all achieved the task would be successfully completed.

Thus the first step of putting the problem in solvable form has been completed. For the purpose of this case study, we will report as the next step the investigations of function No. 4, "control."

The control system, which keeps the refrigerator within predetermined limits of temperature, costs $9. Considering the advancements in the art since its design, the complete function that the customer wants it to accomplish, and the skills that either are in the group or can be called in, this problem was made solvable as follows:

Functions that must be performed	Present cost	Required cost
1. Sense temperature....................	$1.00	$0.60
2. Actuate contacts.....................	1.50	0.80
3. Interrupt circuit....................	1.00	0.50
4. Provide adjustment...................	1.00	1.00
5. Mount and protect....................	4.00	2.00
6. Please customer......................	0.50	0.10
Total cost..........................	$9.00	$5.00*

* In this case, while making the control function "solvable," the preliminary examination of the six functions indicated that it would be reasonable to expect to accomplish a cost of $5 rather than the $6 assigned while examining the overall product.

Note that the expected achievable cost, or "value," tentatively assigned to each function is determined by the precise situations surrounding that particular function, not by general rules or application of "blanket" percentages to all functions.

With this problem now in solvable form, the problem-solving system and other techniques were used, with the following results:

1. A gas was used to *sense temperature*. Its property of contraction when cooler was used. A modified gas, which had the property of condensation and therefore a much greater change in volume at a given pressure right at the needed control temperature, was used. The sensing *bulb* was not needed. The tubing was changed to capillary tubing only.

2. The bellows, which reacted to the change in volume and/or pressure of the gas, was made much smaller, thus increasing its sensitivity and decreasing its cost.

3. The contacts were made differently, halving their cost, with the same functioning properties.

4. The system of mounting and protecting was made much simpler and smaller but still performed the functions with the same effectiveness.

5. Some cost in aesthetics was ended. It became well understood that the only contact the customer had with the control was the knob. Its appearance and ease and convenience of operation were the sole reason for aesthetic cost. Customer aesthetics on the knob pointer were improved somewhat but other so-called "aesthetic" costs in the mount and support assembly were ended.

The overall result was that the control function was accomplished for a little less than the $5, and a $4 contribution was made to the overall $25 task from only a $9 item. Similar procedures produced suitable results on the total project.

4-4 *Problem-setting and Problem-solving Overlap*

The final *problem setting* is accomplished during the *problem-solving* work, described in the next chapter. In the *analysis* step, the problem-solving system, after much information has been secured, the precise problems to be solved and the order in which to solve them are "set." This frequently means a recycling back into *information searching* on the real problems as finally set for solution. Very often, after the information searching and during the analysis thinking, the real problem is clarified, narrowed, divided into two or more separate problems, or changed altogether. Thereafter the disciplined thinking of the creative problem-solving system is utilized on precisely the right problems.

When a problem is properly set, it is organized into a group of functions (or a single function), which are often interrelated but which accomplish one significant purpose—they permit common information search, analysis, creativity, and judgment. If a group of functions is formed, it should not be so involved that incisive thinking becomes impossible or so separated that "pieces and parts" instead of "functions" are being studied.

SUMMARY

Before investing important resources of time and energy in the task of solving a problem only to find later that either it was not quite the right problem or that it was so inclusive, exclusive, or mixed that good solutions did not result, penetrating thought should be given to dividing or grouping the problem right and stating it right.

All costs are associated with the functions or subfunctions they accomplish. Manageable function groups or individual functions are then made into specific problems, which are stated in function terms that are in similar parameters and lend themselves to comparisons and alternatives.

The final work of establishing the exact problems to be solved is done in the analysis step of the problem-solving system. At that time the initial problem will often be made more solvable.

chapter 5

Problem-solving System

5-1 A Good System Contains Everything the Task Requires

Good results, consistently, in any sphere of man's activity arise from the use of a good system. A good system has everything it needs, arranged so that each part is used at the time it is needed, to the extent it is needed, and accomplishes its function well. A telephone is a system—so is an airplane or an automobile. *Value engineering* is a system, but, instead of parts, it consists of approaches, understandings, and techniques—for one sole purpose, *the efficient identification of unnecessary cost.*

All realize and "feel" the futility of trying to get good results with the telephone—which is a system of parts—with even one *wire* or *connection* absent. The secretary would provide a rather "unusual" letter if she were forced to type on a machine lacking *only one key*. Yet, when it comes to performing cost-oriented work, it is *customary*—not even the exception—to use only the approaches and techniques that have been learned, which would certainly be lacking in one-tenth to perhaps one-half of the approaches that would propel one toward a solution. The remaining techniques that are needed but absent are not missed because others have not been observed using them. Thus, mentally comparing the results secured with the results possible is like comparing the effectiveness of a telephone with all parts in place with one lacking 10 per cent of the needed parts.

The overall system of value analysis or engineering includes an array of parts to deal with specific needs. The problem-solving system includes the parts, approaches, and actions required to get better answers to problems more efficiently. Most of these approaches are organized into a *job plan*.

Efficient actions rest on suitable plans. In actions in which cause and effect have immediate obvious relationships, good plans are the rule. In other actions which are more involved so that effects from the various parts of the plan are not so directly tied to their specific causes, plans often become haphazard and less effective.

As a simple example, the repetitive operation of getting into the car and driving to work in the morning involves carrying out a plan:

Open the garage door.	Get out of the car.
Open the car door.	Close the garage door.
Get into the car.	Reenter the car.
Close the car door.	Close the car door.
Insert the ignition key.	Engage the gear.
Turn the key.	Look again for children.
Depress the starter.	Depress the accelerator.
Engage the gear.	Enter the street.
Look out for children.	Release the accelerator.
Depress the accelerator.	Depress the brake.
Release the accelerator.	Change gear.
Apply the brake.	Depress the accelerator.
Open the car door.	

All the steps of this plan are followed every time and, normally, very good results are secured. Omission of any one of the steps would hamper the accomplishment of the objective.

In contrast, effort which is oriented toward identifying and removing unnecessary costs has commonly been carried out without an effective overall plan that includes all essential steps. Besides, when it has seemed inconvenient or difficult to accomplish a step in the plan, the step has been omitted. For the achievement of high-grade results in the objective of removing unnecessary cost, it is no more possible to omit one of the planned steps than it is to omit one of the necessary steps in the handling of the car and still achieve good results.

The reader will learn that, in effect, the value analysis job plan requires that those using it:

Recognize and face the problem, with the functions to be accomplished clearly in mind.

Secure the needed information.

Analyze information and assumptions for meaning.

Do the essential creative work.

Select from the results of the creative work the best choices of action.

Minimize the disadvantages of the best solutions.

Establish effective programs pointed toward execution of these best solutions.

End the "stoppers," or "roadblocks."

Execute the established program without faltering.

5-2 *Essential Preliminary Step Is "Mind Tuning"*

A very clear understanding and "feeling" of "what we are really trying to do" is vital; then later actions and inactions are more readily understood. In effect, the one or more minds involved must be tuned to exactly the same task at precisely the same time. It is often startling how much more effectively a group will work if group mind *tuning*, or *setting*, has been thoroughly accomplished.

On this project, what are we really trying to do in relation to

The competitor?	Our market position?
Our factories, long range?	Our factories, short range?
Our earnings, long range?	Our earnings, short range?
Our sales costs?	Our sales prices?
Our product?	Our investment?
Our management?	Our design engineers?
Our manufacturing engineers?	Our field salesmen?
Our buyers?	Our finance manager?
Our stockholders?	Our labor?
Our good technology?	Our standardization?
Our jobs, present?	Our jobs, future?
Our quality?	Our product obsolescence?
Our quantities?	Our pride in past work?"

Now with a clear and complete "feeling" of what it is that is to be done, proceed with the job plan for problem solving.

5-3 *The Value Analysis Job Plan*

In the *job plan* the problems are recognized and faced, with the functions to be accomplished clearly in mind. It is a five-step process. First, information surrounding the problem area is intensively and extensively secured. Then it is thoroughly analyzed for meaning and *sense of direction*. Next the essential creative work is done. Afterward and separately, the judicial work is done, followed by suitable developmental work. Each of the first four steps is a different type of mental activity. Each is exclusively followed and thoroughly completed before *any* of the other steps are begun.

1. *Information Step*

The foundation for effectiveness is built in the information step. What are the facts? What are the truths? What have been thought to be truths? Only when thorough and complete knowledge of the situation is obtained can valuable new thinking be done. Often, when complete information is in view, good solutions grow rapidly. Carefully separate out the assumptions. Review each. Determine if facts can be substituted for parts of the assumptions. Seriously question assumptions of long standing.

What is to be accomplished? What is it that the customer really needs or wants? What are the desirable characteristics with respect to size, weight, appearance, durability, etc.? Secure all pertinent information: costs, quantities, vendors, drawings, specifications, planning cards, and manufacturing methods data as well as actual samples of parts and assemblies where practicable. In the case of new products, secure all information that is available: all design concepts, preliminary sketches and drawings, preliminary cost estimates, etc.

Examine the basic engineering with the engineer—ask questions, listen, and develop through him a thorough understanding of the experience with the product to date. Examine the basic manufacturing with the manufacturing experts—ask questions, listen, and study manufacturing methods that have been adapted for the operation in question.

Make three lists: (1) facts, (2) assumptions (beliefs), and (3) information needed but not known. Allow no interpretation, analysis, or idea generation. What is known? What is believed? What is done? Where? By whom? When? At what cost? What are the service factors? What are the maintenance factors? What are other customer factors? Why was it done this way? When? What changes? Why changed? Why not other changes? etc. What are marketing, engineering, manufacturing, purchasing, inventory, and all other factors?

Write everything down. Surround the situation with more facts than one person has yet viewed in one picture. This work may be done by individuals or by groups of any number of persons, providing each person present has some information or knowledge or assumptions used, and further, that the leader manages the meeting so that there is deep "dredging" for pertinent information, with positively no wandering half-thoughts of analysis or possible solutions.

2. *Analysis Step*

In the analysis step, extensive essential "function" thinking is developed. Functions are "evaluated," and problem setting is made precise. Functions are separated for single study and then are grouped as needed for best solution. Moreover, it is readily discerned that, in effect, the preceding information step is an essential prerequisite to precise and final problem setting, as illustrated in Chapter 4.

What are the meanings? What are the total problems? The individual problems? The reasonable goals and plans? What are the key problems to be solved first? What solutions seem reasonable? What end result is reasonable? What steps—first, second, third, etc.—are indicated? What additional information is required? What unlisted assumptions are being made? Are the assumptions now valid? What solutions does it make sense to search for? Approximately what savings or benefits might each of the best approaches bring? Exactly what parts of the problem or overall problems should we seek out better solutions for first? What specific needs, when well met by better solutions, would "unlock" very beneficial solutions for the project?

Normally, there will be one or more specific problems in each of the following classes.

Class-1 Problems

Seemingly very difficult, with large benefits if solved.

Class-2 Problems

Require penetrating thought and creativity, with substantial benefits when solved.

Class-3 Problems

Small need for new search and/or creativity and small but probably worthwhile benefits to profits.

In performing the analysis step, two people are the optimum number unless a third individual has special technologies that are constantly needed for that project and the mental skills required to "pull" in mental harmony with the other two at each instant of their joint work. Of course, others should be consulted as required.

Case Study

**EVALUATING FUNCTION IN ANALYSIS STEP
RESULTS IN REDUCING MANUFACTURING COSTS
75 PER CENT**

A few hundred fiber washers, ⅛ inch thick and 1½ inches in diameter, were needed. They were made by purchasing fiber rod 1½ inches in diameter, drilling the center hole, and cutting them off like wafers. This required no special tooling and was easy to accomplish in any machine shop. The cost was 16 cents each. As the product involved became successful and the quantities increased to many thousands per year, the washers continued to be made by the same process. The function was evaluated at much less than 16 cents. As a result, the washers were made from sheet at a total cost of 3½ cents.

3. Creativity Step

Einstein said that when there is a problem to be solved, "Creativity is more important than knowledge." Having acquired understanding and information, we have laid the foundation for the application of various techniques to generate every possible solution to the overall problems involved, to the parts of problems, and to the individual problems. To derive the fullest benefit from our creative power, we must now encourage free use of the imagination.

It is useful to consider the human mind as containing certain knowledge *bits*, or pieces, and an ability to bring these diverse knowledge bits, which have never before appeared in the "same mental picture," together into one focus long enough to consider "What benefits to my present project might result if I combined them in the solution?" In this concept good useful creativity is maximized if the individual is in possession of two factors: (1) the knowledge bits required to deal with the task at hand and (2) the mental ability to readily join diverse, unrelated bits of knowledge into one temporary picture.

To meet real-life situations, the strategy of value engineering must:

a. Provide logic.
b. Communicate emotionally in credible terms.
c. Identify new types of knowledge needed.
d. Provide research techniques that will find that knowledge efficiently.
e. Cause creativity that will usefully combine the knowledge from diverse sources.

A chemical not yet compounded does not exist, and a metal not yet developed does not exist—not because they are not possible, but because the required combination of creativity and knowledge has not yet been associated.

To accomplish the functions that the customer wants for half or a third of the historical or expected cost and at less than the competitor's cost, a situation must be created in which the necessary creative ideation and essential knowledge are blended extensively and intensively.

Three to ten people are optimum.

Defer all judging. This will be much more difficut than expected.

Use the various methods to accelerate creative activities from the mind. (These were originated by the late Alex Osborn and are extended and taught by the Creative Problem Solving Institute of the University of Buffalo and elsewhere.) Since creativity is joining bits of knowledge in new combinations, it may be desirable to include people in this step who have some knowledge related to the subject; however, they *must* accept the discipline of deferred judgment, or *they must not be there*.

Penetrate each of the problems in classes 1 to 3 thoroughly, listing all suggested approaches.

Encourage free association of ideas.

Use preliminary judgment.

Select the approaches that show so much promise that it is believed they should be thoroughly studied, extended, and judged.

Case Study

**CREATIVITY STEP REDUCES COST OF
SHIFT-LEVER BRACKET 80 PER CENT**

A shift-lever bracket (Figure 5-1) on an appliance was used in quantity and made of ⅛-inch-thick steel 3 inches wide. A die the size and shape of the required part was used. It blanked each item as required from the material, leaving a slight amount of trim all around. The part cost 11 cents. Its function was evaluated at between 2 and 3 cents.

In the creative phase of study, dozens of possible approaches were listed; for example:

Make of wire form
    Plastic
    Standard angle
    Flattened tubing
Eliminate it
Combine with the handle

One phase of the creative study developed suggested changes for the tooling used in making it. One suggestion was to cut off the piece instead

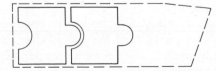

Fig. 5-1 Normal stamping operation with one piece formed at each stroke of machine and waste around edges.

of stamping it out. It was then discovered that the part had an unusual symmetry in that its edges were parallel and its top and its bottom could be identical. A new punch was made which would provide identical tops and bottoms to the part and which was itself the size of the required stamping. A slightly narrower steel material was ordered so that there would be no waste on the sides, and the stamping operation would change to a cutoff operation. Since the stamping die was then exactly the size of the part required and either the bottom or the top would cut the shape required, the material was moved the length of two parts at each stroke and the punch acted to shear off one part with its leading edge and another with its following edge. The result, as shown in Figure 5-2, was that instead of one part with each stroke and waste all around, two parts were secured with each stroke and no waste whatsoever was made. Cost became 2 cents each.

Fig. 5-2 Improved stamping operation with two pieces formed at each stroke of machine and no waste material.

4. Judgment Step

This step is performed by one person, consulting others as required. What approaches show the greatest promise of yield and accomplishment? Do not discard ideas. Develop and improve the better ones. Study intensely ideas with high dollar value, determine their limitations with great objectivity, and then seek to eliminate, overcome, or minimize the objections.

Which approaches are now ready for the development planning step? Which should be referred back through another cycle of information, analysis, and/or creativity step? What solution has so many advantages that the minimizing of its specific disadvantage becomes the new principal problem?

5. Development Planning Step

One person performs this step, consulting others as required and assigning specific actions to others as appropriate for development.

Select the best specialists for consultation.
Select the best vendors for consultation.
Establish a program of investigation that will provide the latest information on, and the latest capabilities of, each of the approaches that shows promise, such as the casting approach, the fabrication approach, the plastics approach, the wire-form approach, etc.

Supply all needed information to the specialists and to the vendors in order to stimulate new, applicable, and effective solutions.

Pursue constantly, regularly, thoroughly, and intensively each of the avenues set up in the program-planning step until all the suggestions have been appraised and evaluated.

Periodically provide more information and encouragement to the specialists and the vendors, and help them to overcome problems they find in applying their materials or processes.

Work with specialists and vendors until they come up with alternatives or otherwise terminate their efforts.

Case Study

A SILVER CONTACT ASSEMBLY—TREATMENT
UNDER THE VALUE ANALYSIS JOB PLAN

INFORMATION STEP: The function of this assembly is that of operating an appliance on a 110-volt circuit. This requires making and breaking the circuit several million times. It makes the circuit with a maximum starting current of 10 amperes and breaks the circuit with a maximum of 3 amperes and with known amounts of circuit inductance. It operates at

Fig. 5-3 Electrical contact.

ambient temperatures in a moderately dry and reasonably vibration-isolated environment.

The contact is found to be used in quantities of 1 million, and the amount of silver necessary to withstand the making and breaking of the circuit for the required number of cycles has been determined. The silver is purchased as a small part and is welded to the brass support. Drawings, specifications, vendors' names, costs, ordering quantities, and all allied information are available. The cost is $22 per thousand. As with other electrical contacts, the practice has been to provide the necessary amount of silver for the making and breaking surfaces and to support this silver on a copper base material which will readily conduct current and efficiently conduct away heat.

ANALYSIS STEP: To make the contact requires much "doing." Silver sheet is bonded to brass sheet, and buttons about ¼ inch in diameter are punched from it. They are coined and shipped from the vendor. Brass strip is punched and cut off, and contact buttons are brazed to each. Only the very small point of silver actually makes contact—less than one-tenth of the area.

Several contacts in newer products in similar high-volume service were tentatively examined. For low-volume applications the present contact made good sense, but observing the superior design ingenuity of some of the high-volume contacts supported the conclusion that $22,000 per year was an excessive cost to accept for the function of this contact.

The function was evaluated at $10,000 per year, or $10 per thousand. It was also judged that although the mating contacts were of somewhat different design, they could probably use the solution developed for this contact.

CREATIVITY STEP: Every possible solution to the problem is now sought. By applying intensive creative imagination, in the neighborhood of, say, one hundred different approaches may be brought forth for consideration. This is a likely result to be derived from creative work, which might run along such lines as this:

QUESTION: How might the circuit with the established requirements of current, voltage, inductance, life, temperature, and other conditions be satisfactorily opened and closed a suitable number of times?

SUGGESTIONS:

1. Use steel strip.
2. Use steel strip to which silver is welded or brazed.
3. Use brass or copper strip.
4. Use brass or copper strip to which silver is welded.
5. Use steel wire.
6. Use brass or copper wire.
7. Use silver-plated wire or strip of iron, brass, or copper.
8. Use silver wire.
9. Weld silver wire to base metal of iron, brass, or copper.
10. Weld silver wire continuously to strip of iron, brass, or copper and cut off.
11. Weld silver wire continuously to iron, brass, or copper, cut off, and coin.
12. Weld silver strip to brass strip, cut off, and coin.
13. Weld shaped silver strip to brass strip and cut off.
14. Use silver rivets in iron, copper, or brass base metal.
15. Weld or braze silver balls to iron, copper, or brass base metal.
16. Buy present contacts more competitively.
17. to 100. Etc.

JUDGMENT STEP: This produced comments like the following ones, which are typical though not complete.

Alternative 1: "Use steel strip." Steel has not been found satisfactory as an electrical-contact material required to conduct necessary amounts of current for the necessary number of cycles.

Alternative 2: "Use steel strip to which silver is welded or brazed." A strong belief by qualified technical people that nonferrous metals should be used, combined with a reasonable question concerning the amount of heat generated if steel were used, makes this one of the less desirable alternatives.

Alternative 3: "Use brass or copper strip." This is not considered satisfactory for the operating conditions.

Alternative 4: "Use brass or copper strip to which silver is welded." Probably a right solution, this is the way it is being done now. Later suggestions cover this arrangement in more specific terms.

Alternative 5: "Use steel wire." Probably steel-to-steel elements make and break contact unsatisfactorily under the specified working conditions.

Alternative 6: "Use brass or copper wire." Possibly a satisfactory solution; however, technical beliefs and much technical momentum back the use of silver as the face metal in making and breaking contacts under the particular conditions.

Alternative 7: "Use silver-plated wire or strip of iron, brass, or copper." This is probably a good alternative. If plating could be provided economically enough and thick enough at the points needed, it might accomplish the function for the lowest cost.

Alternative 8: "Use silver wire." This alternative is ruled out by high cost.

Alternative 9: "Weld silver wire to base metal of iron, brass, or copper." This is a workable approach to be further investigated.

Alternative 10: "Weld silver wire continuously to strip of iron, brass, or copper and cut off." This possibility should be investigated in connection with alternative 8.

Alternative 11: "Weld silver wire continuously to iron, brass, or copper, cut off, and coin." This should also be investigated in connection with alternative 8.

Alternative 12: "Weld silver strip to brass strip, cut off, and coin." This is a practical approach but probably not as useful as alternative 13.

Alternative 13: "Weld shaped silver strip to brass strip and cut off." A workable approach, this needs to be investigated in detail.

Alternative 14: Use silver rivets in iron, copper, or brass base metal." This workable approach should be further investigated.

Alternative 15: "Weld or braze silver balls on iron, copper, or brass base metal." A workable approach, this deserves further investigation.

Alternative 16: "Buy present contacts more competitively." Review of purchasing effectiveness is called for.

DEVELOPMENT PLANNING STEP: From the foregoing, the indications are that actions should now be set in motion to further explore the possibilities of the alternatives identified. This requires programs to cover each of the alternatives thought to be the most likely ones to produce reliable and useful choices.

Accordingly, alternatives 7, 9, 11, and 13 to 15 were assigned to particular specialists or suppliers who, it was felt, led in the technologies involved. Effective ways of searching for and selecting such experts formed the first need. Then, steps followed to provide these people with all the pertinent information and with proper motivation so that they would propose whatever contacts they believed would meet this application and also furnish costs. As for alternative 16, it was assigned to purchasing for action.

Whenever there is an attempt to accomplish a specific job in a different way, new questions arise. Each of the six suppliers or specialists were assigned a definite individual to be referred to for more information and provided with guidance in the adaptation of their technology to the precise function. Their questions were answered promptly, and they were assured that the user would match their efforts in endeavoring to work out any problems involved in making it practical to utilize the lowest cost-value alternative to reliably accomplish the function.

VALUE ANALYSIS SUGGESTION SHEET

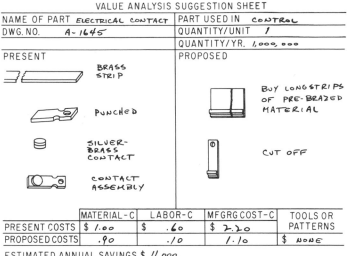

NAME OF PART ELECTRICAL CONTACT	PART USED IN CONTROL
DWG. NO. A- 1645	QUANTITY/UNIT 1
	QUANTITY/YR. 1,000,000

PRESENT — BRASS STRIP, PUNCHED, SILVER-BRASS CONTACT, CONTACT ASSEMBLY

PROPOSED — BUY LONG STRIPS OF PRE-BRAZED MATERIAL, CUT OFF

	MATERIAL-C	LABOR-C	MFGRG COST-C	TOOLS OR PATTERNS
PRESENT COSTS	$ 1.00	$ .60	$ 2.20	
PROPOSED COSTS	.90	.10	1.10	$ NONE

ESTIMATED ANNUAL SAVINGS $ 11,000.

COMMENTS
BRASS STRIP HAS BEEN PURCHASED AND PUNCHED.
SILVER BRASS PRE-FORMED CONTACT BUTTON HAS BEEN
PURCHASED AND BRAZED TO BRASS PART.

SUGGESTIONS–
PURCHASE STRIP BUILT UP OF PROPER AMOUNT OF
BRASS AND SILVER.
CUT OFF PUNCH HOLE, AND USE.
COMPLETELY INTERCHANGEABLE
CONTAINS SAME AMOUNT OF FUNCTIONING SILVER
AND BRASS.

Fig. 5-4   The electrical contact suggestion sheet.

The result was that a number of the alternatives showed equivalent performance at lower costs. The choice shown in the suggestion sheet (Figure 5-4) was selected. It provided all of the functioning materials of the original, was also an interchangeable part, necessitating no changes of any other parts, and reduced the cost in half.

The job plan is a framework that organizes thought and action and prepares the project for the thought and action of its next step. The following case study will show the depth of penetration sometimes required in following through the plan and also the effectiveness of the plan in meeting practical situations. In this case, depth use of the plan provided $83,000 reduction in cost on one small item, adding about $40,000 to the earnings of that operation each year for the design life of the product.

Case Study

THE PIVOT PIN—DEPTH AND THOROUGHNESS
REQUIRED

One morning's mail brought a little stainless steel pin about ¹⁄₁₆ inch in diameter and about ³⁄₈ inch long. A manufacturing man sent it in with the following statement: "We are paying $3.65 per thousand—that's a third of a cent apiece—for 50 million of these a year. Is it good value?"

On receipt of the facts relating to this pin, we found that it was bought from a supplier, and on further study, it was determined that it was not worth that kind of money. We put this finding up to the supplier's sales manager who then, in a two-page letter, told us that the tolerances were so tight that they could do nothing about it. This motivated us to arrange for a meeting of the sales manager, accompanied by his factory superintendent (so we would have the facts), the engineer who had designed the pin, and the buyer who bought it.

Among the questions discussed at this meeting were the following:

1. What purpose does the pin serve? It is the pivot used to support the pinions and gears in an electric clock. Several of them are used in each clock.

2. How is the gear put on the pin? Pressed on. The pinions, made from thin, laminated, carbon steel, are blanked in a small punch press and pressed directly onto the pin. Gears and pinions are held in place by friction with the pin.

3. Why is stainless used? To avoid corrosion.

4. Why use No. 440 stainless which is twice as hard to machine as the others? Because it has 100 points of carbon and can be satisfactorily hardened.

5. Why harden it? In pressing on the tight gears and pinions, the surface of the pin otherwise is sometimes slightly scored, and as this surface serves as a bearing surface, the scoring would result in erratic and short life. The sole function of the hardening is to avoid damage to the pin surface while the gears are being pressed on. Since the pins are running in

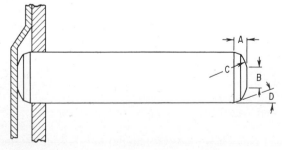

Fig. 5-5   The pivot pin, greatly enlarged.

copper bearings, it is felt that the steel would be sufficiently hard for good bearing operations even without hardening.

6. If the gears are carbon steel and do not corrode or rust, why should the pins? We tried carbon steel for the pins and it does corrode. The gears are made of a very thin cold-rolled steel, and it seems probable that the supplier uses some rust inhibitor in his process which is good enough. If we thoroughly clean the pinion steel by acid or other method, it too will rust.

7. Why the chamfer D? To provide entry into the gear.

8. Why chamfer both ends? To save labor. Otherwise each pin must be picked up and examined before it is located with the proper end up.

9. Why the flat B? The flat presses against the end plate and locates the pin axially. It is desirable for the flat surface to be at a minimum in order to reduce end friction.

10. Why the radius C? The radius is for the purpose of connecting the chamfer to the flat.

11. Why have both the chamfer D and the radius C when the combined length of both is 0.010 inch and may, within tolerances, be as little as 0.005 inch? A chamfer or suitable radius is necessary to provide entry into the gear, and a small end bearing surface is necessary to limit end friction. We presume that the other details best fit into the manufacturing arrangement of the supplier who helped to work it out. A desirable end from this viewpoint would be a semispherical surface. However, such a surface would extend clear back into the bearing and eliminate the cylindrical portion which is now the bearing surface.

12. Why only ±0.001 inch on the length tolerance when it is observed from actual assembly that there is an end play of around 0.015 inch on each pin? Due to the build-up of tolerances, there may be friction between gear faces if more than 0.001 inch is allowed. The tolerance on the studs which separate the end plates is ±0.002 inch, and if it were more economical to hold them to a closer tolerance than the pins, the tolerances might be reversed, allowing +0.002 inch on the pin and making the stud to ±0.001 inch without adversely affecting the assembly.

13. Why only 0.00025-inch diameter tolerance? To provide dependable interference fit when mounting the gears and pinions.

14. There are other ways of providing the features which have been discussed. In general, what prompted this particular design? The part has quite a history; it was made by ourselves and possibly others. The present vendor showed particular interest and aptitude for the job, and some of the design details are prescribed to coincide with his manufacturing processes.

15. Why does the pin cost $3.65 instead of 45 cents per thousand? Because of the ±0.001-inch-length tolerance, the 0.00025-inch OD tolerance, the chamfer-radius end construction, the No. 440 stainless steel, and the hardening.

16. How is it made now? It is made of material in excess of the desired diameter and cut off too long. Then, after hardening, the ends are ground

to length and the outside diameter is ground to size. There are twelve operations in the making of the pin.

17. How much does the stainless material alone cost? Forty-five cents per thousand pieces.

18. How much would carbon steel cost? Around 10 cents per thousand.

19. Can wire be purchased to the diameter tolerance required? Yes.

20. Will automatic screw machines cut it off to the ±0.001-inch-length tolerance? Probably not. We would expect ±0.003 inch from them.

21. How close will wire-forming equipment shear it to length? Good equipment will hold it to ±0.002 inch.

22. Why not cut it off on a form cutter which will provide, in one operation, the necessary chamfer, radius, and end flat? It might work. The problem would be to cut it off to the tolerance of ±0.001 inch and to maintain the form cutter.

23. Some cutoff methods would normally leave a small tip in the center. Wouldn't it be desirable to do so? We would expect so, providing the tip was closely enough controlled so that the distance from end to end of the tips would come within the length tolerance.

Based on this and other discussions, the vendor was requested to quote on the following five alternatives:

Using the entire 0.0005-inch diameter tolerance, which would also allow as substantial reduction in rejected pins. Also, inspection cost will be re-evaluated based on sampling methods.

Same as above except that wire of smaller diameter is to be used, reducing the number of passes from three to two and also reducing attendant losses.

Same as second alternative except that allowable length tolerance is to be 0.003 inch instead of 0.002 inch.

Same as second alternative except that allowable tolerance is to be 0.004 inch instead of 0.002 inch.

Same as second alternative expect for the substitution of No. 1090 carbon steel for No. 440 stainless steel.

The vendor's quotation read: "Our production department has been doing a lot of work in connection with better and more efficient handling and feeding methods. This, plus the concessions discussed, has resulted in some rather startling cost reductions, which are reflected in the prices shown below."

PIVOT NO. 41626-8

Method No. 1. Based on using ±0.00025-inch diameter tolerance, plus attendant drop in rejects and lower inspection costs, we quote $2.05 per thousand.

Method No. 2. Same as method 1 except that by using only two centerless grinding passes, we quote $1.90 per thousand.

Method No. 3. Same as method 2 except for a total length tolerance of

0.003 inch instead of the present 0.002 inch. This larger tolerance should allow us to furnish radius ends instead of slight flats. Using this method, we quote $1.79 per thousand.

Method No. 4. Same as method 2 except that to use SAE No. 1090 carbon steel instead of No. 440 stainless would allow us to quote $1.55 per thousand.

Method No. 5. Same as method 2 except for an increase in the length tolerance to 0.004 inch. Our costs would be the same as under method 3, so the same selling price would apply.

Subsequently, the engineers approved of alternative 2, and the cost went down from $3.65 per thousand to $1.90 per thousand, for a saving of $83,000 on a use quantity of 47 million pins a year. As will be noted, this accomplishment derived from:

Using all allowable diameter tolerance
Using smaller stock, and eliminating one centerless grinding pass
Charging for only sampling inspection approved by our engineers rather than 100 per cent
Eliminating some handling

It will be seen in studying the value analysis job plan that all parts of the plan are not necessarily used in connection with every function reviewed. However, all the parts are tested for effectiveness in application to the function being studied, and all those parts that appear useful are applied. This means that nearly every part of the value analysis job plan must be used to achieve high efficiency and a high degree of value.

5-4   *Utilize Good Guidance from the Past*

The value analysis problem-solving system contains means for efficiently using good experience from the past. Often, familiarity with the past disqualifies men to reach hard enough for totally new and better approaches, which are required to cope with the present and future. Nevertheless, the knowledge of these men is invaluable it if can be objectively utilized without "freezing" the present thinking into the past.

Some percentage of people have the range of mental resilience to build the new, different, and good upon their knowledge and information from the past. They are searched out and often given more and more to do. They are made managers. They are given a scope of responsibility that far exceeds their "hours of the day." They must delegate task after task. Then comes the eternal management opportunity—how to get the benefit of these effective minds, with this storehouse of useful knowledge, into each project, still leaving complete delegation with the people to whom the task is assigned.

To meet this need, to multiply the manager's effectiveness, to "move" the assigned problem-solving work, and to efficiently get good answers that will cope with competition, a *manager guidance point* is introduced at key work points in the probem's solution.

5-5   *Manager Guidance Points in the Job Plan*

Most tasks originate from an assignment from a president, general manager, or other manager. A quick review by him at five crucial times will make sure (1) that the work is centering on the maximum opportunity area, (2) that it is proceeding at the optimum rate, and (3) that it has the benefits from key inputs which management and experience can provide.

Guidance Point 1

After the assignee has completed his study and thinking on "Just what am I trying to do?"

Guidance Point 2

After the information step of the job plan. Basic information, some unusually interesting information, information concerning fact-assumption separation, the new listing of assumptions, and the information needed but not available are discussed. Often more extremely valuable information is provided to the project at this point. Often additional, vital areas for information search are suggested.

Guidance Point 3

After the analysis step. The meanings from the composite of information and assumptions, the values (appropriate costs) tentatively established for functions and groups of functions, the adjustments made to the solvable problems to make them even more solvable, and the specific class 1 to 3 problems, which now go to the creativity phase, are all discussed. The manager adds from his knowledge. The stage is now set for a high order of results in the efficient solution of the "right" problems.

Guidance Point 4

After the creativity step and after some preliminary judgment has been applied. Important different approaches, the ideas that show high promise for more study, some key advantages and disadvantages of some new approaches, some disadvantages of good approaches that should be made into new specific problems for recycling through the job plan, and the approach or approaches that are to be considered for thorough judgment thinking in the next phase are discussed.

Guidance Point 5

After the judgment step. The final approach or approaches that will go into development and will meet the needs and original objectives are discussed.

When time as well as results are important factors, the manager will assign tentative dates to each of the five guidance points at the time he assigns the project.

SUMMARY

Value analysis is a system containing techniques specifically arranged for efficient problem locating, setting, and solving.

Problem solving proceeds by the use of one mind "tuning," or "setting," period followed by four periods involving totally different types of mental work, each of which is separately completed before the next is begun. In mind tuning the question "Exactly what are we trying to do?" is asked and discussed. It usually requires from half an hour to half a day to get all the minds involved in the start of a project in good tune with what, at that stage, seems to be exactly the right problem, whose solution will bring real opportunity.

The four different types of thinking, each of which exhaustively completed before the next is begun, are:

1. *Information step*, in which the search is for: What happens? What has happened? What are the facts? What are the valuable related facts? What are the assumptions? What are the quantities? What are the costs? What facts are needed, obtainable, but not present? Etc.

2. *Analysis step*, in which a belief in the meanings contained in all of the information is developed. Functions are established, and solvable and comparable groups of functions are established. Functions are evaluated. The exact problems to be solved in succeeding thinking are given precise wording.

3. *Creativity step*, in which all judgment thinking is deferred, the precise problems set in the analysis step are individually used, and the widest possibe range of possible approaches to the solution are listed.

4. *Judgment step*, in which the listing from the creativity step is searchingly, thoughtfully, and creatively combed, basically by one man, to provide one or two new approaches, which, after minimizing disadvantages, will meet the needs of the business or service.

This is followed by *development and refinement* work in which definite steps toward implementation are taken.

CONDENSATION AND SCHEDULE OF MANAGER GUIDANCE POINTS

On critical or difficult tasks, when it is mandatory to achieve superior results often within a short time, the five "manager guidance points" afford guidance, evaluation, and the proper amount of assistance from the manager.

First, after deciding,

> "What are we really trying to do?"
> Review with supervisor _____
> date

Second, after information step.

> Information and assumptions study
> Review with supervisor _____
> date

Third, after analysis step.
 Function identification and
  understanding
 Function evaluation
 Making problems solvable
 Selection of specific problems
  for creativity step

> Review with supervisor _____
> date

Fourth, after creativity step.

> Review with supervisor _____
> date

Fifth, after judgment and development planning steps

> Review with supervisor _____
> date

chapter 6

Setting and Solving
Management-decision-type Problems

Successful management must make decisions as good as or a little better than their competition in a wide variety of matters, some of great and some of moderate importance. Some of the representative types of problems that management must solve are listed here.

6-1 Some Types of Management Problems

Shall we use the present equipment or get a new machine?
Shall we make this product in one line or two?
Shall we operate as one division or two?
Shall we own some of our delivery equipment?
Shall we expand our employee training program?
Shall we install and use some automatic communication facilities?
Shall we combine our purchasing work?
Shall we change our sales representation?
Shall we build a completely new plant?
Shall we provide a warehouse in the Chicago area?

Shall we discontinue, as obsolete, our records filing area?

Shall we increase the competence and effectiveness in our New York sales area work?

Shall we buy some knowledge we need from consultants?

Shall we repair the warehouse building or build a new one?

How can we reduce maintenance cost of the filter system?

How can we double the capacity of our compressed-air system?

How can we get the most of what we need for our medical payments?

6-2   *Setting the Precise Problem To Be Solved*

Usually between two and five persons are involved in the first stages of problem setting.

First

Precisely what are we (the five of us here now) trying to do? Encourage many short statements. One person should write them all down. The objective will clarify and become one precise clear objective. Usually in 15 to 30 minutes results will be achieved.

Second

Exactly what are we trying to achieve by the expenditure of money that we will pay for this service? Again, record every statement. Do not judge the statements at this time. Encourage short concise statements. The time required will depend upon the problem; however, in 30 minutes the principal desired specific acts will often stand out rather clearly. Meanwhile all of the minds in the group have again become "tuned" into one direction of thought.

Third

Now the group should agree upon a precise, simple statement of what it is desired to achieve. Often one precise simple statement will not suffice. Then the group should agree upon two or more such statements, which constitute precisely the important results desired. In those cases it will be observed that there is not one problem but two or more, and that each will have somewhat different parameters and controllers. It will also be observed that each separate problem now has become considerably "more solvable."

Decide which problem should be well started first, then second, then third. Reexamine problem No. 1. Modify the wording, if possible, so that it points attention as directly as possible into the area that must produce the solution. Now the problem has been "set" and is ready for the thinking of the "problem-solving system."

Case Study (with Detailed Information Concerning the Problem Setting)

PROBLEM: NOW THAT A PRODUCT WAS PROVED
AND THE MARKET WAS ESTABLISHED AND
GROWING, SHOULD A COMPANY BUILD
MAUFACTURING FACILITIES FOR AN IMPORTANT
PURCHASED ASSEMBLY?

In developing a new product, a control regulator was needed. It consisted of about 1 cubic foot of electrical and mechanical equipment. Its function was to control speed, load, fuel, etc., in response to inputs from an operator and a machine. A responsible vendor quoted a price of approximately $5,000 each on the basis of supplying the few hundred needed regulators. Included in his services would be adjusting some of the final details of the design, finishing a few minor tests, making sure that design details were such that assembly would be facilitated, etc.; thus the vendor did make small important adjustments on the drawings.

During the initial three years that the product was earning its place in a very competitive market, the cost of the assembly had been reduced by experience and important modifications to $3,000. The vendor said that he had gone through all parts of his operation and had taken out all costs he could without lowering quality. His quotation for the future, even anticipating increased volume, stood at $2,500.

FIRST (MIND SETTING): *"Precisely what are we (the four of us here now) trying to do?"*
Reduce costs
Assure future business
Be sure of quality
Assure a profit
Assure a reliable source of the essential assembly
Increase sales
Control the unexpected
Build up our factory
Obtain more control over design
Obtain more control over manufacturing
Facilitate future reductions in costs
Facilitate making changes
Minimize possibility of shipment delays
Maximize earnings
Provide a cost advantage over competition
Provide flexibility

Become self-contained
Make an integrated product more practical
Save money
Make competitive selling price profitable

SECOND: *"Exactly what are we trying to achieve by the expenditure of money for this assembly?"*
Control fuel
Control speed
Provide proper amount of fuel for any load
Prevent overspeed
Prevent underspeed
Prevent overload
Protect from overtemperature
Shut down in case of malfunction
Accept operator's call for more speed or less speed
Occupy minimum space
Fail safe
Function independently of ambient temperature

THIRD: *The problem "set" for first action before others would be considered was: "Determine the effectiveness potential of the present supplier."* A reexamination of this problem statement, pointing it toward the solutions needed, resulted in this problem: *"Determine (1) the efficiency of the supplier's manufacturing operations (his effectiveness in lowering his own costs) and (2) his attitude toward progressively lowering his quoted prices."*

The initial "problem setting" was completed, and the "problem-solving system" was then used with the following results. The supplier was apprized of the entire situation and asked to what extent he felt it was in his own best interests to provide manufacturing information. He was offered the help of value analysis trained personnel but advised that, to be effective for him, they must know and work with his costs. He advised that he felt his best interests would be served not by providing cost information but rather by showing the material, machines, and methods used to fabricate and assemble the parts. He then would hopefully receive specific suggestions pertaining to specific parts and subassemblies, which, at his election, he might use to reduce certain costs.

The value engineer spent a few days studying the manufacture of the parts, the assembly, and the subassemblies as well as the various operations in the supplier's plant. On returning to his desk with a full understanding of the way costs are built up in the use of various processes, he made up a sheet for each of the parts and each of the important subassemblies, with estimates of the costs based on the processes he had seen being used. This gave him the information he needed to identify and evaluate the various functions and use the creative problem-solving methods of the value analysis job plan quite effectively. The value engineer was then able to provide positive suggestions to the supplier on further steps that might be taken to lower costs. Further he was now in a position to advise the vendor on approximately what costs he felt appropriate for many of the individual parts and individual subassemblies, and these costs the vendor could then use for comparison with his own costs. The tabulation below includes two items: first, the cost that the value engineer estimated after reviewing the supplier's manufacturing processes; second, the cost that he considered appropriate and that was the basis of positive suggestions made to the vendor. The latter cost is designated "value."

Item	Estimated present cost	Value
Spur gear	$ 15.00	$ 5.85
Gear	20.00	7.25
Sleeve	105.00	90.00
Side plate	2.00	0.00
Block	4.00	0.00
Shield	5.80	1.80
Gasket	1.00	0.05
Gasket	4.00	0.15
Adjusting sleeve	4.00	1.50
Spring	1.30	0.31
Pin	3.00	0.75
Special screw	1.00	0.10
Shoulder bolt	3.10	0.10
Spring retainer	3.50	0.05
Cartridge pump	137.00	89.00

It should be noted that, in making these suggestions, the value consultant brought into play the various value analysis techniques such as utilizing vendors' functional products, buying standard products and modifying them slightly, using specialized vendors, and reevaluating tolerances which make no contribution to performance.

After study and implementation of the alternatives, the vendor was able to make a new quotation of $1,800, and the redesigned equipment retained its capability to accomplish the total function with reliability. His costs had been decreased sufficiently so that his company was still provided with its proper earnings. The attitude of competitive cooperativeness found in the supplier was sufficient to justify ending consideration of the establishment of an in-plant facility.

6-3   Some Management Problems for Deepening Familiarity with Techniques

It has been found to be very useful for management people to objectively "set" a few of their own types of problems in "solvable" form. The following are suggested.

1. You have consistently sold 30 per cent of the 10- to 100-horsepower motors that are sold in California. You have just learned that last month a competitor increased his sales enough to reduce you to 20 per cent. Set the problem.

2. You are operating the public health service in a city of 200,000 persons. You have four professional nurses and two medical doctors. The work is not getting done. There are long delays, filled waiting rooms, and frayed nerves. Set the problem.

3. You have a warehouse in a tricity area. You have a sales office in each city, which receives the orders; some of the orders are c.o.d., and some are paid for in cash. Orders are relayed to the warehouse and serviced from there. The paper work is killing you. Set the problem.

4. You operate a cement plant. Dust-control authorities request you to install a dust collector on one group of six silos in which you accumulate cement for production and from which you later ship. Set the problem.

5. You are responsible for police protection of the citizens of a small city. You have twenty policemen. You find that the frequence and severity of nighttime robberies is increasing. Set the problem.

NOTE: Problems must be skillfully and creatively set, recognizing their severity and limitations and the directions from which in reality solutions will come. When necessary in order to have each problem in solvable form of similar parameters, set it in the form of a few separate unrelated or only partially related problems.

SUMMARY

Experience has taught that a higher magnitude of results is achieved sooner when dealing with management problems if the first step, the "mind-tuning" step ("Exactly what are we trying to do?"), is taken in two steps:

1. Precisely what are *we* (each person in the group personally) trying to do?

2. Exactly what are we trying to achieve by the expenditure of money we are studying?

The greatest of attention must be given in problem setting to clarity of thinking in order to set the problem in action-directing words. For example, the initial problem

Shall we or shall we not build a manufacturing facility?

was changed to:

Determine the effectiveness potential of the supplier

as a first essential step and then was "set" in action words:

Determine (1) the efficiency of the supplier's manufacturing operations (his effectiveness in lowering his own costs) and (2) his attitude toward progressively lowering his quoted prices.

Each of the two subproblems could be solved, using good problem-solving techniques. The course of action most beneficial to the business then became very clear.

Finally, because of the extreme importance of setting management-type problems optimally, some situations are included to provide the reader experience in management problem setting.

chapter 7

Setting and Solving Services Problems

In service institutions, such as hospitals, government groups, schools, and colleges, it is becoming increasingly important to reach better answers sooner. These institutions are usually operating in an environment of expanding need for services to their constituents, so that the problem setting usually takes the general form: "How can we provide more services or better services to our constituents for the same overall cost?" Experience is showing that the better answers are also decreasing costs. Some examples follow.

7-1 *Some Typical Service-type Problems*

How can we, within the same framework of effort, increase the professional contribution of our doctors? Of our nurses?

How can we increase the life of hospital equipment?

How can we increase the usefulness of our supply materials?

How can we decrease lost, wasted, and waiting time for all hospital personnel?

How can we reduce the costs of good maintenance?

How can we reduce to half the taxpayer's time in buying a license, paying a tax bill, securing information, etc.?

How can we improve the effectiveness of our police?

How can we receive information on robberies much faster?

How can we teach world history more efficiently?

How can we use developing student skills more effectively?

How can we provide more classroom space most economically?

How can we locate and interest the mathematics professor we need?

How can we communicate benefits to the alumni better?

How can we get the funding we require for an added facility?

7-2   Pattern for Disciplined Thinking
of Value Analysis on Services Work

The disciplined thinking procedures follow closely the following pattern:

1. What is the overall problem area in which better answers are desired?

2. Divide the overall problem until it consists of individualized, coherent, important, secondary problems, each largely controllable by its own type of parameters.

3. Determine which problems can be solved concurrently and which must be solved consecutively. Establish the starting order.

4. Now start and follow through the thinking and search processes of the job plan. Force the thinking and language of "function" into all considerations.

   a. What functions are being performed?

   b. What functions are wanted?

   c. What functions are needed?

   d. What functions could be grouped for better solutions?

   e. What functions should be eliminated?

   f. Develop changes in, different groupings of, and alternative means for, accomplishing the functions.

   g. Associate present costs with each function being accomplished.

   h. Evaluate functions and function groups by meaningful comparisons.

Case Study[1]

VALUE ANALYSIS APPLIED TO HOSPITAL
SERVICES AND EXPENSES

One project related to *admissions, room assignments, and laboratory tests.* Annual costs for the functions provided were $320,000 for labor and

[1] Society of American Value Engineers, Atlanta Chapter, George R. Weeks, Program Director.

materials. In addition there was need for service improvement, such as reducing delays, overcrowding of certain areas, and assorted frustrations.

In problem setting, items such as the following were brought into focus:

1. Overloading the floor secretary with admissions.
2. Multiple tests are erroneously ordered on same request.
3. Inefficiency in running stats one at a time.
4. Need better priority designation than "routine" or "stat."
5. Insufficient information given when floors call in stat.
6. Some routine requests are not in by 5:00 A.M. the day needed.
7. Room transfer delays.
8. Lab notification from emergency room of patient status.
9. Excess amount of nontechnical work to be done in lab.
10. Ordering new supply of lab forms.
11. Wasted request forms.
12. Delays caused by not ordering required tests at proper time prior to surgery.
13. Duplication of lab requests.
14. Inadequate information on requests.
15. Some requests do not have needed specimens attached.
16. Use of control cards.
17. Scheduling outpatients for tests.
18. Notifying affected personnel of test schedules.
19. Conflict of X-ray and lab work.
20. New tests not covered by a request form.
21. Unneeded phone checks from floor concerning emergency X matches in blood bank.

As the result of the problems set in these areas, the information-gathering, analysis, creativity, and preliminary judgment steps were used and the following items either went into implementation or were recycled to maximize their benefits or reduce their disadvantages.

1. Eliminate overloading ward secretary by:
    a. Changing admission hours to 12:00 noon to 2:00 P.M.
    b. Alerting doctors to time of admission
    c. Doctors providing preadmission information and arrival time
    d. Bringing all orders by lab
    e. Admission office stamping forms for all lab work
    f. Buying or renting a stamper for lab
2. Avoid multiple tests on same request by:
    a. Developing better communication between ward secretaries on different shifts
    b. Nurse catching it when checking request
    c. Checking control copies
    d. Including instructions in training for all new personnel
    e. Including instructions on ward bulletin board
3. Reduce inefficiency of processing stats one at a time by:
    a. Collecting several before processing

  b. Running a test every hour

  c. Fixing "sick" PCV machine

  d. Improving space conditions in lab

  e. Assigning complete responsibility for stats to one or two persons

  f. Utilizing one nontechnical person for collecting stats and performing nonskilled tasks in the lab

4. Improve request priority by publishing a definite definition of terms:

  Emergency

  Stat

  Today

  Routine

  Preop (give hour)

5. Eliminate floor *calling* for stats to be worked by accepting no verbal stats

6. Ensure that all routine requests are in lab by 5:00 A.M. the day needed by:

  a. Informing affected personnel of this cutoff time

  b. Not holding request until shift change

  c. Posting scheduled cutoff time (5:00 A.M.) on bulletin board for doctors and ward secretaries

7. Avoid delays resulting from room transfers by placing transfer slips in box after checking slips on spindle

8. Ensure that the emergency room notifies the lab of patient status, which will reduce delays by:

  a. Emergency room notifying lab when patient is admitted

  b. Improving communication between the emergency room and the admissions office to prevent duplicating CBC's (by attaching control copy to emergency room form, which goes to the admissions office)

9. Reassign nontechnical lab work by:

  a. Hiring nontechnical personnel and listing duties

  b. Obtaining voluntary help (six months only)

  c. Obtaining voluntary help for weekends to answer phone, etc.

  d. Appointing a collector

  e. Establishing an IV team and a blood-collecting team

10. Reduce the cost of request forms by:

  a. Reducing the number of different colors on the forms

  b. Using ten colors and five checked forms

  c. Getting all hospitals to use the same form

11. Reduce wasting of request forms by publishing cost of a form on the bulletin board

12. Avoid delays caused by not ordering test at proper time prior to surgery by:

  a. Having anesthesiologists check all patients

  b. Explaining to the doctor the importance of notifying the lab

  c. Using preop flags

  d. Providing early notification to the operating room when a patient is placed on the operating room schedule or of any change in the schedule, so that the three-to-eleven shift can do surgical CBC and urine routines, thus avoiding stats

13. Avoid duplication of lab requests by using the control copy
14. Improve the adequacy of information on requests by:
    a. Listing specifications for "funny" tests on each floor
    b. Including diagnosis on all slips
    c. Listing tests that cannot be done simultaneously, for example, BSP and IVP
    d. Updating the procedures book
15. Prevent delays caused by requests not having needed specimens attached by:
    a. Not accepting slips without them
    b. Improved communication
    c. Bulletin-board instructions
16. Increase the effectiveness of the control cards by:
    a. Improved filing system
    b. Destroying cards when report is received
    c. Attaching a card to emergency room form when patient is admitted to avoid duplication
17. Avoid delays involving the scheduling of outpatients for tests by:
    a. Scheduling arrival prior to 9:00 A.M.
    b. Using appointment cards
    c. Posting test schedules in doctors' offices
    d. Scheduling clinic patients and standing orders
    e. Giving appointment and schedule information to information desk
    f. Publishing test schedules in *Kennegram, Cup of News,* and on the bulletin board.
18. Notify affected personnel of test schedules by:
    a. Using bulletin board (preop, 5:00 A.M., 1:00 P.M., etc.)
    b. Using other methods of communication
19. Eliminate unauthorized stats.
20. Reduce delay of stats and special orders by attaching a red card as a "flag."
21. Reduce wasted phone-call time concerning emergency "cross-matches" by having the lab secretary take the message.

The benefits accrued to the hospital were twofold: (1) a reduction of overcrowding and delays in acquiring crucial additional space needed, and resulting frustrations, and (2) annual expense reduction of $50,000.

Another project was a similar function-cost study of the admission kit. Information was gathered, and functions were studied. Creativity and judgment thinking were scheduled and completed. The savings in labor and material developed were about one-third, or $54,000 per year.

Another project involved the isolation chart. The annual expense reductions developed were $57,000 in labor and material.

7-3 *Progression of Value Analysis*
Work on Services

1. Exactly what are we trying to do?
2. Information step—jot it down. What happens, etc.? (See previous instructions on information step of the job plan.)
3. Analysis step—function identifying, evaluating, separating, grouping, and setting the precise problems that will be solved.
4. Recycle through information step. What else can be known about this precise situation? What knowledge about it? What assumptions about it? Perhaps do some hard work to develop some information that is not known but is needed.
5. Follow with analysis again. Do it thoroughly. What are the meanings, senses of direction, and orders of solution? Reshape or reword the exact problems now to be solved. Put them into proper language to allow creative solutions.
6. Apply creativity to the precise problems from above. Allow no judging. Secure much "free-wheel" thinking. Jot it down.
7. Proceed to judging. Now the task is *not* to eliminate the unsuitable approaches but rather to *select one or two approaches that would have great benefit and minimize their disadvantages.*
8. Often "how to minimize the disadvantages of a solution that has great advantage" becomes the next problem to cycle through the problem-solving plan of information, analysis, creativity, and judgment to a good final solution.
9. Now the development-planning step becomes of great importance. Assign the task of implementation with much care and concern. Schedule the progression of the change. Arrange for follow-up of progress. Expect some unexpected situations to arise to slow or stop the change.
10. Be prepared to take any serious "stoppers" of the implementation plan as new problems, and promptly develop suitable solutions to them by good use of the problem-solving system.

7-4 *Start of Value Analysis Program*
in a City Government

Repeated urgent requirements for higher taxes to support what seemed to be required essential services caused great concern among business and industry leaders in the city. A few had had experience with value analysis in their businesses. Through the chamber of commerce they arranged for the city to receive some knowledge of value analysis approaches.

Steps Taken

1. The city council was provided with 2 hours of orientation and indoctrination so that they would understand, in general, a little about the nature of value analysis and how the system of value analysis techniques would try to accomplish the needed results. ("What are we trying to do?")

2. Teams of two persons from each department were selected by the city management for some training in the techniques. Some of the departments were health, finance, police, fire, water, engineering, and parks.

3. Two-hour sessions of instruction in the techniques were held every Tuesday afternoon for ten weeks (twenty would have been even better).

4. Each team of two persons selected a project on which to apply value analysis approaches during their training. Some of the teams gathered essential information and did effective work on their projects between sessions. About 1 hour of the session was utilized in teaching them further techniques; in the other hour they were assisted in using the system on their own projects.

5. At a special meeting of the city council, each team reported on its attitudes, projects, and future recommendations. (Members of the chamber of commerce were welcome to attend any of the meetings, and some did so.)

Typical Findings of City Employee Teams during Their Value Analysis Training Project Work

1. Health department members studied the functions and subfunctions that needed to be performed, the means by which each was performed, its cost, and alternative methods of performing the functions and their costs. Sensible groupings of functions were so grouped. Very useful problems were "set." Creativity and judgment followed. Some of their findings and recommendations were:

A considerable amount of their professional nurses' time was being consumed in nonprofessional type of work. By separating it out and eliminating the work that was making no contribution to useful functions, the equivalent of two more nurses' time was made available for nurses' work. This ended the nurse shortage, which they had been forced to endure because of budget restrictions. They studied real functions of each clerical operation. Then they grouped or eliminated enough as nonfunction operations to speed up services. Many improvements in the use of their doctors' time reduced client delays and excessive strain on their doctors.

2. One of the projects of the fire department was the examination of maintenance costs of certain equipment, including fire hydrants. One item of expense on the hydrant was a large gasket, which cost $20,000 per year in material and installation cost. Studying its functions and searching for newer and better material to withstand the conditions brought them a new material that required replacing only one-tenth as often and did not cost any more originally. The new gasket would provide the same functions at an annual cost of $4,000, reducing operating costs $16,000.

3. One of the studies made by the team from the finance department was the expense of collecting taxes. In the information step, for example, some of the facts were:

Thirty people were required to write receipts, which were given to taxpayers.

The receipts were written and torn from a permanently bound book.

It was said that the state law required that the receipts be written in and torn from a permanently bound book, which retains a copy.

In the analysis thinking they defined the function as:

Collect money.
Give receipt.

In searching for alternatives, they were shown by equipment manufacturers that for a one-time $30,000 investment, modern equipment could be installed that would handle the entire task with only three, not thirty, people. Since very basic issues are involved, this alternative typically produced a violent disagreement between two members of the team, one of whom felt that the whole matter should be dropped immediately. The other member of the team felt that action should be initiated toward changing what he considered to be an "obsolete law" and slowly transferring the unnecessary people to other areas of city government that were requesting more people but unable to hire them because of budget limitations. In this case, each man made a separate report to the city council, rather than both as a team as in all other cases.

4. Projects from the other departments brought tangible useful suggestions for the city government group, who were hard pressed to meet the increasing demand for services with insufficient increases in taxes.

Case Study[2]

VALUE ANALYSIS OF A COMMUNITY SERVICE

It was decided to offer the services of members of our chapter of the Society of American Value Engineers to our county's Goodwill Industries.

[2] Warren A. Johnson, *Proc. Soc. Amer. Value Engrs.*, vol. 4, pp. 77–79, 1969 (extracted with permission).

This was decided because:

1. Under the recent increase required by the federal Minimum Wage Law, Goodwill Industries had been compelled to lay off numerous handicapped employees, as they could no longer afford to pay them.

2. Goodwill Industries was not able to afford professional engineering services and therefore had been accepting contract work, which was unprofitable.

3. Salvage operations resulting from community collections were also losing money for Goodwill, as their methods of operation were costing more than could be recovered through sales.

4. High operating costs were requiring the handicapped people, who comprise approximately 90 per cent of Goodwill's employees, to be laid off and returned to welfare roles at taxpayers' expense.

The greatest and costliest problems were found in the materials-handling area. All of the items collected from the Goodwill booths throughout the country were brought in by the trucks to the receiving docks for processing. Since these collections usually took place throughout the night, teams actually followed various trucks and filmed the pickup operations. Before dawn, additional films were made on the receiving docks, showing the unloading and sorting activities. From studying these films, improved handling procedures were developed and considerable improvements were introduced to further reduce the time and expense previously incurred through the old methods.

Some other projects were:

1. The analysis and evaluation of all incoming job-shop production contracts to determine which of these will yield the greatest returns to Goodwill Industries. Until these teams (which serve on a rotating basis) began performing this much needed service, this was one of Goodwill's most serious money-losing areas. As a result of these teams' evaluating efforts, this function is approaching the profit level.

2. The direct application of value analysis methodology to products that have been offered to Goodwill for long-term production but are presently too high in cost to meet competitive market conditions. There are numerous contracts of this type, and they received high priority by the team members, as their acceptance can provide the employment of many handicapped people who are unable to obtain jobs.

3. The evaluation and analysis of all incoming salvage to quickly determine the most profitable items to process and the most economical method for disposing of the undesirable materials.

4. The breaking down and planning of incoming job contracts in order to provide the most feasible and economical means of production. Team members working on this phase of the program actually designed special tooling whenever its development would result in work activity for an otherwise unemployable person.

5. The development of a much faster and more effective test procedure that is to be used in selection of appliances and television sets worthy of

being repaired for resale in Goodwill's outlet stores. The method used often required several days of repair time, only to result in a nonresalable item. This team designed and built a simple test fixture that would quickly separate the worthwhile appliances for repair from the time-consuming money losers.

As a result of this action, the Goodwill people became thoroughly indoctrinated with value analysis methodology and are making plans to utilize it in all of their operations as a standard operating procedure.

SUMMARY

When used on a service, the value analysis system may start in the same manner as when used on a product or it may have a different starting point. With a product, the starting point, except for original design, is the product itself, with the development of thinking beginning with "What functions does it perform?" Similarly, the study of a service may start with the entire activity or some separable part of it and move off with the question "What functions does it perform?"

Often, however, the study of a service may advantageously start with a focus on the cost of that service. For example, from the list of expenses it is seen that an item of service costs $25,000 annually. This then becomes the starting point, followed by the question "What functions do we receive for that $25,000?" Then follow all of the techniques of examining each function for its need and appropriateness, separating, grouping, searching for alternatives, evaluating suitable functions and/or function groups, etc. Problem setting and solving then proceed in the usual way.

chapter 8

Results Accelerators

Successful value analysis effort, culminating in the elimination of unnecessary cost, depends a great deal upon skillful application of techniques that will identify unnecessary cost, remove obstacles, and provide a course of action that will ensure the development of value alternatives of merit.

A series of accelerators has been developed and has proved capable of meeting real-life situations. Each of these accelerators—thirteen in all—will be described in this chapter. In some cases, good results are obtained by using only one of the accelerators, but in many more cases, more than one will need to be applied. The situation in each particular instance will dictate whether one, several, or even a whole group of accelerators holds the best promise. That question will be further covered in Chapter 9, Using the System.

The reader will do well to acquire a distinct comprehension of each specific technique and its aim.

The value analysis techniques are:

1. Avoid generalities.
2. Get all available costs.

3. Use information from only the best source.
4. Blast, create, refine.
5. Use real creativity.
6. Identify and overcome roadblocks.
7. Use industry specialists to extend specialized knowledge.
8. Get a dollar sign on key tolerances.
9. Utilize vendors' available functional products.
10. Utilize and pay for vendors' skills and knowledge.
11. Utilize specialty processes.
12. Utilize applicable standards.
13. Use the criterion, "Would I spend my money this way?"

8-1 *Avoid Generalities*

All too frequently a good idea or proposition is swept aside by a good-sounding generality such as, "The farm is no good—never has been and never will be." This statement stops buyers, excludes investigation, and prevents change. Assume that we ask, "Specifically, what is wrong?" Perhaps it will be found that $1,000 worth of limestone will make it the best farm in the township.

Similarly, "This field won't grow potatoes. They never are any good; they have hollow centers. Don't waste any time or money trying to grow potatoes on it." By specifically inquiring why it won't grow potatoes, we might find that $5 worth of magnesium sulfate will make it top-grade potato land.

Such general statements stop progress in somewhat the same way that fog stops traffic. Although there is not necessarily any tangible obstruction in a fog, as a dense, unmanageable curtain it constitutes a good stopper. It is so general and so diverse that problems, if any, within it cannot be seen; nor is there any assurance that the fog shrouds no problems.

In industry, one commonly meets with generalities such as the following:

1. "Every detail of the design of this device has had a thorough review by a special, high-competence review team."
2. "The best manufacturing specialists in the United States have reviewed this and agreed that these manufacturing methods are the best and most economical."
3. "It's not practical to build dies for drop forging when quantities are less than 25,000 per order."
4. "It's not practical to build molds for casting in quantities of less than 5,000."
5. "We had to make these parts by hand because we can't pay for the tools with the quantities involved."

6. "We've made a thorough study of every conceivable way of doing this, and what we have is the only way it can be accomplished."

Recognizing every generality as a force for continuing the status quo, the first step must be to eliminate the generality by coming to grips specifically with "man-size" integers of the problem.

As an example, let us see how we may deal with generalities 1 through 6.

1. First, we must establish precisely what the over-all function is, and also what the partial functions are. By then intensively studying a specific function which is being accomplished, the "fog" will be penetrated. Alternatives which reliably accomplish the specific functions or subfunctions for lower costs will suggest themselves.

2. In this case, we must inquire specifically into what it is that manufacturing must accomplish—oriented, not exclusively to specified drawings, but rather to required functions. Having in mind a precise function, we can determine the manufacturing processes or skills which will result in a product that accomplishes the intended function with greatest reliability and lowest cost. Then the manufacturing problem can be broken down into a series of small, manageable integers, each of which can be studied intensively as a single item and in its relation to the others. For example, in a practical case the manufacturing processes were studied, planned, and put into effect on a water-cooled support and resulted in a cost of $90. Generalities certainly indicated that nothing more could be done on the manufacturing of the item. Application of value techniques to the individual parts and to possible combinations of individual parts showed that two important and costly parts could be combined and made by hydroforming. This provided a thoroughly reliable product, even more desirable in that it was somewhat lighter in weight,—and the cost went down to $36.

In another case, it was reported that manufacturing studies just completed had succeeded in removing a third of the cost of assembling a twelve-piece insulating support. Did the generality that the best manufacturing specialists had looked it over and had made their recommendation mean that little more could be done to lower the cost of manufacture? In the "what does it do" functional approach, it was brought clearly into focus that this item supported 2 pounds of weight, insulated by about 2 inches from a metal frame. An obvious question was, "Does it require twelve parts to insulate and support 2 pounds?" This examination, originating from a study of the manufacturing process, resulted in a very much simpler and equally effective way of accomplishing the total function.

3. In this case, the generality was, "It's not practical to make dies for this quantity." The fact is that:

Parts may vary in complexity.

They may vary in kind of material used.

Different suppliers develop particular skills in diemaking and machine setup.

Nearly each year sees advancement in the art of diemaking, and periodically progress is made in the type of machines in which the dies are fabricated as well as in the simplicity with which dies can be changed.

Different ways of heating metal are developed according to the size and shape of the raw material.

The important point is, "Precisely what is it that is to be forged?" Specifically, what equipment, what processes, what specialists in the industry can contribute to this particular item in the light of today's developments? Unexpectedly useful benefits result when these time-accepted generalities are turned into specifics and an action study is made.

4. As for the fourth generality, the same situation pertains as in the case of generality 3.

5. This generality is one of the substantial reasons why unnecessary manufacturing costs are retained in a wide variety of moderate- and lower-volume products. The idea that "the quantities are too low to liquidate the tools" is very widespread. There are, however, so many products and parts made in moderate quantity that the problem has generated its own solution. Specialists have developed processes for making special types of tooling, for using combinations of tooling, and for making quick changes in and out of the equipment, so that all of the generalities fall by the board. Here again, the question is, "Precisely what is needed? Who is most likely to have the best answers? Where are they? How do we get their specific technology applied to this specific part or function or group of parts?"

For example, a small weld segment, about the size of the palm of the hand, was made from $\frac{3}{8} \times 3$-inch bar stock. One end had to be cut to an irregular contour. Quantities were 3,000 per year. For several years it was made by manual effort on power equipment. It cost $1.41. The generality was, "For material $\frac{3}{8}$ inch thick, tools cost entirely too much to consider buying them to produce a quantity of only 3,000 a year." When this generality was discarded and vendors of the type who specialize in "low-quantity stampings" were approached, it was found that, with a tool cost of $75, they could produce the segments for 39 cents each. The yield in this case, after it was determined to not accept the generalities trap, was $3,000 a year for a $75 investment.

6. The last item was, "This is the only practical and reliable way of doing it." Here again, let us establish what is to be accomplished. What are the subfunctions which must be accomplished in order to achieve the overall function? Precisely what are the alternatives for accomplishing these subfunctions, and what are the relationships between them? With

the total general problem thus divided into its integers, the generality applying to the whole is no longer applicable. Where this particular generality has protected the status quo for a period of time, the yield from the use of value analysis techniques is usually especially large.

To summarize, avoid the generalities trap. Recognize that if a generality exists it has probably deferred effective value action in the past. Proceed to break the situation down into specific, man-size integers of function and cost. Then apply the appropriate value techniques and watch the results.

Case Study

DEVELOP SPECIFIC INFORMATION

For one application, forty thousand ¼ × 3-inch screws were required. It was necessary that they be threaded all the way to the head. Standard screws contained only a 1 inch length of thread, but they were purchased and then put in a screw machine for extension of the threads to the head. The costs became 12 cents. The arrangement satisfied all involved because (1) purchasing could buy available standard screws with no problems; (2) manufacturing had the equipment and welcomed the work which could be put on its machines; and (3) the engineers obtained the screw they needed. As is so often the case, all considerations except those of value were properly cared for. The use of value analysis techniques showed that the function was not worth 12 cents. Accepting no generalities as a basis for decision, suppliers were asked for bids on supplying screws with the proper full-length thread initially. This resulted in a change to buying the screws ready for use for 2½ cents each. The purchase and modification of standard products may be a good-sounding generality that does not guarantee best value.

A second and most important phase of the rule of dealing with specifics is to remember that specifics are needed to sell an idea and to stimulate action. To suggest or ask for a change to a less expensive material in a product without furnishing specifics is not the value specialist's way. His procedure must be to describe, with no ambiguity, the specific material, its characteristics, and how it is proposed to be used. Similarly, it is not enough to know that a casting, for example, costs $5. The specifics that count here are: how much of the total represents material, labor, extra costs for complicated coring, costs of scrap and rejects, costs of patterns or die maintenance, tolerance, flash removal and machining, inspection and handling, and the many other factors that contribute to cost.

Many times a sand casting is used because of a general opinion that sand castings are the cheapest method for producing short-run cast parts. Later it may prove that necessary machining operations price the part out of the market. Only by a specific analysis of cost can these details be pinpointed. Here, it is not enough to ask, "What does this part do?" The question should be, "What does this tolerance on the part do?" Be specific, not general.

Case Study

CRYSTAL OR WINDOW GLASS

In each area of activity, habits and accustomed practices prevail. Specific information, when developed, often leads to changes that bring large improvements in value.

In the drafting department of an electric clock factory, the word "crystal" was always used to designate clock faces, as a matter of habit. They were called clock crystals. This meant that drawings delineating the exact shape and dimensions of clock faces always specified these as crystals.

In the general auditing of freight bills, it became accepted practice to expect the crystals to require a very high freight rate. However, when the time came for making a special audit of freight rates, the question arose, "How does a clock factory use so much crystal?" The investigation which followed disclosed that the clock faces were indeed window glass, warmed and sagged. The investigation also brought forth the information that the transportation of crystal, a very expensive grade of glass, is extremely costly, while window glass, in any form, travels at a very much lower rate.

Crystal shipped "less than carload" costs 1.25 times the first-class freight rate, while "bent window glass," which correctly described the product being shipped, travels at only 0.85 times the first-class freight rate.

The result was that the name was changed on the drawings, in the specifications, on the orders, and on the bills of lading so that, instead of being wrongly called crystal, the material was correctly called bent window glass. The freight rate was cut by 32 per cent. *Always, "specifics" are important.*

Value analysis is an intensive study; its very basis is dealing, item by item, with specifics, not generalities. It requires reviewing every operation on a planning card; checking every radius, every corner, and every hole shown on a drawing; looking critically at operations performed and at material purchased but not used and diverted to scrap; and establishing all else that affects cost.

It follows that no effort must be shunned to get at and present the essential facts. This may seem like a big job because, while some of the specifics may be easily obtainable, others may take real effort to nail down. When this is the case, the value analyst will do well to remind himself that he may let an opportunity go by unless he gets together more specifics than anyone else may easily lay his hands on.

Whenever the objective is to promote beneficial change, always use specifics. Generalities serve only to prevent changes and protect the status quo.

8-2   *Get All Available Costs*

Meaningful costs bear the same relationship to good value as meaningful tests bear to good performance. Unfortunately, it is not uncommon to find that far-reaching and important decisions are made without accurate and meaningful costs. In contrast, important decisions affecting performance are no longer made without meaningful test data.

To have available and use meaningful costs is more vital and more difficult than may be immediately apparent. It is vital because cost is influenced by every decision on every part, component, or subcomponent of a product. If meaningful cost is a criterion in each decision, then value may be secured. Otherwise, value is not obtainable.

There are a variety of reasons why it is difficult to obtain meaningful costs.

Cost figures normally developed are for use in a basic system intended to ensure proper income tax accounting and proper overall profit accounting for the total business and also to provide some manageable basis for liquidating necessary charges of all types. It is a popular misconception that these costs are meaningful for the purpose of decision making about engineering, manufacturing, or other value alternatives. They are not. They accomplish their intended purpose very well. However, when the purpose is important enough and the user understands the problems involved, they may serve as a basis for meaningful costs.

The resultant cost figures, however, bear little relationship to those provided by the normal cost system. As a homely example, the same types of materials are put together and the same types of processes are used in making vehicles of various kinds for the transportation of people. One vehicle, the automobile, is intended for transport on land and is very effective for that purpose. Another type of vehicle, or vessel, intended for transportation on water, accomplishes that purpose very effectively. A third type, intended for transportation by air, may accomplish its purpose very well with the same resources of materials, processes, and men's talents put together for its different intent.

So it is with cost systems. Anyone who believes that costs which have been put together in a form to accomplish one purpose can also be used for other purposes and so protect the business' interests arrives at a very faulty decision.

The cost situation is so involved that different people in the accounting business use different names to cover different combinations of the various types of cost. A few of them are:

Material cost	Decision cost
Labor cost	Shop cost
Overhead cost	Standard cost

Fixed overhead   Manufacturing cost
Variable overhead   Incremental cost
Burden   Variance cost
Prime cost

What does each of these terms include? What does each of them mean? What types of costs are included in the terms used in the company involved?

Meaningful costs are difficult to develop because of the matter of overhead. In practice, nearly every machine and nearly every process actually consumes a different overhead. Still, for convenience of accounting, they are bunched together in some sort of grouping. How should the fixed overhead for the buildings, the depreciation, and the management of the company be apportioned? How should the work of maintenance people, janitors, service people, etc., be factored into individual costs? What effect on all of these expenses would different alternatives actually have?

The problem here lies in the fact that it is necessary to provide not only an answer that is satisfactory to the head of accounting or to the manager, but an answer that is also satisfactory to the economic system. An incorrect method of preparing so-called meaningful costs may be directly responsible for making wrong decisions which preclude good value in the product.

Another reason for the difficulty of getting meaningful costs is that habits, practices, and procedures are already established in most areas. People and machines are in place and things are being done in a certain way. Vested interests exist. Change often seems wrong to the people involved. Change always brings uncertainty and a measure of insecurity to the people concerned. Because means of allocating costs have been empirical and arbitrary, the tendency is to prolong the use of existing types of costs.

Does "labor cost" mean the amount paid to labor? Possibly, but probably not. It may include only part of the payment to labor; the remainder may be in a variance or other account caused by labor rate increases since the item was planned and the various costs set up.

Does the "material cost" show the amount which was paid to vendors for material? Perhaps so and perhaps not. Frequently, the accounting practice is to add certain overheads into this account. Someone must purchase, receive, inspect, and protect material. Additions of from 3 to 20 per cent to the actual material cost for these operations are not uncommon. Thus, the material cost may actually include some overhead.

Where labor and material costs include just the total of labor and material, are the figures meaningful? The assumption in this case is that the machines, the buildings, and the supervision are all in place and nothing needs to be added to the bare cost of the labor and material involved. The answer is obvious: These are indeed not meaningful costs. Obviously, the business results will be affected negatively by taking advantage of time, people, and facilities paid for in other budgets. Decisions made on this basis will not bring value to the product.

If we add overhead to labor and material, that is, if each part or product is assessed its share of the overall overhead so that the item takes in the total of material, labor, and overhead, does the cost become meaningful? Certainly not in itself. Many items of overhead in the business continue, and will continue, regardless of whether the particular part or assembly is made on one machine or another machine, is made in one assembly area by one method or in another assembly area by a different method, or indeed is purchased from an outside supplier. Many more overhead items are affected in varying degrees, some rather directly and others most indirectly.

The purpose here is not to penetrate deeply into accounting practice— a subject on which text books are available—but rather to provoke recognition that the mere inclusion of overhead does not bring meaningful costs for value decisions.

What happens if we concern ourselves with labor and material plus partial overheads? It has been reasoned that overhead is divided into two groups: fixed and variable overhead. Fixed overhead takes in such items as costs of buildings and equipment; depreciation; and general management of the company, research, and other operations that will go on regardless of the value decision pertaining to any one product. Variable overhead covers the expense occasioned by the particular way in which the particular product is designed and manufactured, such as carrying charges of special machines and equipment used, foremen and supervisory personnel, and other items, exclusive of labor, which are caused directly by the particular manufacturing or design alternative chosen. Do we now have a meaningful cost? Perhaps the problem lies in the danger of using arbitrary or habitual percentages which may not in the slightest way show how the business is affected. For each engineering and manufacturing alternative, these various overheads are probably affected somewhat differently. Therefore, it becomes necessary to understandingly study the specific alternatives involved so that the amounts of overhead expense and other additions will be in harmony with the economic system and not necessarily with the practices of the past in the area involved. Any margin of error between what is believed to be meaningful cost and what is in reality the true economics of the way the business is affected is decreased value.

What then is meaningful? To prepare meaningful costs for the purpose of making correct value decisions, the true effect of the use of the different alternatives must be interpreted in terms of dollars for several areas.

How is the business really affected?
How is the product affected?

How will sales be affected?
How will other products be affected?
How will the company's future pans be affected?
How will the development of new technology be affected?

Attainment of the desired degree of reliable performance is commonly no problem except in the case of newer products that are the result of recent research and development, and these might embrace 10 per cent of the industrial production. *Where the problem does lie is in getting reliable performance at low-enough cost.* Cost is the important factor in decision making in every phase of product planning, designing, and manufacturing. For nearly every function and for nearly every manufacturing situation, there exist many alternative solutions, all of which will accomplish the purpose reliably. Proper selection depends upon meaningful costs, and only when such costs serve as an essential criterion in the decision making will good value be achieved.

Without meaningful cost, decisions will not, and cannot, be made to provide good value.

EXAMPLE 1:   There are no costs. This is a normal situation when value analysis work is done before design. It forms a satisfactory starting point. Meaningful costs must be developed, however, for each of the alternatives that might be used.

EXAMPLE 2:   Costs exist but are not provided. Seldom, if ever, is value work efficiently done if costs which exist are not brought forth. Getting good value is difficult. All possible help is needed. Knowing present cost sets certain floors and ceilings with relation to different types of alternatives. This saves time and helps show where the work will probably be most effective.

In contrast to performance-oriented work, it is often desirable, in order to secure good creativity, to avoid knowing how others have accomplished the desired function until some study has been made. Otherwise the thinking is often channeled into the types of solution that are known to have been used previously, with the consequence that excellent value alternatives which might accomplish the total function reliably for a small fraction of the cost are not brought into view.

To summarize, start out with the best costs that exist, understand them, know their deficiencies, and gain all possible benefits from them.

EXAMPLE 3:   Data exist but only labor and material costs are provided. This situation is sometimes found in areas in which competition has not forced a high degree of value. Normally labor costs are known, as are material costs. Furthermore, it is known precisely how much of each applies to the product in question. The easy, habitual way is to accept these as the costs. No interpretation, no imagination, no direction, no forethought, and very little effort are required. In contrast, if some or all of the pertinent overhead figures are included, the questions arise: Which one? How much? What percentages? etc. These require thought, study, and understanding. Where only labor and material costs are provided, the action taken is usually justified by various forms of rationalization; for example, "Direct costs of labor and material are about all that are affected by a change anyway; overheads continue relatively the same."

Again, efficiency of value work is reduced to the extent that pertinent costs are not brought into the picture.

EXAMPLE 4: Decision cost—so called "out-of-pocket cost"—in make-or-buy decisions.

A general statement, specific enough to have some validity, is that meaningful costs for use in make-or-buy decisions will include:

Labor
Material
Variable overhead
Some amount of fixed overhead

Normally, all labor, material, and variable overheads are included. But, considering all of the effects on the business, on costs, on sales, on other products, etc., the question is: What percentage of fixed cost should be added to arrive nearly at an out-of-pocket cost which will show how the business will be affected?

Although there are many important factors, the most significant consideration normally used is the amount of work in the plant compared with its capacity. When machines or facilities are only partially loaded, it will be observed that some machines are idle, floor space is not filled, some people are on short time, and other people are obviously "stretching" less important work in order to make a full day of it. It is generally felt that the costs for make-or-buy decisions are lower in this situation than when the plant is working at full capacity or over. Figure 8-1 illustrates an approach that is sometimes used.

It will be seen that the amount of fixed overhead liquidated in the cost of the particular product is reduced as the plant load decreases to bring more work into the plant. Again, as the plant work load increases, the amount of fixed overhead applied in the comparison figures is increased, tending to minimize "keep-busy work" and to open up capacity for essential, productive, profitable products which must be manufactured in the area.

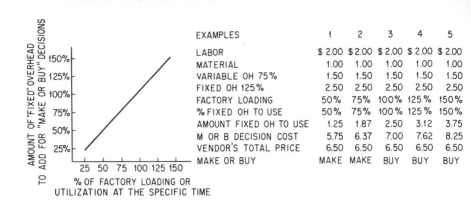

EXAMPLES	1	2	3	4	5
LABOR	$ 2.00	$ 2.00	$ 2.00	$ 2.00	$ 2.00
MATERIAL	1.00	1.00	1.00	1.00	1.00
VARIABLE OH 75%	1.50	1.50	1.50	1.50	1.50
FIXED OH 125%	2.50	2.50	2.50	2.50	2.50
FACTORY LOADING	50%	75%	100%	125%	150%
% FIXED OH TO USE	50%	75%	100%	125%	150%
AMOUNT FIXED OH TO USE	1.25	1.87	2.50	3.12	3.75
M OR B DECISION COST	5.75	6.37	7.00	7.62	8.25
VENDOR'S TOTAL PRICE	6.50	6.50	6.50	6.50	6.50
MAKE OR BUY	MAKE	MAKE	BUY	BUY	BUY

Fig. 8-1 "Make it or buy it."

EXAMPLE 5:   Decision cost involving make one way versus make another way in the factory.

The general practice is to use labor plus material plus variable overhead plus or minus significant changes in the way fixed overhead is affected.

In conclusion, the costs used often make the decision. Therefore, any wrong action taken in preparing cost means a wrong decision and resultant poor value in the product.

Case Study

UNMEANINGFUL COSTS USED FOR DECISION MAKING CAN BANKRUPT THE BUSINESS

Word was received that severe customer resistance had developed to hamper the selling of an important electromechanical control. Advices were that all the assemblies, subassemblies, and parts were laid out for study and that each was labeled with costs, quantities, etc.

Even first examination showed that costs were extremely high. For example:

Twenty-cent items often cost 50 to 70 cents.
Two-dollar items often cost $4 or $5.
Three-cent items cost 50 cents.
Eight-dollar subassemblies cost $21.

Study was undertaken to determine why costs were so high. Some of the reasons follow:

1. Parts were being made on less than optimum equipment.
2. Parts were often made by skilled labor when they required none.
3. Inventories of some parts were extremely high.
4. A "blanket" fixed-overhead rate was used on all items whether the fixed assets used consisted of a screw driver or a $20,000 machine.

INTERPRETATION: Cost figures which were used for decision making and which had been responsible for overpricing the product were not meaningful because:

1. The use of blanket fixed overhead regardless of the fixed assets used prevented decision makers from knowing how the business was really affected by the various alternative methods for accomplishing the necessary functions.

2. The job was used as a "filler" to take up the slack in the factory. Whenever machine time opened up or men had no other jobs, parts were made for inventory. Labor costs were not meaningful for decision making between alternatives because they were often based on uneconomical short runs and on the use of much higher skill than the particular items required. Setup costs were not meaningful for decision making because they were based, not on needs of the job, but rather on conditions of "factory slack absorption." In fact, no costs—labor, material, or setup—were meaningful for decision making because they were based, not on the needs of the design or the job, but on other considerations.

3. The volume of the work in the factory was being reduced because, unfortunately, the selling prices of the product were being influenced by the summation of these costs.

Even a glimpse at the cost realities shows that included in these "carefully delineated" costs of parts, subassemblies, and assemblies were these costs:

1. The legitimate cost of producing the functional parts, subassemblies, and assemblies as they were designed

2. Completely extraneous costs for factory load balancing

3. Costs for totally unused items of fixed assets

It was decided that two activities would at once proceed.

1. Determination of appropriate costs, strictly applicable to the particular parts and assemblies being manufactured

2. Using the value analysis techniques, evaluation of all functions of the product

With the meaningful figures of cost for accomplishing the various functions by means of present designs and with a clear view of the value of these functions, alternatives were developed where poor value existed.

The result was practical alternatives as a basis for decision making which would reduce the total cost to less than half.

8-3   *Use Information from Only the Best Source*

Lack of full information and use of misinformation are frequently the cause of a poor degree of value. In recognition of this, the search for pertinent information in value analysis must be a continuing one, and likewise, the sources from which the information comes must constantly be weighed to ensure that they constitute the best ones available. The more diligent and effective the search for the best information, the better the value attained.

Questions by the score must be raised, and answers must be accepted only from the highest level of the best sources in each case. Some examples of the sort of questions that should be asked are:

Why is this square?
Why is it painted red?
Why does it have a double set of contacts?
Why is it "hogged" from solid bronze?
Why is there a 0.0001-inch tolerance on the diameter?
How does the customer mount the base?
At what atmospheric conditions must it work?
In what positions can it be mounted by the customer?
What limits its market?
What causes it to be noisy?
What benefits does the F4 finish on the inside of the cover bring?

Answers traditional to the thinking within any area are readily available. Experience shows that such pat, traditional answers must not be accepted. Whatever the pertinent question is, only the best source must be allowed to answer it. The following examples are offered in verification of this statement.

Who is the best source, the engineer or the sales manager? In the value analysis of a moderate-sized piece of electrical equipment, a partial inside cover was found which had a cost of $5. The analyst, in analyzing functions, could find no function for it. Accordingly, in reporting to the engineer in charge, he said, "This cover costs $5 and I can find no function for it." The engineer immediately answered, "It has no function, but the customers require it." The analyst at once recognized this as quite a normal situation, in which the engineer voiced his belief; in fact, he voiced the criterion on which the decision to retain this cover had been made for years. The analyst's suggestion, therefore, was, "Why don't we ask the sales manager why it is that the customers require this cover if it seems to us to have no function." When the question was subsequently put to the sales manager, his answer was: "Does that cost $5? Take it off. I have only one customer who uses it. The others take it off and throw it away. I will see to it that this particular customer pays a special charge for extra equipment."

Again, who is the best source, the sales manager or the purchasing agent? At a manager's staff meeting, it was being determined whether or not it was practical to increase production of some appliances from 2,000 to 4,000 per week. The marketing manager said, "In this market we can now sell all we can make. However, with the shortage of steel, we can't get enough to support a schedule of any more than 2,000 a week." This statement contained what he believed, for the very good reason that he had made inquiries. He had talked from time to time with purchasing and had read in trade magazines about shortages of steel. Just before the group made its decision, the engineering manager said, "Shouldn't we call in our purchasing agent and get a direct up-to-the-minute reading from him on this shortage of steel?" That was done and the purchasing agent, like most competent men, knew more about "his business" than anyone else. When told that they wanted to increase the schedule to 4,000, he told them to increase it; he would furnish the steel. Thus, a loss of potential business was narrowly averted by merely going to, and accepting the answer from, the best source. What the purchasing agent did was to buy some of the necessary steel components in a partly finished or finished form, and by so doing, he properly utilized the steel allotments of various component manufacturers for whom he provided good business at the same time that he met his own quota of 4,000.

Who won't approve it, the Underwriters'? A value alternative suggested for a small transformer would reduce its cost 20 per cent and seemingly provide all the functions, as well as efficiency and reliability. The answer from the engineer was, "The Underwriters' won't approve the change." For the answer to the resultant question, "Why won't Underwriters' approve?" communication was made directly with the Underwriters'. The answer from the appropriate personnel in the Underwriters' office was: "Proceed with the change. Several years ago, under different conditions of application, we felt that the transformer should be made in a certain way. However, we have since changed this requirement as the added expense makes no contribution to safety or performance."

Case Study

THERE IS ONLY ONE SUPPLIER

A special instrument required a glass cover, about 10 inches in diameter, having a curved shape similar to a cereal bowl and having a ¼-inch hole through it. Its cost was $1.25, and the quantity used was about 20,000 per year. The value analyst was told, "There is only one supplier for this type of part, and though we recognize that the cost seems high, we have little choice."

Realizing that the buyer in a specialty department was not the best source for knowledge relating to clock and instrument faces, the analyst asked the buyer at a clock factory if he could suggest suppliers for the part. The answer came back, "We have six excellent suppliers for this type of part." Drawings and specifications were sent to some of these suppliers, and the result was that, for exactly the same item, the cost became 50 cents rather than $1.25.

It always pays to locate and consult the best source.

8-4   Blast, Create, Refine

This is a special technique usually helpful in reaching value objectives. Its purposes are many. First, it serves to eliminate what is in immediate view so that the mind is no longer channeled and so that thinking in totally different, more effective directions is not stifled. Second, it directs thinking to basic considerations. Third, it provides a mechanism for building that which is needed on these basic considerations.

The use of the technique is often very painful to the originator of a design or a plan. His solutions are his brain children, so to speak. In arriving at them, a great deal of effort was expended. Studies were made, money was spent, the aid of others was solicited, and so on. With the concept evolved and the plan put together, the designed and manufactured product has truly become a part of the individual. To him, the idea of "blasting" is inwardly revolting. It is as though a part of his being were about to be destroyed.

These mental reactions are emphasized here because the whole technique of blasting, creating, and then refining is a mental, not a physical, one. It can be extremely productive when people are mentally trained to understand and use it.

In the technique, the function or functions are first brought into very clear focus. Then the possible means of providing the functions are reduced to oversimple terms. The necessary complexity is then added. Alternative means for adding the complexity come next. Where good-grade value is required, this procedure is necessary to eliminate the causes of why things are done as they are. The common controlling factors are the habits and knowledge of the people at the time the particular thing, whatever it be, was first done and when it later was modified as different processes and materials and other people came into the picture.

For example, the three-room house so typical in the Middle West in earlier days provided accommodations for living, cooking, and sleeping. Sanitary facilities were outside in a nearby building. This house was functional and appropriate to the circumstances of the time as they were then known and interpreted by the people involved. Later, a lean-to was added to include two sleeping rooms as both girl and boy children came along. There followed a lean-to for the hired man. When the family became overcrowded, another lean-to for the kitchen was added and the former kitchen was converted into eating space. With the advent of modern plumbing, a further lean-to was provided for a bathroom and the outside facilities were likely to be remodeled into a tool shed.

Intense study of any product shows that it is, to a greater or lesser degree, the result of such a chain of happenings. Even the new products that value work will bring forth will be, to some extent, of a similar nature.

This situation raises the following vital questions in the search for better value:

How can this chain of influence be periodically stopped?

How can a function needed today, in the light of today's knowledge, be looked at objectively?

The technique of blasting, creating, and then refining is specifically directed toward accomplishing these objectives. The aims of the three steps in the use of the technique are:

1. *Blast.* In this stage (keeping in mind the basic functions to be accomplished, but not expecting necessarily to entirely accomplish them) alternative products, materials, processes, or ideas are generated. These alternatives should, first of all, qualify for accomplishing some important part of the function in a very economical manner or, at least, serve as an economical base for modifications that are likely to accomplish an important part of the function. At the same time, the precise amount of the function which would be accomplished and the specific cost which would result are brought into clear focus.

2. *Create.* Using intense creativity, as described in section 8-5, this step should serve to generate alternative means by which the concepts revealed by the blasting can be modified to accomplish a large part of the function with pertinent increases in cost. In this creative part of the technique, definite integers of increased function are associated with definite integers of increased cost.

3. *Refine.* In this final step, the necessary created alternatives are added to the functions which would be accomplished by the blasted product. These are further sifted and refined, adding additional integers of function with additional integers of cost, until the refined product fully accomplishes the total function. It is not uncommon for the resultant newly constructed product concept to accomplish the total functions with the same reliability and overall benefits for a cost of one-half to one-tenth of the original.

The following are examples of execution of the three steps. The selection of the three most common simple fasteners—the nail, the screw, and the bolt—is made purposely for the sake of clearness.

Nail

To blast a steel nail, let us compare its cost with that of steel wire of the nail diameter, which surely is capable of performing an important part of the function of a nail.

In our blasting of the nail, it is recognized that additional work must be done on the steel wire to make it accomplish the total function of the nail. Our next step must be to create, for review, a list of alternatives which will serve for the function of the head, such as (1) bend the wire at one end, (2) flatten it at one end, and (3) weld a small piece at one end.

In refining, we first look again critically at the total function of the nail. Second, we review the basic cost of the material from which the nail is made, as found in the blasting, and also the amount of function which the wire alternative fails to accomplish. Third, we develop the ideas arrived at in the creative approach to a point where the ones most practical can be selected for further consideration, and we then select one or two of the approaches which will provide, at a minimum cost, most of the required additional function. Fourth, we critically review the new approach, which embodies the blasted concept plus the created additions, and determine whether the function is totally accomplished with complete reliability. Also, we ask: Have the lowest-cost practical solutions been selected? If the function is not totally accomplished with complete reliability by the selected combination, we must refine further by adding additional increments of function and cost so that the new product becomes totally usable.

Screw

To blast a steel screw, it seems reasonable to compare it first with steel wire of proper diameter and then with the nail. In each case, we identify appropriate costs.

Starting with the alternative of a nail, we proceed to consider (1) cutting the thread, (2) rolling the thread, (3) coining the thread, (4) accomplishing the function of the screw without a thread, (5) coining a slot at the head end, and (6) milling a slot.

Again, we combine the best alternatives produced by the blasting and the creating, adding in each case the integers of function and the integers of cost. Then we study the precise function for which the screw is to be used and make necessary refinements by adding additional function and additional cost until the product will accomplish the total function completely and reliably.

Bolt

To blast a steel bolt, we may similarly compare it with steel wire or rod of the appropriate diameter and in the appropriate amount, then with a steel spike or nail, and finally with a steel screw. In addition, we study the function which is intended for the bolt and, if possible, draw comparisons with other basic ways of accomplishing the same fastening function at a much lower cost.

From among the blast alternatives, we may start here with the wire or rod necessary and proceed to (1) create alternatives at the end as was done in the case of the screw, (2) create alternatives at the head end, and (3) examine the function to determine what variation of alternatives can be provided for the particular application. In each case, we should attempt to bring into view, at least for preliminary consideration, a considerable number of alternatives.

For the refining, we follow the procedures described above in connection with the screw. The more complicated the product, the better are the opportunities for wide use of creativity and for searching investigation of value alternatives which will accomplish total functions reliably for very much lower cost.

The blast approach may often be used also on individual elements of the cost. For example, let us take the case of a counterweight that cost 6 cents.

Its function was to provide weight. It was used in a completely enclosed assembly with no parts other than its support near it. Simple analysis showed that its use value was 100 per cent and its esteem value 0 per cent. The amount of $2,000 per year was paid to grind a small flash from the casting. This flash did not affect the weight or the mounting or the environment.

The "function" secured for the expenditure of $2,000 was blasted and revealed that the grinding provided no use function. With no esteem function, any expenditure which does not provide a use function represents total waste. Accordingly, the grinding operation was blasted to zero and eliminated from the cost.

Looking back, it is seen that it was quite normal to accept the $2,000 cost because it is normal to grind the flash from castings. It is the way such things are done. It represents the way people who are used to handling castings operate. It is accepted by them, on the basis of their years of experience, as a normal, proper, and necessary operation to add to casting making.

The reader will learn to recognize that the accomplishment of outstanding results will depend, in some instances, upon expertness in the use of the "blast" portion of this technique; in others, expertness in use of the "create" portion will be largely responsible for extremely high-grade results; in still others, extreme expertness in the "refine" portion will bring forth the optimum results. It is important that the value of effectively using each portion, when and as it is needed, be understood and, further, that the emphasis in each case be placed where it is needed. The examples that follow will aid in recognizing the validity of this statement.

EXAMPLE 1:   A needed part (Figure 8-2) was a piece of ¼-inch copper tubing 1½ inches long. Its cost was 4 cents. Here are the results of applying the three steps of the technique.

Blast. The basic cost of the required amount of copper tubing at the mill was found to be ¾ cent.

Create. The first alternative was to draw the tubing straight at the mill, box it in 20 foot lengths, and ship it to the factory for cutoff. The second alternative was to draw the tubing but wind it in coils and ship to the factory for straightening and cutoff. The third alternative was to arrange to have the tubing cut off at the mill as it was drawn and so eliminate the need for boxing straightened lengths for a costly shipment or for coiling the tubing and having it straightened at the factory.

Refine. Putting together the costs, the figures for alternative 3 were:

Material	$0.0075
Cutoff	0.0010
Boxing and freight	0.0017
Total (delivered ready for use)	$0.0102

Quite obviously, the third alternative appeared to be the proper one to subject to refinement. What refinement was necessary? In the particular application, it was essential that there be no burrs. Therefore, the cutoff equipment had to be inspected and samples of its work had to be examined for burrs. This examination proved that the high-speed cutoff equipment accomplished its work effectively without leaving burrs. The final result was that the cost for the part changed from 4 cents to 1.02 cents.

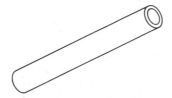

Fig. 8-2   Copper tubing.

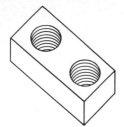

Fig. 8-3 Clamp bar.

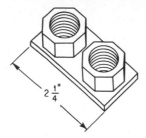

Fig. 8-4 Clamp bar: same function, one-fourth the cost.

EXAMPLE 2: The clamp bar shown in Figure 8-3 is made of steel, 1 × ½ inch, with two ½-inch threaded holes. It is 2 inches long. Required quantity is 4,000 per year.

What is the function? Half concealed inside heavy equipment, this clamp bar performs a basic function which could be provided by two ½-inch nuts. It does, however, also provide the secondary convenience function of compensating for the fact that there is no space in which to insert a wrench to hold individual nuts during the tightening operation. Further, the clamp bar is desirable to keep individual nuts from becoming loosened during the use of the equipment. The overall function, then, consists of a holding function, approximately equivalent to that which would be performed by two nuts, plus some type of secondary fastening function, such as could be provided by welding the two nuts together, welding them to a common piece of metal, or pressing them into some sort of holder which would keep them together.

Blast. The basic function for which this part was designed, we find, could be accomplished by two nuts which cost 1½ cents each. Hence, the value of the basic function is 3 cents. This represents a typical blast finding. We have an alternative which will provide an important segment of the function, though it will not accomplish the overall function. To do that the two nuts must somehow be fastened together.

Create. How to fasten the nuts together is the subject of the second step, and we arrive at these solutions:

1. Weld the two nuts side by side.
2. Weld the two nuts to a piece of wire.
3. Weld the two nuts to a piece of sheet metal.
4. Press the two nuts into two holes in a piece of sheet metal.

Approximate costs for the above alternatives are brought into view.

Refine. Particular complications or problems to be solved in each case are now generally considered. While so investigating, we find that a vendor makes and sells weld nuts of the proper size. Further, we find that the factory has proper facilities for making a small stamping and for welding the two nuts into the stamping. The result of the blasting, creating, and refining is the double nut assembly shown in Figure 8-4. Its cost is 8 cents, while the cost of the clamp bar had been 32 cents. In other words, by applying the technique, an alternative is provided which reliably accomplishes the overall function for one-fourth of the cost.

EXAMPLE 3:   Here we are concerned with a small radio-frequency transformer (Figure 8-5) about twice the size of a grain of wheat and costing 39 cents. It is used in large quantities. What is the function? The normal function of a transformer is to effect a useful transfer of electrical energy between two coils. For that purpose, one coil of wire is brought in close physical proximity with another coil of wire. In this type of product, it is most profitable to divert the thinking from the end function to the structural function. Basically, the problem then becomes one of reliably holding two coils of wire in an appropriate physical relationship. In this case, "holding" was found to be accomplished by winding both coils of wire on a very small spool. Four almost microscopic holes were then drilled in the ends of the spool, and the four necessary ends of the two coils were threaded through and pulled out of these holes. Study showed that the two coils of wire accounted for less than 10 cents of the cost. The cost of the spool, the drilling of the ends, and the threading of the wires through the holes in the end made up the bigger part of the cost.

Blast. Use only the two coils of wire. Put the two coils on a toothpick-size piece of wood or plastic.

Fig. 8-5 A small radio-frequency transformer.

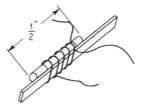

Fig. 8-6 A radio-frequency transformer, identical in function, one-half the cost.

Create

1. Discontinue drilling the spool ends and the subsequent threading of the fine wires through the holes.

2. Use a drop of adhesive to hold the wires in place.

3. If the spool ends are not to hold the wire, they will not be needed, and so we can discontinue using the spool.

4. Use a straight piece of suitable plastic or insulator material, wind on the coils, and secure the wires by a drop of appropriate adhesive.

Refine. By using only the coils as indicated from the "blast" step and the small insulator and adhesive (alternative 4) to maintain them in rigid relationship to each other, the electronic function can be accomplished at considerably less than half the original cost. However, we are now short of a means of supporting the assembly in the equipment. To provide for this, an additional small mounting part can also be secured by the drop of adhesive, as shown in Figure 8-6. The new cost is 19 cents. The annual cost, which had been $78,000, is now $38,000.

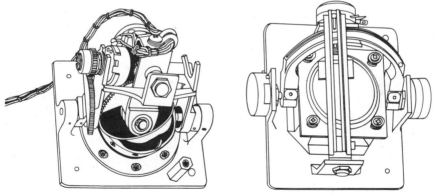

Fig. 8-7   Radar-control mounting.

EXAMPLE 4:   In military equipment of the radar type, it is often necessary to have a control for centering a spot on the televisionlike screen. This "joy-stick" assembly (Figure 8-7) consisted of a mounting plate about 6 inches square with a small lever about 4 inches long extending through the center. This lever could be moved in any direction, and as it was moved, it electronically caused the spot on the screen to move in the same direction. In back of this plate were suitable gears and mounting for the lever and for four potentiometers: two operating at right angles to the other two. The total assembly cost $127. The potentiometers which accomplished the electronic function accounted for $3.60 of this cost. For the required simple, unprecise manual movement of $4 worth of electronic gear, $123 worth of mechanical gear was used.

The overall function was that of electronically providing decreases in certain currents and increases in others so that the spot could be guided to the center of the screen. For the purpose of providing better value alternatives, this total overall function is best divided into a number of subfunctions which become quite manageable valuewise. Basically, the mechanical functions of the device consist in mounting four small potentiometers with an operating handle so that the handle can be moved through the proper range to adjust the potentiometers for proper operation.

Blast. For this item, with which the hand moves a small lever until the eye sees that the spot is in the center, it would seem that a very simple mechanism for mounting the lever and the potentiometers would accomplish the total purpose and would be low in cost.

Create

1. A standard or a modified ball-and-socket mounting with suitable linkages to operate the potentiometers.

2. A simple "double axis" mounting with the axes at right angles

3. Standard control levers with their mountings, as already provided and available for other applications

Refine. A study showed that the principal reason for the high cost was that the potentiometers had to be moved through 300 degrees to get their complete variation, and to that end, it was necessary to have a considerable number of gears back of the panel in order to magnify the 90-degree motion of the lever through the panel. It was further found that a plus or minus 20 per cent variation tolerance was properly specified for the potentiometers, because in this application, any specific benefits from close tolerance would be canceled out by differences in the motion of the hand.

The vendor was asked for quotations based on providing potentiometers which would vary through the same range with a motion of 90 degrees. This he was able to do, but the potentiometers became "specials" and a cost increase of 10 cents was added to each. Therefore, instead of $3.60 for the four standards, $4 would have to be paid for the four specials. A basic model was promptly provided for $11 to meet other physical conditions of the equipment. This was further refined to an interchangeable component which met all of the operating specifications and which had the same reliability at a cost of $30. Three-fourths of the cost was removed and all of the performance reliability continued. This is a typical result of applying the technique.

To summarize, the very useful value analysis technique of blasting, creating, and then refining serves first to bring the needed functions sharply into focus. Then the means being used or planned to accomplish these functions are critically reviewed and blasted by comparing them with processes, products, or materials which would accomplish only part of the function but which would have a small fraction of the cost. This is followed by an extensive and intensive creative effort in which a series of significant alternatives for accomplishing the total function or each part of the function or for causing other methods to perform satisfactorily are brought into view. In a subsequent refining effort, the total needs for the application are objectively considered in the light of all the information developed in the function study and in the blast and create phases, and a suitable combination of alternatives is established for reliably accomplishing the total function at a cost lower than that existing.

Case Study

THE ELECTRIC CONTROLLER

Electromechanical controllers, approximately $1 \times 1 \times 2$ feet in size, were required in quantities of 1,000 per year. The product performed its function well and had received good acceptance in the market for several years. With the constant march of progress, it was apparent that the selling price would have to be lowered, which in turn meant that costs would have to be lowered. A team of men from the engineering, manufacturing, purchasing, and cost department was assigned to go over the controller in detail. Their work culminated in the reduction of costs by about 10 per cent. While this reduction was adequate to meet the market conditions at the time, it certainly allowed no leeway for the unexpected. Hence the manager, who had heard of the value analysis approach, arranged to have a man make a value audit of the product using value analysis techniques. Starting again with the functions performed by the assemblies, the subassemblies, and the parts and evaluating these functions, value alternatives were developed which would reliably accomplish these functions.

Some of the items, together with the particular changes affecting them, were as follows:

Small hinges were made by buying an extruded section, drilling the hole for the pin, and then drilling mounting holes in the flat portion. The cost was 28 cents. By using a $\frac{1}{8} \times 1$-inch steel strip, cutting it to length, rolling it at one end for the hinge pin, and drilling it for mounting, the cost became 10 cents.

A steel hub $2\frac{1}{2}$ inches in diameter and $\frac{1}{4}$ inch thick, with a $\frac{1}{4}$-inch hole drilled in the center and six small holes drilled around and near the outer circumference to serve for mounting two small 6-inch diameter by ⅟₁₆-inch-thick aluminum dials, cost $1.27. The search for a specialty product which would perform this function revealed that aluminum companies sell slugs, i.e., round pieces of aluminum punched from sheet stock, for use in impact extrusion machines making toothpaste tubes and a wide variety of similar containers. It was found that one of these slugs, 2½ inches by ¼ inch in size, could be secured for 4 cents. However, it was slightly cupped, and the judgment was that for the application in question it needed to be flat. This could be accomplished by a flattening operation costing 1 cent. The operation of drilling the center hole and the smaller holes for mounting the dials came to 8 cents, giving a total of 13 cents instead of $1.27.

Plastic cams, ¼ inch thick by 2 inches in diameter, having the equivalent of saw teeth, approximately eight per inch, cost $1 each. By reviewing the product with the plastic supplier, it was determined that orders placed approximately twice each year rather than more frequently in very much smaller lot sizes, as had sometimes been done, resulted in a price of 20 cents.

A ⅝-inch ID by ⅞-inch OD by ½-inch-long collar drilled and tapped for a radial set screw cost 36 cents. It was made on a screw machine. By changing the raw material to a heavy-wall tubing which was cut, burred, and provided with a drilled and tapped radial hole, the cost came to 10 cents.

A special jam nut cost 20 cents. A standard jam nut of the same general description cost 1 cent. However, the distance across corners of the standard jam nut was slightly too large—⅟₃₂ inch—to avoid interference with the smallest-size gear which, under some conditions, was used in the mechanism. A slight modification was made in the mounting arrangement, and the cost became 1 cent.

A small spur pinion, approximately ⅝ inch in diameter by ⅝ inch long, was being machined. Its cost was 65 cents. A supplier was found who could provide the pinion stock of the proper size and thread so that the factory merely needed to cut it off and burr it in order to produce an interchangeable pinion for 40 cents.

Three switches and a switch mounting plate were purchased from the same supplier for 85 cents. They were routed to the factory and put together into an assembly. The cost of the assembly was $1.33. The particular supplier was asked to provide the assembly ready for use, shipping only one part instead of four. This eliminated much inspection, mounting, handling, storing, etc. The supplier offered delivery of the assemblies ready to use at $1.

A bracket in the form of a U was made of ⅛ × 1-inch steel bar. The base of the bracket was about 6 inches long, with each end turned up approximately 2 inches. Some suitable holes were drilled. The cost of the bracket was 48 cents. In studying the reason for the high cost of this bracket, it was found that one operation—a special straightening and sizing of the ends to hold the distance between the two bent-up ends within extremely close tolerances—accounted for 12 cents of the cost. This sizing operation was said to be required so that the assembly would immediately go together under all circumstances. Inspection and study of the assembly area showed that a mallet was kept nearby. The operator said that it was used on all of the brackets in assembly. This element of obviously unnecessary and noncontributing cost was eliminated, and some other improvements were also made, with the result that the cost became 17 cents.

A bearing block was made by buying extruded material, cutting it into lengths approximately ½ inch long, and drilling a large mounting hole for the bearing and two transverse holes for mounting the block. It cost 65 cents. It was found that a piece of ⅛-inch steel sheet, with two holes drilled in what would serve as a flat section for mounting and a large hole swaged to receive a flanged bearing in a section that was bent up at right angles, would accomplish the function with the same reliability for 20 cents. It was further found that the bearing which was being used cost 11 cents, whereas a suitable flanged bearing would fit ideally into the assembly and cost 3½ cents.

The device contained a dust cover which was open at the bottom and hinged on the side and cost $5. As reported elsewhere in this text, the cover appeared to have no function, but the engineers believed that it was necessary to provide it on the product in order to please the customers. It was found that only one customer wanted it, so the item was eliminated except for that one customer, who then paid for it as special equipment.

A large assembly called a motor plate pointer assembly was made of ⅛-inch steel approximately 5 inches on each triangular side, with a welded pointer rising several inches and with teeth cut on one edge. Its cost was $1.80. In the value study, its function was evaluated at considerably less. A review of the cost build-up showed that these steel parts were being copper plated, chemically blackened, and then lacquered. Newer processes for chemically blackening steel directly, to provide good surface protection and a good appearance finish, were investigated and resulted in a decrease in cost to 80 cents.

A panel costing $2.28 was also carefully investigated. Each point of specification which caused increased cost was studied, and such actions were taken as were desirable and possible. Among others, care was taken to control the ordering quantities to eliminate unnecessary setups. The cost decreased from $2.28 to $1.

All these and other changes, none of which in the least affected the needed function, were responsible for a 40 per cent reduction over and above the 10 per cent removed prior to the application of the value analysis techniques. Tooling costs in this case were almost negligible—less than one-fourth of the annual saving.

8-5 *Use Real Creativity*

When a new and better method is needed to excel in competition, it may be sought by either of two means. The first and most common is to *observe*, in other products and processes, the approach that accomplishes functions that are similar to the function required and then adapt that approach. The other means is to *produce* mentally a new approach—one that has never been seen and, perhaps, one that has never before existed.

This process is called *creativity*. In using it, knowledge integers, or, in modern-day computer language, *bits*, that have not been associated before are connected, or associated. For example, growing green grass has not been commonly associated with the hood or exterior of an automobile. Some paint-like material is usually associated this way. To consider growing grass, which must be periodically cut, as the finish for an automobile is a new association. Thinking that could later spring from this association has a better chance of being totally new. Unfound good solutions are more likely to be found, and the finder can reap the original benefit during the period when these solutions are being copied by competitors who are not using creative problem solving.

When value analysis is used for the purpose of assuring profitable success in competitive markets, it is absolutely mandatory that good creative thinking processes be used. As soon as functions are clearly known, the problems can be "set" in sentences beginning with "How might we . . . ," and intense creative thinking can and *must* begin.

The most common obstacle to deriving results from attempts to be creative in developing ideas lies in the natural tendency to let judicial thinking interfere with mental associations. For that reason, the main requirement in applying the creative technique is to defer judgment. Unless that be done, progress is soon retarded by sentiments such as "It can't be done," "It won't work," or "Specifications won't allow it." Such negative thoughts hamper a free flow of imagination; the things that they imply must be left to be explored in a subsequent step.

Another obstacle to getting creativity into action is the tendency to associate creative thinking with intricate and complex problems. The fact is that even the simplest problems benefit from being dealt with creatively. The thing to guard against here is the application of creativity in the wrong directions. For example, in one case on record the problem was to seal off a 3-inch pipe. Here the designer chose to be creative by laying out a special pipe plug that served the function well indeed, at a manufactured cost of $15. Had he applied his creativity to searching out the best plug for the purpose from available supplies, he would, no doubt, have chosen to purchase a perfectly serviceable plug from a local plumber dealer at $3, thus avoiding a needless outlay of $12 that returned no value.

A third cause of restricted use of creative thinking is often found in the difficulty people may experience in getting a chain reaction of ideas ignited and then sustained. In such instances, experience indicates that a brainstorm session with, say, three or more participants works wonders. In the competitive atmosphere of such sessions, one individual's idea soon stimulates other ideas both in the mind of the individual himself and in the minds of his associates. The extent to which this happens is indicated by the following yields of two group-brainstorm sessions. In the one case, the problem was "how to detect that someone is at the front door and wishes admission." The record of that session showed a total of 109 different ideas for solution of the problem. The other instance had to do with how to join together two electrical conductors. Here, the record was comprised of 140 varied ideas.

Sight should not be lost, though, of the fact that an individual by himself can stimulate his own imagination or creative thinking by very simple expedients. For instance, anyone confronted with the problem of how to best join two flat pieces of material may derive helpful suggestions from merely glancing observingly around the ordinary office. As the eyes pause on the paste bottle, the cement tube, the Scotch tape roll, the paper stapler, the hole punch, or the clip tray, the mind is automatically directed toward the alternatives of pasting, cementing, taping, stitching, riveting, and clamping the pieces together.

Whether the application of creativity is exercised by the individual alone or in group brainstorming the important factor, as already indicated, is to let no judicial thinking eliminate any idea that comes to mind, regardless of how ridiculous it may sound at first. Every idea that emerges spontaneously deserves to be jotted down for further consideration. What this means, then, is that whenever the ready flow of ideas stops, each idea on the record must be evaluated in terms of what effect its development may have on the ultimate goal. A farfetched idea may then appear to hold the best promise of yielding the most substantial benefit in its developed state. Thus that idea, rather than the idea that seems the easiest to develop, may be the one to concentrate on. In this connection, it is well to bear in mind that development work on one idea frequently leads to other ideas of even greater benefit. Hence no idea should be forsaken until an attempt has been made to develop it to the extent that it deserves.

EXAMPLE 1: The United States Navy's bulkhead-penetration project culminated in the use of a combination of fiber supports and epoxy-resin sealing by air-gun extrusion. Compared with the standard variety of metal bulkhead penetrations, the cost of the new method came to one-fifth of the earlier cost and opened up opportunities to make sizable savings, more than $70,000 a year in one naval shipyard.

EXAMPLE 2: Application of squirted-in self-vulcanizing material to take the place of ready-made rubber gaskets resulted in a cost reduction from 11 cents to 1 cent per seal. This solution went back to someone's inquisitively asking himself, "Wonder what use I could make of the jar-sealing gaskets that my wife buys for practically nothing at the dime store?" (See Figure 8-20, page 150.)

Because the methodology of creative idea development is a subject that in its own right is illuminated by several good books and many courses in universities and elsewhere, it would be redundant here to include the step-by-step procedures for obtaining good results. Suffice to say that creative idea development must be mastered and used by anyone who expects to use value analysis effectively.

8-6   *Identify and Overcome Roadblocks*

There is hardly a person living who has not been impressed by the effectiveness with which some product accomplished its purpose, only to be superseded some time later by modifications which performed the same function much more reliably at a much lower cost. It is normal to accept, as being "near perfection," the good work which has been done on something that accomplishes its purpose well today. It is shocking to later learn that the same functions could have been performed so much better at a lower cost even at the earlier date.

Why, then, were these functions not accomplished at lower cost earlier? Something prevented it. Most likely, continuation of the study involved ceased, as did work that might have resulted in improvement. Design and manufacture were centered on the product as it was. In some instances the material or process that would yield the function at a lower cost was nonexistent at the time of the earlier design. Experience shows, however, that, in nine out of ten cases, applicable processes or materials or perhaps special products did exist and could, in fact, have been included in the earlier design and manufacture.

The natural question here is: "Would not benefits have resulted from putting into earlier use such processes or materials which accomplish the total function more reliably, perhaps more simply, and at lower cost?" Checks indicate that the answer is usually "yes." What, then, stopped action for better value in nine out of the ten cases? Roadblocks—occasionally real but mostly imaginary, occasionally technical but mostly human.

The purpose of the technique of identifying and overcoming roadblocks is to help develop these situations and prevent value work from so often stopping short of adopting accomplishable value alternatives. A *roadblock*, as that term is used in the present connection, is a decision that prevents timely development of appropriate value alternatives. The cause of it may be a lack of information, acceptance of wrong information, or a wrong belief. These factors cause the decision maker to decide that it is not wise for him to continue to work toward lower costs at the particular time. The sort of roadblock in question occurs after tests have shown that the performance objectives have been met. Value objectives, being less clear and not as measurable, are given secondary consideration, and decisions tend to be made to proceed with the drawing up of the designs, with the buliding of tools, and with manufacturing.

Some of the common roadblocks met with are:

There is no better material.

This is the best process considering quantities.

There is probably no better way of doing it and we are short of time anyway.

This has been proved to work. We won't change it.

Underwriters' wouldn't approve any other arrangement.

This is the result of a lot of study. It will be far better than competition.

We changed that a few years ago and got into an epidemic of trouble. We are not changing it again.

We had to maintain interchangeability.

You can't beat an automatic screw machine for any part that it can make.

We have ten turret lathes; we certainly make money by designing to keep them busy.

There is no other source of supply.

We can't pay for the tools.

It doesn't make sense, but it's policy.

We know more about this than anyone else.

There is no plastic with those properties.

It is impractical to make castings that small.

It costs too much to change the drawings.

The customers like it this way.

It is important to bring these roadblocks clearly into the open and to recognize that they usually represent the honest beliefs of the men who make the decisions. To achieve improved reliability, simplicity, and lower cost in these circumstances, more correct information must be injected into the situation with proper timing and presentation so that the decision maker will use it.

EXAMPLE 1: Rather large quantities of asbestos paper were used for one application at a time when asbestos was in short supply and was, besides, a costly item. Its function was to catch paint drippings in a dip-painting line. When the value consultant questioned the use of asbestos for this, he was told that it was the only material that fit the specification and had the approval of the fire-safety committee.

The roadblock clearly was that the fire-safety committee would not allow the use of anything other than asbestos paper. New information was searched out from manufacturers of special papers, and when it was found that "nonburning" paper could be made, samples were obtained. Tests were made and the new paper proved to serve the purpose reliably. Based on this new information, the roadblock was overcome. The result was an improvement of value and a lessening of procurement problems.

EXAMPLE 2:   A stainless-steel nipple for conducting water into electrical equipment cost 20 cents and was required in large quantities. It was manufactured by purchasing standard fittings and then modifying them. Manufacturing alternatives were later provided in the creative phase of a manufacturing value study. The finding was that the parts, made from tubing by semiautomatic machines, could be purchased for 5 cents each. The roadblock clearly was a statement put on the drawing for the guidance and instruction of the purchasing department. It said, "Purchase stainless fitting #AB 1025, modify as shown by the drawing." Again, with the roadblock clearly in view, action could, as is usually the case, be taken to overcome its costly effects. A review with the engineer disclosed that when the item was designed ten years earlier it was a relatively low-volume item, and the most economical way to provide the fitting was as specified. Sometime during the years, matters changed so that the opposite situation was now true. Of course, there was no reluctance on the part of engineering to immediately strike from the drawing this roadblock specification.

EXAMPLE 3:   *"It is patented."* A rather complicated arrangement was used to support about fifty pounds of rotating equipment on a high-volume product. Application of value analysis techniques quickly brought forth the information that a simple construction for the support would cut the cost by 40 cents and result in an annual saving of $24,000. However, the objection arose that the simple construction could not be used because it was patented. The roadblock came into clear view. Obviously, the simple construction should not be used if it were covered by a valid competing patent and if licensing could not be arranged for at a cost substantially less than $24,000. A patent search was initiated, and soon the attorney reported that there was no patent in existence that read on the simple construction which would most effectively and economically accomplish the function. This eliminated the roadblock and allowed action to simplify and improve the design, with the additional benefit of eliminating the $24,000 of unnecessary cost.

The fact remains that this "belief," until corrected, was just as effective in adding $24,000 to the cost as some additional customer requirement or additional new feature would have been.

EXAMPLE 4: *"Underwriters' wouldn't approve it."* A very simple and functional design for a socket to hold a light bulb was suggested by a value analysis study. The verdict of the engineering people of one company was that the design would accomplish the function reliably but that it would never be approved by Underwriters'. Hence it was not adopted. Again the roadblock was in clear view. It is interesting to note that a socket incorporating the main features of this proposed design was put on the market by another manufacturer a few months later. It bore the stamp of Underwriters' approval as it should have, because it accomplished its function with total reliability and total safety.

This specific technique of identifying and overcoming roadblocks is another item in the kit of tools which is positively essential for the professional value engineer to learn to use effectively.

Case Study

IT WON'T WORK

Truth is indeed often stranger than fiction. A most interesting and typical example of such a situation is the case in which 800 small brass cams were required per year. These cams were being machined from $\frac{3}{16}$-inch brass material, and because of their unusual shape, the machining operations did not lend themselves to any simple mechanical routine. Because the quantities were so low, it had also been determined each time a change was considered that it would certainly not be economical to purchase tools for stamping them out.

The value engineer, in looking at the job and in creatively searching for alternatives, felt that it was worthwhile to consider the use of a Kirksite die. Kirksite resembles lead and is commonly melted and poured into a die around a model of the part required. When it has set, it is hard enough to be used for a tool to blank out a good quantity.

A manufacturing methods engineer, whom the value analyst succeeded in interesting in the project, decided it had a chance of working and thought he would like to try it. Hence, he asked his boss for a shop order of $50 to give it a try. He didn't get it. The boss said, "It won't work." Meanwhile, the engineer's interest in the project grew, and he went on to tell the boss's boss what he had in mind and said he wanted the $50 to try it. Again he was told, "It will never work." By now he had become so enthusiastic about the idea and so involved in it that he decided to run the risk of going to the top and telling the manager of manufacturing about it. This he did; once more he asked for the needed $50 shop order, only to be told that he couldn't have it because "it wouldn't work."

During the following few days, the idea stayed with him, and his frustration turned into constructive emotion. He decided he would do it anyway and charge it to another shop order which he already had. It worked. The demonstration was amazing. He decided to get the worst over first by telling the manager of manufacturing, and when he did, he was immediately given an opportunity to demonstrate. The amazed manufacturing manager called in a number of his subordinates and they were given the same demonstration. These people, in turn, called in a number of their engineers for a demonstration. Each time a few pieces were run off and checked for dimension.

An interesting happening was that, at the end of the day when the parts were viewed, it was decided to send them to the storeroom for use in production; as they were counted, it was found that they made up enough parts for two years of production.

After a roadblock is identified as such and eliminated, it appears very simple; prior to this, however, it is formidable and totally stops action.

Case Study

UNDERWRITERS' WON'T ALLOW IT

An electronic control contained twelve binding screws. The function of these screws was to hold small wires in positive contact on their terminals. Quantities were 50,000 controls per year which meant 600,000 screws. The screws cost $6 per thousand although they were very similar to screws which cost $2 per thousand.

Why this three times increase in the cost? The answer was that although $2 per thousand would buy small No. 8 screws of the proper size and type, the specifications called for No. 8 screws with smaller No. 6 heads. This made the screw a special. The use of technique 12, "utilize applicable standards," showed that two-thirds of the cost might be unnecessary. When the question of "why?" was raised, the answer from technical people involved was, "Underwriters' requires a No. 8 screw." Examination of the assembly showed that, as it was made, the head of the No. 8 screw was slightly too large to facilitate assembly in the installation of one of the twelve screws. Hence No. 6 heads were put on No. 8 shanks for all of the screws. When the question was properly explored with Underwriters', its answer was, "We felt it desirable to specify a No. 8 screw so that it would have a large-enough head to make extra-positive contact with the small wires."

Now that this roadblock was illuminated with more facts, it was obvious that putting the large shanks on the screws at three times the cost made no contribution of any kind. As a result, Underwriters' was asked to reexamine the application, and it subsequently approved a screw which cost $2 per thousand—one-third of the cost—as totally functional and safe.

In this case, as in many others, better answers did not come forth until technique 6, "identify and overcome roadblocks," was applied.

8-7 *Use Industry Specialists to Extend Specialized Knowledge*

Getting an acceptable degree of value means accomplishing functions as well as competition does. Getting good-grade value means doing it better. The former is accomplished by getting answers as good as competition's; to accomplish the latter, better answers are required.

The question, then, is how to get better answers. The procedure is as follows:

Establish clearly in the mind exactly what is to be accomplished, i.e., precisely what functions are desired.

Place better alternatives before the decision makers.

Get an action pattern established so that the information on the best alternatives will be promptly used in decision making.

In providing better answers for the accomplishment of each function, we must first ask: What technology is involved? For instance, does the problem primarily involve:

Circuitry:	Metals:
Electrical	Corrosion-resistant
Magnetic	High-temperature
Conduction:	Heavy-duty
Electrical	Lightweight
Hydraulic	Nonmetallics:
Heat transfer	Paper
Design:	Plastics
Arrangement	Rubber
Styling	Wood
Mechanics:	Processing:
Gears	Material removal
Linkages	Forming
Servomechanisms	Joining
	Packaging

The quality of the answers suggested is dependent upon a number of things. Obviously, one of the most vital is the depth of penetration of the subject matter brought to bear on the problem. If we take the known penetration of any technology as 100 per cent, what depth of penetration into each applicable technology can be expected in any specific instance? Is the answer, say, 25 per cent penetration? Probably not—or at least not in more than a certain few technologies. In most cases it is reasonable to assume that we get down considerably lower.

Let us assume that the personnel concerned with developing and selecting engineering and manufacturing alternatives which establish the degree of value in their product apply a knowledge penetration of 10 per cent on the average. The quality of the answers then arrived at, compared with the answers which could be obtained with available knowledge applied, cannot be good. Special knowledge in depth in the areas involved must be brought into the work to a greater extent before decision making. Furthermore, it must be remembered that knowledge, techniques, and processes are continually being developed in each technology and that only the specialists know of those which have become practical within the last year or two. Of still greater importance is the fact that these industry specialists are continuously working on advancing knowledge in each technology. The developments they complete one year will begin, perhaps, to come into usage the next year and will gain increasing use during the years immediately following. Only by bringing these specialists into touch with the functions needed in the product can the better answers derived from the latest within their technology be obtained so that a good or excellent degree of value may be ensured.

Case Study

DO IT LIKE AN INDIAN

Scarcity of stainless steel and innovation in attractive anodized finishes for aluminum made it advisable to seriously consider a good welded-aluminum construction for an appliance shelf.

After a few months of study, however, it appeared that the project should be abandoned because of an inability to weld suitable aluminum which would take an acceptable finish with sufficient dependability. One engineer dissented, saying, "I don't think we ought to quit. Why don't we try doing it like an Indian would?" When questioned by the engineering manager as to his meaning, he said, "I only mean that an Indian wouldn't weld it, because in the days of Indians, they didn't have welding."

He was put in charge of the job. His first action was to utilize the value analysis techniques to obtain, as quickly and efficiently as possible, all of the industrial know-how from industrial specialists. This resulted in visits to two fence manufacturers to learn approved practices in bending, crimping, twisting, and otherwise fastening wire to wire.

So much technology new to the appliance business but, in fact, old to the fence business came into immediate focus that before long practical designs had been developed, tested, proven, and put into production with retention of the desired aluminum construction. For his accomplishment, the engineer received a special award from his company—a personal gain further recognizing his benefit to his company.

The concept of drawing on industrial specialists to extend the use of specialized knowledge is so simple and straightforward that it ought to be one that is followed as a rule rather than as an exception. That, however, is contrary to the facts. There are several reasons why this is so.

1. Unfortunately for the cause of value, contributors commonly have pride in what they do. Each individual, when he receives an assignment, becomes interested in it, intrigued by it, and challenged by it. He puts his body, his mind, and his emotions into it, and often he develops several answers. When tests show that they, or at least one of them, will work, he develops "pride of authorship." He may have attained neither excellent nor a good degree of value, but physical tests do not show that up. Therefore, he proudly supports any related projects of engineering, manufacturing, purchasing, or management, and the product is born.

2. In the past, when a good degree of performance was required but there was little emphasis on a good or excellent degree of value, it may or may not have been necessary to call in help. Just the same, it has become a quite well accepted practice, if performance problems continue, to call in industrial specialists to help solve the performance problems. In contrast, relatively few people as yet have become used to drawing on the technology of such specialists in order to get better answers which will improve reliability, provide simplicity, and result in lower cost. Habits and attitudes of the past work against this simple expedient.

3. Supervisors and managers, lacking sufficient competitive experience, may interpret the action of drawing on specialized knowledge as a sign of weakness. Even today, superiors will occasionally measure their people by their individual ability to solve the problems they meet up with without calling in extra help. Such an attitude may have been excusable in the past when there was so much less depth of knowledge in the various technologies and when the primary effort was performance-oriented. The fact remains that it has led to staggering, and sometimes bankrupting, amounts of unnecessary cost in products.

4. Individuals sometimes lack recognition of the existence of more knowledge pertinent to their work than what they have at hand.

5. People often do not know where to go to get more knowledge pertinent to their work, although they may feel that it probably exists.

6. The additional knowledge costs money. When a man buys an automobile, he sees, tests, and evaluates the automobile, then pays his money for it. He knows, in general, what he will get before he makes the

decision. The exact opposite is true in the case of acquiring the help of technical industrial specialists. If the accomplishments they can provide were known beforehand, their services would be unnecessary. But the fact that their services must be solicited and will cost money before their contributions can be known is a strong deterrent to their use.

7. Securing more know-how may mean delay, especially if it is called in belatedly at quite a late stage of product development. It seems much easier to go ahead with plans as they are. The product is known to have performance, attractiveness, and suitable features, and often it is assumed that the value is good. That is particularly so when some ingenious moneysaving ideas may have been developed in the course of the value work.

EXAMPLE 1:   *Heat-transfer enclosure.* A complicated metallic enclosure of a space, approximately 2 cubic feet in volume, had the primary function of transferring and dissipating heat from the equipment which it contained. It had fins and other elements of design and construction for accomplishing this main function, which it performed very well. It dissipated the necessary amount of heat and helped to make the product perform entirely satisfactorily. It was made in moderate volume, and its cost was $74.

During a value program, a heat-transfer specialist was invited to look into the application. The result was that, within a week, design and manufacturing concepts were provided which accomplished the total function more simply with less weight and with complete reliability for $16.

EXAMPLE 2:   *The linkage.* As today's products become more and more adjustable and more and more automatic, the development of simple, reliable, low-cost, effective linkage is changing from an art to a science. It is true that virtually any engineer can develop a linkage that will perform any job. The variation comes in the complication, reliability, and cost. It is not unusual for the number of parts to vary from five to one and for the cost to vary from ten to one.

A linkage used for a lifting mechanism, in moderate volume and in rather heavy equipment, had proved thoroughly reliable in accomplishing its performance function. The cost of the linkage, based on the usual volume, was $285,000 per year. During a value study, a linkage specialist was asked to review it and submit suggestions. In a week's time, he came up with sketches and suggestions for a linkage which completely retained the reliability and performance characteristics and, in addition, provided further simplicity, at a cost of $90,000 per year.

EXAMPLE 3: *Gyros.* In a military product in which weight was very important, gyros were used for a specific function. Since cost controls quantities in military purchasing, it too was an extremely important factor. During a value study, electronic specialists examining the functions to be provided advised that an electronic circuit would accomplish the total function of one of the gyros and eliminate weight, provide simplicity, and do away with large amounts of cost. The result was important improvements to the weapon.

The reader will recall that the greatest causes of roadblocks which are responsible for stopping at cost levels as they are instead of continuing projects until very much lower cost levels are attained are:

Lack of information
Wrong information
Wrong beliefs

The technique of using industrial specialists to extend specialized knowledge is usually essential in penetrating roadblocks to achieve very much lower cost levels and very much higher value levels.

To get top-grade value, it is essential that needed functions be clearly identified first. Then, the best of industry specialists must be apprised of the function to the end that they contribute their knowledge and technique to the securing of the simplest, most reliable, and lowest-cost means for accomplishing these functions.

8-8 *Get a Dollar Sign on Key Tolerances*

Why are tolerances specified? The simple answer here is that tolerances are specified *where* and *as* required to obtain a necessary fit or to allow essential assembly. Nevertheless, confusion often causes tolerances to be called for unnecessarily, as illustrated by the following answers to inquiries from actual cases.

The designer or draftsman "thought" that the tolerance he specified was needed to obtain required fit.

The designer or draftsman didn't know, but to "make sure," he included a close tolerance or precise specification.

The designer "thought" it to be standard practice to specify tolerance.

Tolerances were included to avoid an "incomplete" drawing.

The designer "thought" the tolerance used would not increase costs.

The designer "thought" the tolerance to be in harmony with available economical materials specifications.

Variations of raw material in past years made it "seem" necessary.
Interchangeability with former products made it "necessary."
The way mating parts were joined, it was "required."

Case Study

IS THE VALUE $60 PER THOUSAND, OR IS IT $1
PER THOUSAND?

A small precise part resembling the top half of a shingle nail was used in
quantities of 700,000 per year. The cost was $60 per thousand—6 cents
each. What would a shingle nail cost? Perhaps ½₀ cent?

The part was found to be made of carbon steel, to have a very precise
head, and to have a ½-thousandth tolerance on the shank part. In operation, it acted as a valve. The exactness of the head was quite important.
The function of the shank was the normal one of locating the functioning
head. The precision in the head was adding to performance. The precision
in the shank was adding only to cost. The shank precision made manufacturing the part a very costly job.

Suppliers who specialize in economical manufacture of that type of
part were shown the item, shown its performance, shown the precision
needed in the head, and shown the function of the shaft. The result was
a quotation of $1 per thousand. The shank would be held within a toler-
ance of two thousandths.

The engineering group could see no reason why this alternative would
not work and proceeded to find out why the ½-thousandth tolerance was
specified in the drawing. The draftsman recalled a discussion of it with
the engineer at some previous time, when they had both decided on the
½-thousandth tolerance. The reason neither could recall. Tests were made.
No benefit resulted from shank precision. The change was made, the
identical function was obtained, and the cost was reduced to one-sixtieth
of the former cost.

Close tolerances, when they conform to standard practice and are provided automatically from properly adjusted machines, do not add substantially to increased cost in a good many cases. Often, however, from
any list of tolerances, there are one, two, or three which produce shocking increases in manufacturing cost. These must be known for proper
decision making.

The real objectives of tolerances, of course, are:

To assure a product which will work, i.e., provide use functions
To provide a product which will sell, i.e., provide appearance functions
To provide a product which can be manufactured at lowest cost

Regrouped as follows, these objectives become more readily applicable as a guide to study and to decision making.

To provide use functions reliably at lowest cost
To provide aesthetic functions reliably at lowest cost

On each tolerance called for, it is essential to raise the basic value analysis queries of:

What function does it provide?
What does it cost?

For efficient use in identifying unnecessary costs, these questions are here best reversed.

What does it cost?
What function does it provide?

What the key tolerances are is the next point that must be nailed down. If, in reality, the cost of the tolerance is found to be trifling or negligible, then it may be passed up without further consideration in the application of this technique. But if the cost it introduces is substantial and important, the function it provides must be brought into clear focus so that it may be subjected to all applicable techniques to creatively generate and crystallize value alternatives.

This process of associating cost with each function automatically locates key tolerances as far as cost is concerned. For example, iron pole pieces used on speakers, as shown in Figure 8-8, were called for to these specifications:

Length, ½ inch ±0.002 inch
Flange, ⅟₃₂ inch ±0.002 inch
Diameter, ½ inch ±0.0005 inch
Perpendicularity of face of flange to axis of
cylinder, ±½°
Finish:
  Surface of flange, F5
  Surface of cylinder, F5

Fig. 8-8 Pole piece.

The method of manufacture involved the use of an automatic screw machine making 2 million per year. It is obvious that tolerances must be evaluated in relation to each method of manufacture or process which is being considered. In this case, a study of each tolerance as produced on the automatic screw machine—using the annual cost for the normal yearly volume—would promote proper refining and improving of that process.

The yearly increase in cost for each tolerance above that which the equipment would take in its stride at fastest speeds and with minimum maintenance comes to:

Yearly total part cost	$70,000
Special tolerance costs:	
Length, ±0.002 in.	1,000
Flange, ±0.002 in.	None
Diameter, ±0.0005 in.	5,000
Perpendicularity, ±½°	2,000
Finish:	
Flange	4,000
Cylinder	6,000
All other costs	52,000

We now rearrange these costs. For example:

Finish cylinder	$6,000
Diameter, ±0.0005 in.	5,000
Finish flange	4,000

Our study then proceeds along these lines:

What use functions are believed to be provided by the $6,000?
What aesthetic or appearance function does the $6,000 bring?
To what extent are these beliefs valid?
What alternate processes, tooling, equipment, or technology might reliably achieve the valid tolerance requirement for lower cost?

Next, the various applicable value analysis techniques are applied to develop lower-cost value alternatives for achieving the specified tolerances. Similar studies are made for each other significant item of tolerance cost, and then we examine other processes for manufacturing the part, for example, cold coining. A preliminary review shows these figures:

Yearly cost of parts	$50,000
Tolerance costs:	
Length, ±0.002 in.	20,000
Finish flange, F5	10,000
Flange, ±0.002 in.	None
Diameter, ±0.0005 in.	None
Perpendicularity	None
Finish cylinder, F5	None
All other costs	20,000

Proceeding with an analysis, a natural first question is: Why does length plus or minus 0.002 inch cost $20,000 extra? The answer is: Because automatic slug shear cutoff cannot be used; special precision cutoff is required. Now then, what function does the $20,000 buy? Answer: none. The flange of the pole piece is located on the magnet. Magnetic flux comes up through this flange, turns out radially to the cylinder, passes through the cylinder sides into air, and then passes through the cylindrical voice coil which surrounds the cylindrical pole-piece section. The small end of the cylinder is adjacent only to air and a felt cover providing appearance.

What would modifying the tolerance on length from plus or minus 0.002 inch to plus or minus 0.005 inch do? It would eliminate $20,000 of cost and produce no change in either use or aesthetic functions. Similarly, why does flange finish F5 add $10,000? What function does it buy? The flange is in intimate contact with the smooth, flat surface of the magnet. It is desirable to have metal-to-metal contact between each particle in the flange face and the magnet. Any roughness or unevenness on the flange face would result in voids between the metal surfaces and lower the efficiency of operation of the speaker. It is found that true flatness and a controlled high degree of fineness of surface can be achieved by a Blanchard grinding operation after coining. Hence real use function is purchased with this $10,000. That sum represents a useful, necessary, and proper element of cost until and unless another reliable value alternative can be developed which will accomplish it at lower cost. The operation is retained, and the yearly cost of these parts becomes $30,000.

If it is not known how to accomplish a specified tolerance in a potential value alternative, give each tolerance a dollar cost equivalent to the dollars of economy that the use of this tolerance prevents. For example, in the previous analysis, if no known way of obtaining the tolerance of length plus or minus 0.002 inch had been developed, tabulation of tolerance costs, based upon the cold coining process, would be as follows:

Length, ± 0.002 in.	$40,000
Flange finish	10,000
Other tolerances	None
All other costs	20,000

This clearly and appropriately directs attention to the tolerance which is "locking in" much cost and compels study and evaluation of the functions provided by the $40,000 followed by application of the appropriate value analysis techniques to the end of creating suitable value alternatives.

In summary, the important questions to ask in this technique are:

Is the reason for the tolerance valid?
What other design concept, if any, would make it unnecessary?
Is the means for reliably securing the tolerance the most economical?

8-9   *Utilize Vendors' Available Functional Products*

All products are developed to perform one or more main functions. The bicycle, the turbine generator, the airplane, and the baby's crib, for example, all serve principal functions for which they are purchased. Each main function, however, is accomplished by a group of subfunctions, each of which often has its own group of functional components.

The main function of the airplane is accomplished through a number of contributing subfunctional components—the wings, the motors, the body, the tail, etc. In turn, the functions of these various components are accomplished by their functional components. The wing function may be accomplished, for instance, by sheet aluminum, structural aluminum, or magnesium and by rivets, fastenings, hinges, and supports.

Often, need has fostered development and has resulted in specific functional products such as special hinges, special rivets, special tapered structural shapes, and special gasoline-containing bags, to mention but a few. The use of these products often provides a total function more reliably and more economically than specially designed components. When this is the case, design time and design cost are saved. Besides, proved products can be used without expending time or money for testing.

Available functional products commonly have low costs because the specialty supplier has a sufficient lead in his particular technology and sufficient manufacturing volume to produce reliable components most economically.

This all sounds so simple—but! Practical circumstances and interfering factors combine to cause far too little use of available specialty functional products. Some of these circumstances and factors follow.

1. Individuals making assignments may not know or suspect that a suitable product exists, so they proceed to have the design and development work done.

2. Men given the assignments may not realize or suspect that applicable products exist. Hence they carry out the detail development and design of the functional product assigned to them.

3. "Do-it-ourselves" forces are strong in most every phase of human activity. The overpowering feeling is that "we can do it!" This is followed by costly and detailed redesigning of functional products which already exist.

4. "The boss assigned the work to me. He expects me to do it." Men are very hesitant about spending time or money in any direction other than the direct line of their superiors' instructions, as they interpret them. Slow success or failure in direct harmony with bosses' directions is

not as damaging, by a factor of ten, to a man as slow success or failure following a different approach.

5. Often there exists a belief that using the functional products of others is evidence of a shortcoming or weakness and that it is par for the course to be self-capable and self-integrated. This is the same as contending that only the man who does not know how to swim gets a boat.

6. A normal human characteristic is the tendency to place too much confidence in what "we" do and too little confidence in what is done by others. Much excessive "do-it-ourselves redeveloping of the wheel" is backed by an erroneous feeling that better quality will thereby be assured.

7. A self-injuring belief is that to protect "proprietary knowledge" which no one else has, it is essential to design and develop all aspects of a functional product, though it often causes delayed design, uncertain performance, and high cost. Occasionally, of course, such a situation may exist for short periods of time and will bring temporary benefits to offset the inefficient "do-it-ourselves" philosophy. In such instances, very critical reviews should frequently be made to determine when the proprietary secrets have ceased to be secrets.

8. Because the results that a search for functional specialty products may bring are not known before the search has been made, the tantalizing fear exists that, after time and money have been spent searching, no suitable product will be found and that it will be necessary after all to develop and design it.

9. "Do-it-ourselves" work can be planned. The objective, the resources, the effort, the expected results in performance, cost, and time can all be reasonably scheduled.

In contrast, search is more unsure; hence plans to search bring greater insecurity, and the feeling of insecurity in a job, activity, or project is a topmost reason for shunning the search approach. The task of locating something—who knows where—that may or may not exist, compounds insecurity.

10. Groups of people often have the belief that the accepted and proper system is to "do it ourselves." To do otherwise means to deviate from established procedure. Creative search for combinations of available functional products to accomplish the needed function is foreign to their basic beliefs.

11. Men don't know how to efficiently and effectively start the chain from no information on a particular functional product and quickly penetrate haze to build up a valuable fund of information on specialty-product availability, performance, and cost.

12. Often the belief exists that, in some way, various intangible, un-

identifiable benefits come from designing bit by bit and, hence, that much special hardware ought to be made in in-plant manufacturing space. The feeling is that resultant increasing activity in the factory will increase profits, business stability, control of markets, and utilization of resources. In consequence, a search for available functional products is regarded as a search for something injurious to the business.

The foregoing factors will oppose effective searches for specialty functional products that quite commonly aid in eliminating substantial unnecessary costs.

Case Study

SPECIALTY PRODUCT SIMPLIFIED IT

Four thousand small hinges a year were made by producing an extruded metal section which was then cut off and drilled for a close-tolerance hole. A pin, also with very close tolerance, was inserted in this hole so that an interference fit resulted and always held the pin in place. The cost of the hinge and pin assembly was 30 cents.

It was recognized that the main function of the assembly was to act as a hinge and that a secondary function, produced by costly close tolerances, was to hold the pin in place at all times. The construction was brought to the attention of a manufacturer who would make the hinge from sheet metal and roll a suitable portion to receive the pin. His process was found to be very practical except that the tolerances would not be close enough for a suitable interference fit to hold the pin reliably in place.

In searching for ideas and alternatives to overcome this problem, thought was focused on the use of a rolled, tempered sheet-steel pin as available on the market in a variety of sizes. These spiral pins are made with a certain springiness so that, when driven into a hole, they will expand and retain their position. It was found entirely practicable to use such a spiral pin in combination with the sheet-metal hinge, and the total assembled cost came to 10 cents instead of 30 cents.

Available specialty functional products may be divided into two classes:

1. Products that most designers expect to buy
2. Products that, although they often accomplish a needed function at the lowest cost, are not commonly considered as items to be purchased

For clarification, a sample guide of products in these two classes, as compiled for one specific usage, is shown below.

Commonly, designers expect that applicable standards will be purchased to fill their needs, but they often overlook the opportunity to have the desired functions accomplished reliably at the lowest cost by also purchasing suitable specialty forms. (A functional product, in the present sense, may be a plain material, a part, or a composite figuring as a "building block" for more inclusive design combinations.)

ELECTRICAL COMPONENTS

Apparatus type
Generators
Motors
Converters
Rectifiers
Switchgear
Circuit breakers
Control devices
Transformers

Part Assemblies
Dry batteries
Capacitors
Condensers
Potentiometers
Rheostats
Resistors
Coils
Contacts
Magnets
Commutators
Collectors
Slip rings
Brushes
Brush holders
Terminals
Electron tubes
Transistors
Electronic circuits
Etched
Printed
Plated
Antennas
Microphones

Headsets
Loudspeakers

Insulating materials
Cloth
Fiber
Glass
Mica
Paper
Plastic
Porcelain
Rubber
Impregnated
Laminated
Molded

Wiring devices and supplies
Wire
Conduits
Cable
Terminations
Tapes
Cordsets
Harnesses
Junction boxes
Receptacles
Sockets
Plugs
Switches
Fuses

Instrumentation
Test meters
Performance instruments

MATERIALS

Ferrous and nonferrous
Ingots
Rods
Tubes
Sheets
Rolled
Stamped

Nonmetallic
Asbestos
Cork
Felt
Fiber
Textiles
Ceramics

Ferrous and nonferrous (cont.)
- Punched
- Perforated
- Rigidized
- Sandwiched
- Plate
- Strip
- Shapes
- Wire
- Powder
- Castings
- Forgings
- Extrusions

Nonmetallic (cont.)
- Glass
- Paper
- Plastics ⎫
- Rubber ⎭ Molded, laminated, Extruded
- Chemicals
  - Organic
  - Inorganic
- Synthetics
- Paints
- Lacquers
- Varnishes
- Metalizers

MECHANICAL COMPONENTS

Machine type
- Blowers
- Compressors
- Fans
- Pumps
- Engines
- Motors
- Actuators

Parts type
- Housings
  - Boxes ⎫
  - Cases
  - Covers ⎬ Cast, pressed, deep-drawn, fabri-cated
  - Caps
  - Cabinets
  - Shields ⎭
- Bearings
  - Sleeve
  - Ball
  - Roller
  - Needle
  - Jewel
- Shafts
- Keys
- Leadscrews
- Shims
- Retainers
- Spacers
- Gears
- Springs

- Couplings
- Clutches
- Flanges
- Sprockets
- Pulleys
- Chains
- Escapements
- Bellows
- Diaphragms
- Filters
- Shock absorbers
- Mesh
- Trim
- Fasteners
  - Nails
  - Screws
  - Bolts
  - Studs
- Vibration dampers
- Hangers
- Brackets
- Pedestals

Hardware type
- Bumpers
- Casters
- Handles
- Knobs
  - Tie rods
  - Turnbuckles

Hardware type (*cont.*)

Nuts
Washers
Rivets
Eyelets
Staples
Stitches
Clips

Straps
Corners
Hinges
Latches
Locks
Name plates
Tags
Dials

SUPPLIES

Building supplies

Cement
Mortar
Bricks
Cast blocks
Lumber
Coverings
  Roof
  Wall
  Floor
Trim
Heating items
Conditioning items
Lighting items

Maintenance supplies

Brooms
Brushes
Cleaning agents
Buckets
Pails
Mops
Rags
Steel wool
Waste
Aprons
Gloves

Plumbing supplies

Piping
Tubing
Fittings
Unions
Nipples
Plugs
Nozzles
Valves

Faucets
Gaskets
  Cord
  Cork
  Felt
  Rubber
Sealing compounds

Office supplies

Furniture
Equipment
Stationery items
Office machines

Packaging supplies

Bags
Boxes
Crates
Skids
Pasteboard
Excelsior
Shreddings
Wrappings
Cord
Wire and straps
Paste
Tapes
Labels

Shop stockroom supplies

Abrasives
  Cloth and paper
  Compounds
  Powders
  Grinding wheels
  Sanding disks
  Sanding pads
  Sanding planes

Shop stockroom supplies (cont.)

Adhesives
  Cements
  Glues
  Pastes
  Tapes
Compounds
  Caulking
  Cutting
  Dust suppression
  Impregnating
  Insulating
  Sealing
  Descaling
  Rust protection
  Marking
  Soldering
Gaskets
  Felt
  Leather
  Paper
  Plastics
  Rubber
  Fiber
  Metalized
Lubricating agents
  Greases
  Oils
  Compounds
  Guns
Tools
  Axes
  Hammers
  Pliers
  Screwdrivers

Wrenches
Chisels
Planes
Saws
Punches
Nail sets
Hand drills
Augers
Bits
Drills
Reamers
Taps
Dies
Fixtures
Jigs
C clamps
Air guns
Soldering irons
Torches
Shears
Shovels
Pickaxes
Rakes
Hoes
Instruments
  Gages
  Calipers
  Micrometers
  Levels
  Rulers
  Squares
  Scribers
  Compasses
  Straight edges

Productive steps for locating available functional products are:

1. Learn and clearly understand the desired function, the basic step in the application of any of the value techniques.
2. Search directories such as:

Thomas' Register of American Manufacturers
    Thomas Publishing Company, 461 8th Ave., New York, N.Y. 10001
Mac Rae's Bluebook
    Mac Rae, 903 Burlington Ave., Western Springs, Ill. 60558

Sweet's Catalog Files
McGraw-Hill Information System Company, 330 W. 42d St., New York, N.Y. 10036

Consultation of these and other inclusive business directories may be advantageously supplemented by referring to specialized sources such as

Electronic Engineers Master—E.E.M.
United Technical Publications, 645 Stewart Ave., Garden City, N.Y. 11530
Modern Plastics Encyclopedia
Modern Plastics, P.O. Box 809, New York, N.Y. 10036
Modern Packaging Encyclopedia
Modern Packaging, P.O. Box 809, New York, N.Y. 10036
Specialty manufacturers' trade catalogs.

3. Search appropriate trade shows, including exhibits at professional societies' annual meetings and conventions; for instance:

Metals Congress and Exposition
American Society for Metals
National Plastic Exposition
Society of Plastics Industry
Annual Technical Conference
Design Engineering Show
Design Division, American Society of Mechanical Engineering
International Convention and Exhibition
Institute of Electrical and Electronic Engineers
American Welding Society's Annual Meetings and Welding Exposition
American Chemical Society's Annual Meetings
National Hardware Show
Instrument-Automation Conference and Exhibit
Instrument Society of America
Machine Tool and Production Engineering Shows
National Material Handling Shows
National Packaging Exposition and Conference
American Management Association
Society of American Value Engineers Conventions

This listing is but a sampling of the trade-show and convention type of affair that has proved a profitable source in the search for improved value alternatives. Innumerable exhibitions of this kind, covering practically every trade and profession, are held constantly both in the United States and abroad. Where personal consultation at such fairs is not practical, it pays the seeker of new and varied ideas to scan the widely published accounts of what is being shown.

4. Search trade magazines. Where library services are available, request searches by them if needed.

5. Contact, by writing or phoning, competent men in related businesses. Describe to them the functions needed and ask for guidance. Inquiries directed to a dozen or so of those who represent top thought and knowledge in any one industry will often bring a most gratifying yield.

6. Make chain inquiries. Select, say, three men who have the best chance of knowing where to locate what is needed and ask them for guidance. If they don't know the answer, attempt to get names from them of the top two men they would suggest. Continue this process as long as desirable. It is surprising how soon very complete and valuable information can be assembled from competent men in a wide variety of industries.

Once suitable sources of special functional products have been located, do not neglect to: (1) assist the functional product vendor; (2) interpret the needed functions to him; (3) provide him with a broad and deep feeling for the importance of the various functions, for the various operating situations, etc.; (4) help him to develop practical suggestions for using his product or combinations of his product; and (5) secure tangible suggestions from him.

With the aid of a few examples, let us see how this procedure may work out.

EXAMPLE 1:   An adjusting screw that cost 8 cents was used to facilitate adjustment of electrical equipment. In use, a stiff wire was hooked into the hole in the head. The screw was lifted against a spring pressure, turned as desired, and then lowered again, allowing the cross pin to drop into a slot and be held by it.

Manufacture of the screw required $\frac{3}{16}$ and $\frac{1}{16}$-inch diameter steel as the raw material. The larger piece required cutoff, threading, and drilling of two holes. The smaller piece required cutoff, assembly in hole, and staking. The part was deemed so unusual that it was not expected that a vendor made such an item.

A review of the function—not of the part—brought forth the following requirements:

A screw having a hole in the top, or other suitable arrangement, so it can be lifted and turned

A head arrangement that will be pulled back into the slot and held to prevent turning.

A search of specialty products having these two characteristics uncovered the spade bolt shown in Figure 8-10. Its cost was $\frac{1}{3}$ cent

Fig. 8-9 Adjusting screw.

Fig. 8-10 Alternative adjusting screw.

(as compared to 8 cents). It accomplished all of the functions reliably. It was readily available.

EXAMPLE 2: A spacer hub (Figure 8-11) that cost, in steel with machining and drilled holes, $1.27 was undercut and turned from steel bar. Its functions were to mount two disks of aluminum, which were riveted through six holes, and to provide a mounting center for this disk assembly.

Again, few would expect to find as an available product an undercut steel disk of the right diameter and right thickness; probably no one would search for it and possibly no one would find it. But what happens when we consider precisely what the function is?

1. Separate two 6-inch diameter aluminum disks approximately ¼ inch.
2. Provide for mounting them securely in an assembly.
3. Provide a center hole for mounting the assembly.

A search for specialty products which could be readily adapted to accomplish these functions brought forth, among other alternatives, aluminum disks or slugs that could be bought in bulk in a variety of diameters and thicknesses for use in impact extrusion.

One such slug was of a suitable diameter and thickness. It cost 4 cents, but it was stamped from sheet and so was cupped, not flat.

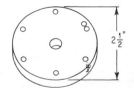

Fig. 8-11 Spacer hub.

Fig. 8-12 Alternative spacer hub.

It cost 1 cent to flatten it and 8 cents to drill the holes. The total cost of the alternative (shown in Figure 8-12) was 13 cents.

EXAMPLE 3: A ⅞-inch diameter thin nut (Figure 8-13) cost 8 cents. Its function was to hold a small 1-pound assembly on its shoulder bushing between periods of use and not allow it to fall off while it was not being used. There was no load on the nut. When in use, the force of the work held the assembly in working position and the nut was not performing any function. A small radial hole was drilled and tapped in the nut for a setscrew to reduce the risk of its loosening. It was made from hexagonal steel bar on which the necessary operations were:

Drill and tap the center hole.
Drill and tap the radial hole.
Cut off.

What precisely was the function?

1. To hold one pound onto the bushing
2. To provide unusual vibration-proof features so that, under all conditions, the nut would not loosen.

A search produced a specialty product for this exact function in the appropriate size and type, namely, a standard locknut (Figure 8-14) possessing exactly the needed characteristics. Its cost was 1½ cents (instead of 8 cents). Besides, tests proved this locknut to be more vibration proof than the former nut with setscrew.

EXAMPLE 4: A high-temperature locknut—castellated nut—(Figure 8-15), including the drilling of the shaft on which it was mounted and the safety wiring on assembly, cost $4.75. The function was to hold a heavy, high-temperature part to a moving shaft which, to some extent, was vibrating.

Search brought forth a variety of locknut arrangements, most of which were judged unsatisfactory because of the extremely high temperature of the application. Then a manufacturer of nuts using plastic locking rings was given the complete problem. His engineer

Fig. 8-13   Thin nut.

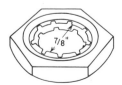

Fig. 8-14   Standard locknut.

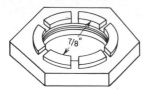
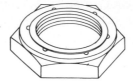

Fig. 8-15 High-temperature locknut.

Fig. 8-16 High-temperature locknut.

said, "In our product line, we have a variety of locking materials used for this function. Each is especially adapted to different environmental conditions. We can provide one which is suited to the high-temperature operation in question. Of course, it will cost a little more than our regular product." What he provided cost 23 cents and eliminated the need for drilling the shaft and wiring the nut. It is shown in Figure 8-16.

Thus identifying clearly the needed functions and then searching creatively for vendors of specialty products reduced the cost of accomplishing the total function from $4.75 to 23 cents per unit. In summary, the steps in this technique are as follows:

Recognize that for most subfunctions suitable combinations of functional products already exist.

Learn how to identify clearly and review precisely the functions needed.

Learn how to locate specialty functional products.

Use them.

8-10 *Utilize and Pay for Vendors'*
Skill and Knowledge

It is unimaginable that any user would design his own nails and buy steel to make them. Nails fall within a group of functional products that we are accustomed to buying. Likewise, few users would design standard screws and buy metal to make them (unless quantities were large enough for continuous runs on the most modern of equipment).

Many users, however, will design special screws and similar parts and go on to buying metal and making them. The alternative is to inform suppliers, who have the proper general type of equipment and accumulation of skills, of precisely the functions that are required and knowledge of the limitations on size, weight, shape, stress, etc. With such information at hand, suppliers will gladly provide suggestions and quotations. Often the costs of this procedure are from one-fourth to one-half the costs of the "do-it-ourselves" method.

The objective in product development is to get the best solutions to the problems involved in the shortest time and at the lowest cost. The best solutions will accomplish the function the customer needs and will provide the appearance that he wants. At the same time, they will do so at lowest manufacturing cost and with a minimum of manufacturing problems or quality difficulties.

The technique of utilizing and paying for vendor's skill and knowledge yields exceptionally high returns when effectively used, for the following reasons:

Large amounts of special knowledge exist in every field, and much of this knowledge is not possessed by people in other fields.

Only a relatively small amount of the total special knowledge bearing on any technology exists in any one place at any one time.

Special machines, fixtures, tooling, and equipment exist in large numbers.

New developments known only to the engineers concerned with them are in progress in most good supplier's plants. They represent the best materials, processes, or parts to use "tomorrow" within the particular technology. They can be put to use only if the supplier is called into the job to which they are applicable. Suppliers want their new developments to follow actual needs in the market and they are usually searching for practical new ways of applying their technology. They benefit and the user benefits by working together.

It is important to note that the use of skills and know-how of others in the field of securing new performance is quite commonplace and quite fruitful. Such use is motivated by tests showing that suitable performance has not been secured. Faced with known unsuitable performance, the search for better answers is self-forcing. In contrast, since value is not measured, simultaneous realization that better answers are required valuewise is lacking; hence the course of action often taken is to choose from the alternatives immediately at hand, and in reality, an integer of value loss results.

Case Study

THE THREE SPRINGS

An electrical control used three springs:

One 1 inch long by ¾ inch in diameter, plated steel, 23 cents; $23,000 per year

One ¾ inch long by ¼ inch in diameter, plated steel, 11 cents; $11,000 per year

One ⅛ inch in diameter by ½ inch long, tension loops on ends, phosphor bronze, 17 cents; $17,000 per year

A supplier who had an established reputation as a top specialist in good-value springs as well as for good performance in springs was invited to look at the job. It was suggested to the sales manager of this specialist vendor that he take the product, the drawings, and such other operating and specification information as could be provided by the engineers, have his technical people suggest precisely what springs to use, and then provide suggested costs for them. His answer was surprising: "I can't afford to do it."

When asked to explain his stand, he said experience had shown that when an engineer has had the drawing details and specifications of an exact spring made up, it is offensive to him to receive a quotation unless it is confined to precisely the geometry requested, and in the long run, the submittal of a quotation is injurious to the supplier who makes the suggestion. Only when the buyer who was taking part in the value audit of the product brought the sales manager into direct contact with the engineer and the engineer asked him to make a quotation did he consent to do so.

The springs were of such a standard nature that they could be made on completely standard spring machines and the supplier offered to submit five sets of samples for each of the first two springs and two or three sets for the third. He said he would provide twenty-five samples each and would furnish both a sheet of descriptive information telling exactly what each spring was and a sheet of test data telling precisely what each spring would do. This he did. The engineer was amazed and delighted. The cost for the various alternatives generally ran from one-fifth of the present cost up to the present cost.

After study of the test data and completion of some additional tests, springs were selected with the following costs:

$16,000 per year instead of $23,000 for the first group
$3,000 per year instead of $11,000 for the second group
$9,000 per year instead of $17,000 for the third group

Besides, a modification of material on the third group provided improved operation and greater stability throughout the life of the product. *Utilizing available supplier skills and capabilities pays off.*

The business of industrial suppliers is organized along one of two lines:

1. Make a product or provide a process which will accomplish some known and needed function or group of functions, and then sell the product or process. Examples are turbines, motors, lathes, hammers, airplane autopilots, printed circuits, photoforming.

2. Develop a group of skills, a body of knowledge, and a family of facilities capable of accomplishing certain types of functions or certain

types of work, then merchandise this capability to those who have corresponding needs.

This second type of business is most vital to our economy but much more difficult to merchandise than a product or process. The value analysis technique that we are concerned with here ties in principally with the second type.

To locate the best suppliers of this second category requires active and effective search on the part of the user, especially since a vendor cannot know what the needs are until he is located and told. The search is not simple. The first half-dozen or so vendors to whom the needs are communicated may not be the few having the special know-how needed, and thus the results become negative. Particularly high yields will be in proportion to the skill and effort applied in using the technique. Again, a series of questions must be raised, such as:

What functions are required?
What processes might contribute?
What vendors lead in each area?

When the answers to these questions are established, the definite actions to take are as follows:

Get in touch with the indicated vendors.
Describe the technical situation clearly to bring out what is really needed—the various functions; the limitations of size, weight, and dimension; the essentials of strength and appearance; etc.
State the economic situation clearly and fairly.

If there should be a prejudice by decision-making people against using any item, such as, stampings, castings, forgings, plastics, aluminum, or whatever, and the vendor's interest lies in that particular area, tell him just what the situation is. If he is competing against in-plant manufacture, tell him so and tell him the basis of the competition. If the product, even after development, has a questionable market volume, tell him that too. Only then can the supplier appraise the total situation and decide what amount of his resources it will be good business for him to commit to the solution of the problem.

The next step should be to allow the vendor's technical people time to study alternatives, to develop and test new answers, and to make a solid and new contribution. It is vital at this stage that the vendor be given every opportunity to ask more questions about what is important and what is not important, and also that he be assured that his suggested solutions will be given attention by people who decidedly want the proposals to be satisfactory for the particular purpose.

Alternatives submitted should be reviewed objectively and the best-appearing value alternatives should be selected for possible further improvement. Objective information on shortcomings should be taken back to the submitter and help should be given him to overcome the objections, if possible.

Usually, of course, only one supplier can win, i.e., earn the business. Several may work for it, but one commonly earns it. That is the nature of doing business in the competitive system. The suppliers realize this before they start work, and they fully expect that the supplier with the best answers will get the order. All of this points up the great importance of completely advising them *before* they start work. They must be made acquainted with all of the "rules of the game" before they decide to go into it.

After a vendor has produced the best answer—one substantially better than the one used prior to his work on the project—he has earned the business and must be given the opportunity to retain it for a reasonable length of time to fairly repay him for his development work.

It is indeed wrong, and cannot be tolerated, to:

Draw up his ideas and send them out to other vendors for quotation
Allow factory personnel to decide that they can make it that way in the plant

Such actions will cause the best vendors to stop wasting their good technical talent on the products or processes of the manufacturer involved. Besides, they will thereafter turn to assisting his competitors instead of continuing to help him. Paying for his work by placing orders with him if he has contributed is not only the ethical thing to do but is also, selfishly speaking, the only course of enlightened, long-range self-interest.

> EXAMPLE: *Handle for machine tool adjustments.*
> An operator uses this lever to make necessary adjustments by turning it clockwise or counterclockwise. Screws in the ends have opposite threads, one right-hand and the other left-hand; hence rotation in one direction lengthens the handle and rotation in the other direction shortens it.
>
>   What functional properties are required?
>
>   A rigid handle to be axially expandable and contractable
>   A handle capable of 300 pounds pressure
>   A surface on the handle for ready hand grip
>
>   What process might contribute?
>
>   Machine from bar; knurl and tap

Machine from tubing; knurl, plug ends, and tap

Make from aluminum impact extrusions; plug open end and tap both ends

Make from aluminum extruding tubing; plug ends and tap

Make from sheet metal, rolled and crimped; plug ends and tap

Make from suitable plastic

What vendors lead in each area? Select one or two good vendors in each of the indicated areas, the number depending upon the importance and amount of business involved. Follow through the remaining steps of the technique, as outlined above, with each of them. Help each to apply his expert knowledge and facilities.

The results of the technique will now be apparent. The special function required in the product will be reviewed in the light of the most advanced skills, techniques, and facilities within several technologies. All resultant alternatives will be unveiled before the decision maker to enable him to promptly increase the value of his product.

8-11   *Utilize Specialty Processes*

Generally speaking, all processes serve for one of two purposes.

1. They accomplish functions that can be performed in no other way.
2. They accomplish performed functions equally well but at much lower cost.

The second group takes in an extremely large number of processes, which are of vital interest in value-oriented work and which will be the group for further study in this section.

All processes might further be divided into two classes.

1. Processes that are known and are reasonably well understood by those who are making decisions
2. Processes that are not known to the decision makers but which would be applicable and would accomplish the desired ends at very much lower cost

Again, it is this second class that we shall deal with. Let us first see how processes which will accomplish functions reliably at very much lower cost but are not known to the decision makers at the particular time may be brought into view and how their benefits may be utilized in value work.

Of course, what is a special process today commonly becomes the standard process of tomorrow. Therefore, a line between the special and the standard process does not really exist, the differences being a blending of shades of gray. For practical purposes in securing important benefits from the technique in question, the best definition seems to be that a specialty process is an applicable process which would reliably accomplish the needed function for significantly lower cost and which either exists or could, and would, be developed by some one who leads in the technology involved if he understood the need for it.

For example, to the design and manufacturing engineers who designed the J bolt shown in Figure 8-17 as a cut thread part costing 11½ cents each, the process of roll threading at a cost of 1½ cents would be a specialty process. Similarly, the hollow-forging method would be a specialty process to engineering and manufacturing men who did not know that hollow forgings 2 feet in diameter and 10 feet long could be made with very high grade properties for $3,000 each after finishing machining to take the place of a similar part made from solid material at a cost of $6,000 each after machining.

The capabilities of specialty processes to accomplish functions per dollar of expenditure extend far beyond what is normally recognized. Such recognition by professional people engaged in technical value-oriented work normally lags about three years behind capabilities. General recognition lags about ten years behind.

A good estimate seems to be that the recognition of normal decision-governing design and manufacturing engineers lags about five years behind capabilities. It is the purpose of the technique under discussion to eliminate an important part of this five-year lag.

Most specialty processes go hand in hand with the never-ending development of special tools. As a simple example, perhaps at some point in the history of industrial development three types of hammers existed: one for work with stone, one for the blacksmith, and one for the carpenter. As a variety of work was brought to the carpenter, the familiar claw hammer was developed to facilitate the nail-pulling process. Successively, this tool has been further developed into a heavier hammer for the process of laying oak flooring and a lighter and very much differently shaped hammer for tacks, with the still further development of the magnetic head to make the tacking process even more economical. Similar

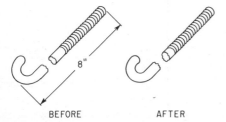

BEFORE   AFTER   **Fig. 8-17**   J bolt.

developments have taken place in hammers for metalworking and other fields. Probably few engineers know all the various stages of development of the simple hammer, each for the express purpose of improving a building or manufacturing operation of a specific type, and generally for the main purpose of improving value.

For another example, the casting process starts with the basic sand casting and spreads into almost hundreds of different types of casting processes. Some of these are uniquely appropriate to achieving a certain function by the use of some particular metal or temperature range; others fit for the attainment of specified tolerance, lack of porosity, desired appearance or surface conditions, etc. A group of typical casting processes are:

Sand casting	Miniature casting
Precision casting	Die casting
Shell molding	Mercury cast
Permanent molding	Insert molding
Lost wax process	

Case Study

MOUNTING HOLES FOR PERFORATED SHEET

For an appliance, a $\frac{1}{32}$-inch-thick galvanized-steel sheet, $1\frac{1}{2}$ feet wide by 6 feet long, was used. To perform its function, it was necessary to punch 10,000 holes in each sheet so that it became perforated. This punching cost 68 cents. To facilitate mounting the sheet, six more holes were punched near the ends at a cost of 28 cents, bringing punching cost to 96 cents.

The 10,000 perforated holes served an essential function in the appliance, while the six additional holes served merely for mounting the part. When these required functions were brought into clear focus with men throughout the country who had specialized manufacturing know-how, a supplier of continuous perforating equipment showed that the material could be continuously perforated in the long uncut strip and that some of the holes could then be used for mounting.

Investigation showed that the ends were bracketed and that cutting through the perforated area would detract from neither usefulness nor appearance. The change was made with a reduction of 59 cents per sheet in punching cost.

Application of the technique of utilizing specialty processes involves three steps.

1. Recognize that processes which would accomplish the desired functions for very much lower cost (a) may exist and not be known, (b) are

being developed, or (*c*) would be developed if competent men in the technology knew of the need.

2. Put in motion actions which will increase the likelihood that specialty competence knows about, and becomes interested in, the needed functions.

3. Assign time and effort to stay with each item until the minor problems, minor objections, and minor misunderstandings which always arise in any new approach have been illuminated with useful and factual information. The aim here is to ensure that the results to be expected from the status of science at the particular time will indeed be developed and made applicable to the particular project.

For a listing of typical specialty processes see Chapter 10. It should be recognized that such listings may lag from three to five years behind actual industrial capabilities. Also, available tables are useful guides but do not supplant the further step of making direct contact with individuals who lead in any technology.

EXAMPLE 1: The undercut screw shown in Figure 8-18 was being used in quantities of 20,000 per year. It was made on a screw machine from steel bar, was $2\frac{1}{4}$ inches long, and was undercut as shown. A study of the functions revealed that the screw was a suitable means of accomplishing the functions, provided the undercut could be produced more economically.

A specialty manufacturer who produced cold-headed and roll-threaded screws was among the ones contacted and informed of the need. He did not have a process "on the shelf" which would serve economically but he took the following approach: "I believe I can adapt the roll-threading process to remove the metal from the undercut portion. I will try to first roll a thread and then roll another thread so displaced as to remove the metal left by the first process. Next, if necessary, I will complete the operation by rolling enough successive threads until the metal has all been eliminated." He became very much interested in adapting his process to the need, so he tried it and it worked. The cost with the use of this specialty process became $1\frac{1}{2}$ cents each, not 15 cents.

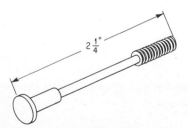

Fig. 8-18 Special screw at one-tenth the cost.

EXAMPLE 2:   The small bracket shown in Figure 8-19 was used in large quantities and served to support a small spring assembly in an appliance. It was made of steel on well-mechanized equipment. Nevertheless, the drilling and tapping of two small holes brought its cost to $13 per thousand.

The functional study showed that this was a simple and practical way of accomplishing the function, provided the cost of tapping the holes could be lowered substantially.

Search for a specialty process brought one forth. A supplier recognized this type of part as being sufficiently common in industry for him to build a good business by creating special equipment around it. In his special tooling, he bent the material and drilled and tapped the holes all in one continuous process. As a result, he quoted a delivered price of $3 per thousand for the identical part made from the identical material.

EXAMPLE 3:   *Tube support gasket* (See also example 2 in section 8-5.)

A molded-rubber gasket (Figure 8-20), a few inches in diameter and costing 11 cents, was used in large quantities. The functional study brought forth a number of alternatives for accomplishing the function. Most of the alternatives involved the use of rubber or rubberlike material but not necessarily a molded gasket of the precise type used.

The search for an applicable specialty process identified a manufacturer whose equipment applied rubber directly to the needed parts in plastic form. The desired result was obtained by placing a small machine in the production line and applying the plastic rubber directly to the parts in an operation that required but a few seconds. The total cost for a functional product of the same high quality as the former product became 1 cent instead of 11 cents.

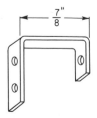

Fig. 8-19   Bracket.

BEFORE   AFTER

Fig. 8-20   Tube support at one-tenth the cost.

All cases of the profitable use of this technique to accomplish functions for very much lower cost have the following in common:

1. No applicable specialty process is known.
2. There is no assurance that such a process does not exist.
3. The functions needed in the product, together with alternative means for securing the functions, are brought clearly into view for study.
4. Based upon the likelihood that such specialized processes do exist, or would be created if proper information were provided to the proper suppliers, a search is started and the information is furnished to men in the technologies most likely to contribute.
5. Work is done with these specialists to obtain further information, to overcome minor misunderstandings, and to change meaningless specifications to allow adaptation of the specialists' processes to accomplish the needed functions at very much lower cost.

Case Study

THE TEMPERATURE-SENSITIVE CONTROL (See also the case study in section 4-3.)

An electrical control, made in relatively large quantities, consisted of a copper tube about 2 feet long attached to a bellows. The tube contained a gas which was very sensitive to temperature. Expansion and contraction of the gas operated the bellows to open and close electrical contacts. The copper tubing, for most of its length, was ⅛ inch in diameter, but for about 4 inches at the far end, it was ¼ inch in diameter. It was believed by the engineers that the larger volume at the end was required in order to give the desired sensitivity of control. The full length of the copper tubing cost 10 cents or for a million per year, $100,000. Value work was started in a number of directions.

Cost analysis showed that the proper lengths of the two sizes of copper tubing cost 5 cents and the joining operation cost 5 cents, equivalent to $50,000 a year. This immediately focused attention on the process of joining which was accomplished by brazing. Searches for other processes of joining failed to bring to light any useful alternative. Hence the function was more clearly examined and it was found that what was needed was a small end about ⅛ inch in diameter for mounting to the bellows and a larger end to contain sufficient gas in the temperature control environment. It appeared that possibly what was in between did not matter. This brought forth the idea of using a ¼-inch tubing and the process of swaging it down. The cost would then become $70,000 per year instead of $100,000. That alternative started a chain of useful results.

One process investigated was that of starting to draw the piece ⅛ inch in diameter and then, by some ingenious way, automatically opening the die so that the 4 inches on the other end would not be drawn to the smaller diameter. This solution proved very feasible. Samples were provided and proved excellent; the cost would be $60,000 per year.

Meanwhile, the engineers working along with the job continued taking basic data and making basic tests to determine precisely the length of the larger diameter needed at the end to give the sensitivity required. In doing this, they discovered that, because of improvements in providing gas with very much better temperature sensitivity than had been the case in years past, the same control was attained without any enlarged portion on the end. The tests proved that the use of copper capillary tubing somewhat less than ⅛ inch in diameter throughout its length and without any enlarged section at the end provided the excellence of control needed. The cost of this tubing came to 4 cents each, or $40,000 per year. The search located two useful processes but the final best result came in this instance from eliminating the need for the process.

8-12   *Utilize Applicable Standards*

To include this technique in the work guides of sophisticated industrial people sounds almost too elementary. It gives the impression of something amateurish. It is like being "for motherhood and against sin." Of course, everyone is. The reader will soon find, however, that the technique, once used, becomes very valuable. Some approaches for applying it successfully will be discussed.

The full meaning here includes not only use of applicable standard parts and processes but appropriate utilization of *parts* of standard products, engineering concepts, manufacturing concepts, manufacturing processes, and materials. It means, also, do not use standards that do not apply.

So much has been so effectively written in the field of utilization of standards that our intent will be not to repeat but rather to supplement. Perhaps the best instruction on how to utilize the technique will develop out of some specific examples.

EXAMPLE 1:   *A standard product*

A special tube base costing $6.80 versus a standard tube base (Figure 8-21) costing $1.80 each accomplish the identical function with the same reliability. Naturally, after a search has been made and the standard is found, it is a matter of direct substitution.

EXAMPLE 2.   *A specialty product*

A small aluminum knob and pointer were machined for use on airborne electronic equipment. The cost was $2.25 per knob. The function was to provide for manual adjustment of a small potentiometer. Available specialty products (Figure 8-22) in the form of

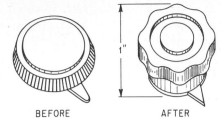

BEFORE   AFTER

Fig. 8-21 Standard tube socket at one-third the cost.

Fig. 8-22 Knobs at one-ninth the cost.

suitable plastics with metal inserts would accomplish the total function with the same reliability for 25 cents.

Once this information has been secured and it is known that the 25 cent knob is available and will accomplish the function with the same reliability, its direct substitution is a straightforward matter.

EXAMPLE 3: *A standard process detail*

A small spring was required to have hooks at each end (see Figure 8-23). One of these hooks, rather than being of the usual turn form, was of an elongated shape. The cost was 9 cents. A study of the cost showed that, by changing from the standard process of providing a spring end hook and going to the special process necessary to produce the elongated end hook, the cost of the spring was increased from 3 cents to 9 cents.

With this information uncovered, a study of the application was made, and it was found that, with a minor change in the location of the hole of the mating part, the standard spring-end process could be used. By this change, the cost of the spring dropped to one-third of its original cost.

EXAMPLE 4: *Do not use inapplicable standard materials*

Suitable standard wire screen was purchased, fitted, and properly mounted for an electronic shielding function in which a certain

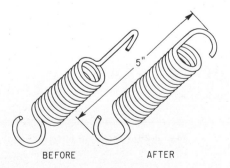

BEFORE   AFTER

Fig. 8-23 Springs, 9 cents to 3 cents.

amount of ventilation was also essential. A study of the function of the screen and its adjacent parts, together with an evaluation of the mounting and the supporting functions of both the screen and the components, raised the question of whether the use of this standard screening was the most efficient way to accomplish the functions.

Value alternatives were developed which diviated from the standard material in that they were based on using a solid material which had been subjected to a standard perforating process (Figure 8-24). The finding was that functions which cost 28 cents when the standard wire mesh was used could be performed with the same reliability by the perforated sheet metal at a cost of 18 cents.

EXAMPLE 5: *Do not use inapplicable standard products*

One million small eyelets were used in an electronic device. These eyelets were made of brass and cost $1.75 per thousand. Examination of the required functions showed that, while the eyelet accomplished the functions reliably, all of the features of the eyelet were not needed for this application. Discussions with eyelet manufacturers revealed that, with a quantity of 1 million, the eyelet machines could be adjusted and special runs made to provide special functional eyelets for the purpose in question at 80 cents per thousand.

From hundreds of examples in which standards have been reviewed—some used and some rejected—a few common criteria stand out for standard materials, processes, products, parts of materials, parts of processes, parts of products, etc. Knowledge of standards of all types is the basic ingredient around which all deviations for the benefit of value improvement must be organized.

If cost and applicability data have not been developed with regard to the function required, the chances that the needed functions are being accomplished at near their lowest practicable cost are decreased considerably.

The matter of correctly selecting standards, nonstandards, or partial standards in products, materials, or processes is similar to all other phases of decision making. The principal task is one of first locating sufficient applicable information and then making correct decisions

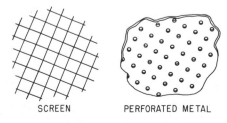

SCREEN   PERFORATED METAL

Fig. 8-24   Shielding screens of wire mesh and perforated metal.

within the various shades of gray. This will result in sometimes using standards, sometimes rejecting standards, and often using certain standardized functions but rejecting overall predigested standards.

Case Study

STANDARDIZE THE PACKING?

Although a range of sizes, stylings, and types of electric clocks were being made to fit into the decor of each room of a house, it was recognized that there existed a substantial market for a utility alarm clock. Therefore, one clock was designed and marketed which included a minimum of cost for producing aesthetic factors and features. It was a very successful product and sold in large numbers. During a value audit on the clock, one of the expense items investigated was the packaging. In line with techniques 7, 9, and 10, the best competence which could be found for this type of package was invited into the job. One of these packaging specialists was very enthusiastic and felt that he could provide a package with added marketing benefits to protect the clock even better and to cost decidedly less.

Two weeks passed and nothing more was heard from him. When contacted by telephone he replied, "We stopped our study of that." When asked why, he said that in his investigation he was confronted by a man who had the assignment of promoting standardization. This individual held that the packages now used on the whole line were a standardized family of packages—all based on the same philosophy and with each deviating only as much as necessary to fit the individual clock. Therefore, to develop an alternative would be a waste of time.

Nevertheless, the vendor was encouraged to develop the alternative in line with his original plan, and this was done. The use of the suggested new package for this one extremely high volume clock would reduce costs $150,000 per year. With this full-blown value alternative in hand, the decision was promptly made to delete the particular item from the standardized group in order to decrease costs and improve the package. *Overstandardization does not bring the best value.*

8-13   Use the Criterion, "Would I Spend My Money This Way?"

It has been said that the system of value analysis concepts and techniques is organized and illuminated common sense. Most certainly, any successful individual in the competitive economy has learned to use common sense in applying the criterion, "Would I spend my money this way?"

The average person, in evaluating his own expenditures, is governed by the following typical conditions:

He has a limited amount to spend.

He strives to secure maximum use function and appearance function from his expenditures.

He expects to get such functions within reasonable limits in return for his expenditures. If that is not in view, he at once sets out to make appropriate changes or, at least, to do so when he again is ready to expend his funds.

He knows that he cannot get reasonable value in exchange for his resources unless he has value alternatives clearly established and uses corresponding information as criteria in decision making.

Before he spends his money, he will have clearly in view the relative use values, the relative aesthetic values, and their relative costs.

The reader may recall for a moment that, in achieving value, it is vital to do what makes the best sense. Any deviation from the answers that make the best sense results in either diminished performance or decreased value. Diminished performance can usually be identified promptly by tests. Decreased value, on the other hand, often remains to be identified by buying resistance. Even then, cause and effect are so separated that the particular answers which do not make good sense are not necessarily in clear view.

Both motivation and direction are provided by the effective use of the technique with which we are here concerned. Unless the answers by design engineering, manufacturing engineering, purchasing, and management in all areas involved in decision making can affirmatively meet the test, "If it were my money, would I spend it this way?" it should be seriously questioned that a good degree of value exists. The application and effect of this technique will become more understandable as it is seen in a number of typical examples.

EXAMPLE 1:   A 3-inch diameter hand wheel on a small valve cost $3. Its function was to provide manual opening and closing of the valve.

"If it were my money, would I spend $3 for the valve handle?" With this motivation, manufacturers who produced handles for valves were sought out. It was found that hand wheels of the same size for the same function, specially cast and machined for this application and made of the same material, could be provided for 60 cents each.

EXAMPLE 2:   A moderate quantity of heavy solid-steel trunnion bolts (Figure 8-25), approximately 8 inches long with hex heads 3 inches across flats and with a bolt section 1½ inches in diameter, were needed. Round bar was purchased and the bolts were machined completely from it. The cost was $11 each.

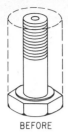 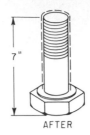

BEFORE   AFTER

Fig. 8-25 Trunnion bolts,
$11.00 to $2.28.

Does it appear to make sense to machine away all of this metal and arrive at such a high cost? Although the manufacturing people involved believed it was the only way that the bolt could be provided in this quantity, motivation from the question, "Would I spend my money this way?" caused a further search.

As a result, a hot-upset bolt blank already containing the hex head was found to be procurable, and the total cost of an interchangeable trunnion bolt which accomplished the total function with the same reliability became $2.28.

EXAMPLE 3: A hub and a shaft used in large quantity were machined and then assembled together (Figure 8-26). In order to provide reliable assembly, very close tolerances were held on that part of the shaft which mated with the hub and that part of the hub which mated with the shaft. The assembled cost was $1.12. Value study of this item followed the line of questioning the wisdom of being forced to provide close tolerances on two mating parts because of their relationship to each other. After assembly, the money paid for these close tolerances did not further contribute to the operation of the overall device. Application of the technique of

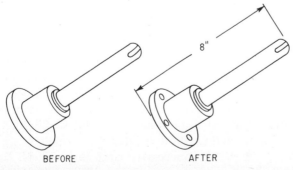

BEFORE   AFTER

Fig. 8-26 Hub-and-shaft assembly after change cost about half.

asking, "Would I spend my money this way?" developed the conviction that it simply did not make good sense. There must be a better design philosophy.

Study of the function was followed by a study of alternative methods of securing the function and also by a study of ways of connecting the two parts without the need for high-cost close tolerances. The final result was a change in the design philosophy eliminating the necessity of close tolerances. The hub was cast on the shaft, and the finished part, machined, interchangeable, and ready for use, then had a cost of 63 cents.

EXAMPLE 4:   *A small support clamp*

On a high-volume product, a part ¼ inch in diameter was supported by a small clamp. As a consequence of technological advancement, a part ⅛ inch in diameter was found to be capable of accomplishing the total function with the same reliability and at a cost of $50,000 per year less than formerly. It was expected that the change would be made at once.

Several weeks later it was noted that the ¼-inch diameter parts were still being assembled which meant that the added cost of $1,000 per week was continuing to be incurred. Personnel conducting the value study asked why the change had not been made. The answer was that owing to the loading in the tool room a twenty-week cycle was required for tool changes, since a $350 change would have to be made in the dies to make the small supporting clamp. When sufficient facts were laid before the decision-making men, the condition which allowed an additional expenditure of $20,000 on the product while waiting for the fabrication of $350 worth of special tools was seen to be so contrary to "the way I would spend my own money" that corrective action followed immediately.

EXAMPLE 5:   *Assembly of parts*

It is normal for people to want to do things themselves. That is true in engineering, in manufacturing, in purchasing, in management, and in all other walks of business life. It is no surprise, therefore, to find that manufacturing people believe they should do as much as possible themselves in manufacturing a product. They feel that they can control quality and make improvements and can, in a variety of ways, benefit their employers and their customers by doing so. This general belief, like other general beliefs, produces decisions which, in specific cases, keep large amounts of unnecessary costs in products. In the present example, a group of parts was purchased from one supplier and brought into the plant for assembly into a subcomponent. The subcomponent was ultimately used in the overall product. The delivered cost of the parts was 86 cents. The labor, handling, overhead, and inspection involved in testing added 49 cents, so that the factory cost of the subcomponent was $1.35.

In studying the value of this assembly in terms of the technique in question, the conviction was brought forth that it just did not make sense to buy a number of separate parts, receive them, inspect them, handle them, and reinspect them as an assembly which is then stocked and ready for later use. It would seem to make sense to buy one part, test one part, stock one part, and use one part when it is needed. The answer to the question, "Would I spend my money this way?" was negative.

The result was that an alternative proposal was developed with the supplier, based upon his assembling the parts and providing a finished and tested subcomponent. This saved so much handling, packaging, etc., in the supplier's plant that he was able to deliver the complete assembly ready for use at 88 cents, which meant that 47 cents of unnecessary cost was identified and eliminated through the motivation of this one technique.

EXAMPLE 6:   *Machine parts*

For good and specific reasons, rules, regulations, and instructions exist in every area. The instruction involved in the case of this example was: "Prevent unnecessary inventory."

For a "one-shot" order, the buyer received a requisition to purchase 5,000 screw-machined parts which would cost 10 cents each—$500 in total. Being trained in value techniques, the buyer immediately developed alternatives and determined that the part could be made also by the cold-upsetting and thread-rolling processes. The minimum order quantity was 15,000 at a cost of $300, i.e., 2 cents apiece.

This meant that the buyer was faced with the problem of either ordering a 5,000 quantity as instructed at an additional cost of $200 or bringing in an unwanted inventory of 10,000 and, in the overall, saving $200. His instructions were clear. However, his belief in the application of the technique, "If it were my money, would I spend it this way?" would not allow him to follow instructions, so he developed an alternative. He issued the order for 15,000 of the parts at $300. He sent instruction to the receiving room that he was to be notified when this order arrived. He planned to go out and personally scrap 10,000 pieces on the spot. He reasoned that there would be no inventory excesses and that his company would benefit by the $200 reduction in the purchase cost.

As so often happens where actions of human beings are involved, an amusing occurrence took place. Here is what actually happened. Somehow the buyer's letter to the receiving room was mislaid and he was not notified as requested. As far as he was concerned, nothing further happened in this connection until the end of the year when he received the dismaying notification that he was charged with $600 worth of excess inventory on the part. Having correctly advised his accounting department to charge the total $300 against the 5,000 parts used, it had booked the 5,000 quantity in at 6 cents each and liquidated the total purchase price of $300 against the job. However, when the 10,000 excess parts showed up at inventory time, accounting again used the 6 cents per piece cost figure, and thus the buyer received the startling debit of $600.

EXAMPLE 7:   *The 1-cent check*

Although the illustrations used in this text generally refer to products and processes, the effectiveness of the techniques is in no way restricted to those areas. The present technique is especially helpful in many other connections. For example, an engineer who, during a certain month, had taken out various cash advances and submitted covering expense accounts and refunds unfortunately made an arithmetic error and returned to the accounting department 1 cent too much. In order to balance the books the accountants drew a voucher on a New York City bank to pay the engineer back the 1 cent. The average cost of this procedure, according to an investigation with the management of the accounting unit, turned out to be $5 per voucher because of a great deal of detail involved. Engineering and manufacturing people, often hard pressed to reduce overheads, were startled to find that a practice existed whereby so much money was spent to disburse so little. The reaction of each was, "If it were my money, I wouldn't spend it that way." The practice of incurring $5 of expense in order to pay 1 cent, or for that matter to pay $1, was brought into the open for very serious questioning by application of the technique.

The present-day endeavor to establish systems which, almost regardless of people, will produce good results is certainly a most worthwhile trend. No matter how well a system is planned to take care of certain situations, there still remains room for the individual—thinking clearly—to make considerable contribution toward improvement. It is for that reason that the present technique is included in value analysis. Unless it is used and used effectively, experience in practical life shows that large amounts of identifiable unnecessary cost remain unidentified.

SUMMARY

Although the basic problem-setting and problem-solving system is applicable to any type of problem, the results accelerators in this chapter are quite specific to the task of locating and making it practical to prevent or remove "unworking" elements of cost.

This is a pragmatic chapter. Every item in it arose from the need, in situations where it becomes essential, to get better than normal cost results while maintaining high-grade performance.

To be unusually effective the user must:

Always end generalities—get into specifics.

Get and understand the makeup of pertinent costs—often very difficult to accomplish.

Get and use information *only* from the *best* source in every situation. Give no credence to any other.

Mentally blast the situation—tear it apart. Mentally build anew.

Mentally refine—minimize disadvantages.

Use real creativity. Bring the new and better solutions into mind, without waiting to see them on a competitor's product or process.

Learn to identify stoppers or roadblocks for what they are. Deal with them effectively. Do not allow them to stop progress or to prevent results.

Help industry specialists to know the exact functional need and offer their assistance.

Relate exact costs to the causes of various increments of cost, and then relate the exact function produced by those increments of cost to the amount of the cost.

The best search for ready-made solutions to problems that face the product or process designer uncovers only a part of the available "off-the-shelf" help. Confront the suppliers with the functional needs, and help them secure a good hearing and apply their products, processes, standards, skills, and knowledge to the needs of this job.

New and better solutions are more readily created when the persons involved believe or "feel" that the present answers certainly are not optimum and hence, in analysis thinking, develop a feeling of "What *I* think and how *I* feel" about the cost in relation to the function being accomplished.

chapter 9

Using the System

As we have seen, the techniques are tools for efficiently identifying unnecessary costs and removing obstacles to better value. Usually several of these tools are used in each case. Furthermore, they are often used simultaneously with one blending into another. They may be compared with the tools used by a blacksmith. With his tongs the smith brings the heated metal to his anvil in order to shape it with his hammer. Then he measures, uses the hammer again, measures once more, and perhaps reheats the work for repetition of the process.

There is great similarity in the selection and use of the value analysis tools for the identification of unnecessary cost. As in the case of the blacksmith, very seldom can good work be accomplished with just one of the tools. Efficient value work proceeds along the lines of:

Choosing the appropriate techniques
Arranging them in best order for the particular job
Using each imaginatively and effectively
Ending the use of some and emphasizing the use of others as knowledge is gained

Continuing through the steps of the value analysis job plan until the useful information developed is suitably summarized to clearly point out directions for decision and action

9-1 *Three Basic Steps*

It promotes good selection of techniques and good progression in achieving required lower costs to begin to think in terms of *three basic steps*. Each step is completed with thoroughness, using the appropriate techniques set forth in the earlier chapters, before the next step is started. It will be learned, however, that in pursuing the second basic step groundwork is often laid for the third.

The basic steps are:

1. Make clear precisely the functions the customer wants.
2. Establish the appropriate cost for each function by comparison.
3. Cause the required knowledge, creativity, and initiative to be used to accomplish each function for that cost.

9-2 *Example of Procedure*

The best explanation of the procedure in using the techniques in combination with the basic steps under the job plan may be by way of an example comprising two items of an assembly (Figure 9-1). Item 1 is a stainless-steel button, and item 2 is a carbon-steel pin.

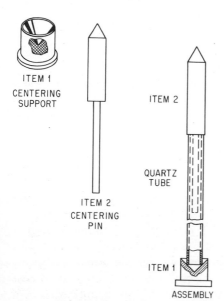

Fig. 9-1 Centering support and pin assembly.

Basic Step 1: Identify the Function

The two items are parts of a heat-sensitive device which consists of a nichrome tube having a high coefficient of expansion and an inner, smaller, concentric quartz tube having a low coefficient of expansion. As the ambient temperature changes, the difference between the coefficients of expansion provides a motion which operates electrical control equipment. Item 1 is secured in one end of the nichrome tube, its function being to provide a self-centering receptable in which the $\frac{1}{4}$-inch diameter quartz tube may reliably rest. The function of item 2 is to transmit the motion from the opposite end of the quartz tube into the control device. Accordingly, it is necessary to provide one part which will be supported on one end of the tube, i.e., something in the nature of a flange, and another part which will extend about an inch beyond the other end of the tube into the control device, i.e., something in the nature of an elongated member, such as a portion of a nail. Also, a part is needed which will extend into the center of the quartz tube for a distance of perhaps an inch in order to keep the quartz tube and the metal part now being studied in the approximate center, axially, of the nichrome tube.

Basic Step 2: Evaluate the Function by Comparison

It will be observed that this is a tentative evaluation which will be revised as the various techniques are used in greater depth later in the study. Before making even a tentative evaluation of function, it is necessary to know the quantities involved (50,000 per year), since quantities required have a major controlling influence on the number of processes that can be employed.

For the purpose of centering and supporting the $\frac{1}{4}$-inch diameter quartz rod, comparison may be made with a washer, perhaps $\frac{1}{32}$ inch thick and $\frac{5}{8}$ inch in diameter. Instead of the usual hole in the washer, a conically depressed center will provide the self-centering and supporting feature. The washer is evaluated by comparison with a standard stainless-steel washer, which would have a cost of about $\frac{1}{4}$ cent. However, since this would not be made in quantities as large as ordinary washers and would, perhaps, need some special tooling, a comparison figure of 1 cent is set. Thus we now consider the value of the function of item 1 to be approximately 1 cent, which is, in effect, the same as saying that it is believed that, considering every suitable process, material, and idea, the function can be reliably accomplished for that amount.

Item 2, when compared with a nail of about the same size, would cost $\frac{1}{10}$ cent. Nails, however, are made in extremely large quantities, and a nail in its usual form would not be suitable. The head would have to be coined in the center, and a more refined point would probably be required. In that light, this function also is evaluated, by the adjusted comparison, at 1 cent.

Basic Step 3: Cause Value Alternatives to Be Developed

Suitable value analysis techniques that will cause value alternatives to be developed are now selected. In the present case, the techniques initially chosen are:

2. Get all available costs.
4. Blast, create, refine.
5. Use real creativity.
7. Use industry specialists to extend specialized knowledge.
9. Utilize vendors' available functional products.
11. Utilize specialty processes.
12. Utilize applicable standards.

While still in the "information step" of the job plan, these facts are established:

Item 1 is made on a screw machine from stainless-steel bar; its cost is 6 cents. The applicable drawings, specifications, and planning cards are sought out.

Item 2 is made on a screw machine from ¼-inch diameter steel rod. Its cost, likewise, is 6 cents. Manufacturing and use information concerning it are also accumulated.

By now proceeding into the "speculative step" and applying technique 4, "blast, create, refine," and technique 5, "use real creativity," a wide range of possible solutions is opened up. "Brainstorms" are conducted and different approaches are explored. Likewise, a start is made with the application of techniques 7, 9, 11, and 12.

First, the functional requirements and some ideas for accomplishing the functions are set forth so that specialists can search their available functional products and study the use of their specialty processes in relation to this need. Second, a search for applicable standard items is started.

In next moving into the "development step" of the job plan, certain programs are established. Two of them cover the following actions. Specialists who use the coining process and specialists who use the cold-upsetting process are encouraged to apply their particular knowledge and to adapt their processes for the functions of item 1 and item 2.

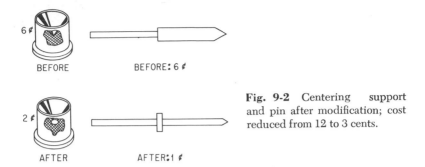

BEFORE　　　　BEFORE: 6 ¢

AFTER　　　　AFTER: 1 ¢

Fig. 9-2 Centering support and pin after modification; cost reduced from 12 to 3 cents.

By the various parts of the "judgment step," it is determined that one of the probable best selections for item 1 is the coining process and one of the probable best selections for item 2 is the cold-upsetting process.

In the "development step," the suppliers selected are provided with every possible assistance to assure accomplishment. Since the assembly is small and is already in production, the suppliers are provided with actual assemblies as well as necessary drawings and, perhaps fully as important, with encouragement and with prompt answers to their questions.

In the "development step," suggestion sheets are made out from the results provided. These show that, with retainment of complete interchangeability of parts, the cost of item 1 can be reduced from 6 cents to 2 cents, and the cost of item 2 can be reduced from 6 cents to 1 cent. The sheets also indicate in general how to proceed to accomplish these results. Folders of supporting data are provided to appropriate people in the decision and action area to enable them to identify and promptly remove unnecessary cost.

It will be observed that the process is an objective, action-oriented, searching study of:

What is to be accomplished

What is the best way of accomplishing it, i.e., the lowest-cost way of reliably doing it

What are the best answers from the best sources using the latest knowledge and technology

What clear information is to be crystallized for the basis of decision and action

As skill is acquired, less attention is necessary in selecting the right tools or techniques. For the sake of effectiveness, however, each of the basic steps, each of the provisions of the job plan, and each of the special techniques should be well learned and should be applied as a well-arranged part of the user's procedure.

9-3 *Interrelation of Basic Steps, Job Plan Steps, and Results-accelerating Techniques*

Basic steps	Step of job plan	Accelerators often used
1. Identify function	1. Information	1. Avoid generalities 3. Get answers from best sources 6. Overcome roadblocks
2. Evaluate function	1. Information	1. Avoid generalities 2. Know costs 3. Get answers from best sources 6. Overcome roadblocks 8. Put value on key tolerances 9. Use vendors' functional products 11. Use specialty processes 12. Use applicable standards
	2. Analysis	1. Avoid generalities 3. Get answers from best sources 4. Blast, create, refine 7. Use industry specialists 13. Spend money as own
	3. Creative	4. Blast, create, refine 5. Use real creativity 13. Spend money as own
	4. Judgment	1. Avoid generalities 3. Get answers from best sources 8. Put value on key tolerances 9. Use vendors' functional products 11. Use specialty processes 12. Use applicable standards
3. Create alternatives	3. Creative	4. Blast, create, refine 5. Use real creativity 7. Use industry specialists 9. Use vendors' functional products 10. Use vendors' skills 11. Use specialty processes 12. Use applicable standards
	4. Judgment	1. Avoid generalities 3. Get answers from best sources 6. Overcome roadblocks 13. Spend money as own
	5. Development	4. Get answers from best sources 6. Overcome roadblocks 7. Use industry specialists· 9. Use vendors' functional products 10. Use vendors' skills 11. Use specialty processes 12. Use applicable standards

At this point, it may be useful to work through an example evaluation for the purpose of checking the techniques that it is necessary to use in order to achieve an effective result.

Basic Step 1: Identify the Function

A terminal (Figure 9-3) of a small electrical device receives and must reliably hold a No. 6 copper conductor wire. Although the wire is usually inserted by moving it parallel to its own axis, sometimes other means of fastening the wire makes lowering it into the terminal more convenient. It is desirable, therefore, to be able to open the top of the terminal under such circumstances. In starting the investigation of this terminal, it was found that the manufacturing department had a fairly large battery of automatic screw machines and the necessary milling machines to produce this terminal as a screw-machined and milled part. Accordingly, they felt it unwise to invest time and resources in investigating other methods, which might result in making this good equipment useless.

It was found that engineering was very pleased with the performance of the terminal. There had been some quality problems a few years earlier. When the nuts were tightened down too much, the prongs of the terminal would snap together and slip threads. This was corrected by providing a washer with a center tongue which prevented this snapping together. The product accomplished its function well. There were no longer any quality problems, and there was other necessary work at hand for engineering talent. Therefore, engineering was not disposed to solve this problem by opening up new design and manufacturing considerations. (The sales department was meeting customer resistance but was seeking its solution by attempting to develop more effective sales methods.)

The essential information had to be secured and these roadblocks had to be overcome by some means, or else the value work would have ended prematurely. Techniques 1, 3, and 6 were put to use.

$\frac{7}{8}$"

BEFORE

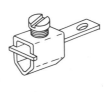

AFTER

Fig. 9-3   Electrical terminals.

Basic Step 2: Evaluate the Function
by Comparison

It was found that the quantities had been large, and although they were decreasing, they were still very substantial. The cost of the three pieces, which included two screw-machined parts and the stamping, was 20 cents for each three terminals used on the device. Preliminary study included various terminals used in other devices and in other industries. Terminal specialists were consulted. Vendors of terminals were invited to make suggestions. The technical people of vendors' organizations were advised of the problems and of the needs. Manufacturers utilizing specialty processes which might be applicable were given an opportunity to understand the function needed so they could apply their processes and suggest appropriate alternatives. Applicable standards were searched.

The initial comparison with available products indicated that this function could probably be reliably accomplished for something in the neighborhood of 6 cents per set of three terminal assemblies if the best combination of ideas, materials, and processes was brought together.

A creative study was then conducted, and in it, every possible alternative, and even impossible alternatives that could be suggested, were listed. These alternatives included contributions which might be made by various materials, by various processes, by various design approaches, by various manufacturing combinations, etc. Preliminary evaluation of them confirmed the 6-cent function value.

Basic Step 3: Cause Value Alternatives
to Be Developed

Now, having in view a 20-cent set of terminals with an estimated value of 6 cents, more extensive creative work was indicated. The suggestions which came out of the preliminary creative work were examined. Especially effective avenues of approach were selected. Creative effort was made to produce a larger range of alternatives to provide ways of accomplishing some of the most effective approaches and also to provide suggested sources for better information and for later approaches.

With this move, sufficient information was accumulated so that, in the analytical phase, good information from knowledgeable specialists and covering estimates, or quoted costs, made it practicable to narrow down the selection of probable best alternatives. The succeeding analysis indicated that a reliable terminal, which would be convenient to use and which would accomplish its function well and be most economical, would in all likelihood be made, not on rotating machinery, but on punch presses or stamping machinery.

Therefore, in the development step of the job plan, emphasis was placed on working with industry specialists having appropriate skills and techniques. Also, more intensive studies were made along the lines of using vendors' functional products and applicable standards, including modifications of such products and standards. Technical people in the plants of vendors making terminal-type products from flat material were further assisted and encouraged to suggest alternatives which would utilize their company's materials. Several good alternatives were developed.

The status summary and report was issued covering an alternative made of one stamping, a piece of tubing, and a standard screw at a total cost of 9 cents per set of three terminals. The best alternative in this case, brought forth by technique 11, "utilize specialty processes," was provided by a vendor whose specialized equipment and specialized knowledge qualified him to furnish simple, high-grade, functional terminals capable of accomplishing the total function reliably at the lower cost.

It will be observed that in carrying out this typical value study, which identified half of the cost as being unnecessary, substantially all of the techniques were used and most of them made an important contribution. Of course, since this was not a close-tolerance job, technique 8 served only for a check to make sure that the specification on the terminal did not include any close tolerances. After that, no further thought needed to be given to the tolerance question.

9-4   *Examples of Appropriate Progression*

To help in gaining familiarity with an orderly application of these tools, each is shown in its appropriate progression in the following example.

Basic steps:

1. Identify the function.
2. Evaluate the function by comparison.
3. Cause alternatives to be developed.

Steps of job plan:

1. Information gathering.
2. Analysis.
3. Creativity.
4. Judgment, minimizing disadvantages.
5. Development planning and action.

Results-accelerating techniques:

1. End generalities and get down to specifics.
2. Obtain and understand all available costs.
3. Obtain and use information *only* from the best source.
4. Blast, create, and then refine.
5. Use real creativity.
6. Identify and overcome stoppers and roadblocks.
7. Use industry specialists to extend specialized knowledge.
8. Get a dollar sign on key tolerances and cost adders.
9. Find and utilize vendor's available functional products.
10. Utilize and pay vendor's skills and knowledge.
11. Utilize specialty processes.
12. Utilize *applicable* standards.
13. Use the criterion "Would I spend my money this way?"

EXAMPLE 1:

	Basic step	Step of job plan	Accelerators
The item is a 2-inch diameter V-belt pulley (Figure 9–4) for light duty on ¼-horsepower motor shaft.	1	1	13
It is planned to machine it from a 2-inch steel bar.	2	1	
Its planned cost is 60 cents.	2	1	2, 13
Specifications and drawings are accumulated.	2	1	
There are no close tolerances.	2	1	8
Quantity will be 60,000 per year.	2	1	
Comparison with available pulleys which are similar but not precisely usable shows the standard to cost 10 cents.	2	2	
An addition of 5 cents to add special requirements gives a tentative value for the function of 15 cents.	2	2	4, 5
Tools most likely to produce the best solution are chosen.	3	2	4, 5, 9, 11, 12

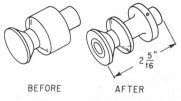

BEFORE   AFTER
$2\frac{5}{16}''$

Fig. 9-4 A pulley, for which drawings and specifications are available, and an alternative pulley.

Searches are made for different ways of doing it; for different methods of fabrication and manufacturing; for different materials, processes, and ideas; for different approaches to the problem.	3	3	4, 5

	Basic step	Step of job plan	Accelerators
Search for standards. Get in touch with suppliers of specialty functional products. Show them the need and interest them in the job.	3	3	9
Get in touch with specialists using specialty processes, show them the need, and interest them in the job.	3	3	11
Judgment indicates that two alternatives may justify intensified study. They are: Modify vendor's standard. Make as die casting in plant.	3	4	
Get in touch with proper vendors and arrange for information to be developed on the basis of a standard product suitably modified.	3	5	9, 12
Arrange for manufacturing and cost alternatives to be developed for in-plant manufacture.	3	5	
Follow each of these alternatives, providing more information as needed and making more suggestions to help each succeed.	3	5	
Prepare a status summary and conclusion sheet showing original intended cost of 60 cents with two alternatives: Modified standard, 25 cents In-plant manufacture including tool liquidation, 23 cents	3	5	

As experience is gained, the steps become automatic, the selection becomes rapid, and without omitting any significant steps or techniques, efficiency and effectiveness are improved as the techniques blend into and through one another.

Another example of the use of the basic steps, the job plan, and the techniques may be helpful.

EXAMPLE 2:

	Basic step	Step of job plan	Accelerators
The purpose of the stud (Figure 9-5) is to hold an electric motor on high-volume equipment and space a dust cover over it. It offers no appearance or aesthetic values to the customer. It is a use part. It costs 15 cents.	1	1	13
Quantities are 400,000 per year. The material is steel. There are no close tolerances. It is made on automatic equipment from standard steel rod. There are no quality problems. Its cost in labor, material, and overhead is 15 cents.		1	13

	Basic step	Step of job plan	Accelerators
Drawings, planning cards, and samples, including an assembled and a disassembled sample of the product using the stud, are at hand.	1	1	2–13
With the function clearly established as a holding function and a spacing function, comparisons are now made to place the value on each function. The cost of the holding function can be compared with that of a screw of similar dimension, which would be about 1½ cents. The spacing function can be compared with a piece of tubing cut to proper length or a piece of flat metal rolled to form a spacer. In either case, the cost would be in the neighborhood of ½ cent. Therefore, by comparison, the sum of the combined functions is evaluated at 2 cents.	2	2	4, 5
Intensive creative work, using the brainstorming technique, follows to develop a wide range of possible alternative means for accomplishing these two functions. These means are listed. Although several useful alternatives were identified, only one will be pursued through the remaining steps of evaluation.	2	3	5
Discuss the requirements with industry specialists, search for vendors' functional products, provide information on the functional need to vendors' technical people, provide information to suppliers having specialty processes which might be applicable, and search for standard products.	3	3, 4	7, 9–12
A supplier of cold, upset, and roll-thread parts proposed a suitable screw as shown in Figure 9-5 at 1½ cents.	3	4	11
A supplier of rolled spacers, which were a specialty product for him, proposed a suitable cylindrical spacer at slightly under ½ cent. This spacer and the roll-thread screw assembled together ready for use would be an equivalent part costing 2 cents.	3	4	9

Fig. 9-5 Spacer stud, 15 cents to 2 cents.

A suitable program was set up with the supplier of the special screw so that samples were made and provided. On a quantity of these were mounted the rolled spacer from the spe-

	Basic step	Step of job plan	Accelerators
cialty supplier. With quotations and samples at hand, the move was made to the next step.	3	4, 5	
Preparation of the status summary and conclusion sheet revealed:			
Initial cost, 15 cents			
Cost as changed, 2 cents			
Yearly reduction in cost, $52,000	3	5	

9-5 Examples Dealing with "Generality" Stoppers

As may be quite obvious, it is seldom known in advance what technique or techniques may best produce the results sought. Nevertheless, it will be illustrated by the additional examples which follow that emphasis on a particular technique is often the key to the identification of large amounts of unnecessary cost. In these examples, the complete framework is omitted and only the parts of the evaluation being studied are detailed.

EXAMPLE 1: *Electrical terminal*
The function was to facilitate reliable connection of wire to electrical equipment. The terminal, shown in Figure 9-6, was made from copper strip by fully automatic processes on a four-slide machine. It was used in very large quantities.

Effective value work on this item was retarded by a prevailing belief that "made automatically from sheet stock on high-speed four-slide machines, it simply cannot be beat." Being a simple part, it was made from the lowest-cost form of its base material, copper strip. The controlling generality was that all experience of the past had proved this to be by far the most economical, simplest, most straightforward way to make that type of part.

In the light of accelerator 1, it was apparent that even effective

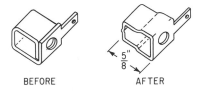

BEFORE   AFTER

Fig. 9-6 Electrical terminals.

attempts at good-grade value work were being stopped by this generality. Therefore, it was decided to temporarily disregard the belief and to develop objective data.

Using accelerator 11, it was found that a specialty supplier had so improved his processes that he could produce copper tubing for almost the cost of producing copper sheet and strip. He also possessed very ingenious machines for making a variety of fabrications from this tubing. Further, his organization possessed a high degree of skill in adapting its special equipment to the special needs of its customers.

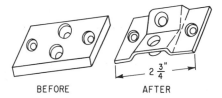

BEFORE AFTER

Fig. 9-7 Spring-locating parts at one-tenth of former cost.

This attack brought forth an interchangeable part accomplishing the identical function at sufficiently lower cost, with the result that the function was secured for $8,000 less per year.

The professional user of value analysis techniques will soon learn to recognize situations in which any one of the techniques does not fit and also that each accelerator, in its own right, becomes the real cause of accomplishment for those particular types of products and situations for which it is provided.

EXAMPLE 2: A part (Figure 9-7) machined from steel bar served the function of locating the ends of two compression springs. Quantities were 5,000 each year. It was produced, however, in conjunction with some other similar machine work. In the information phase, when costs were requested, the answer was that costs were "unavailable." It was thought that because the part was being made in conjunction with a number of other things on equipment which might otherwise stand idle and by workmen during setup time and in odd periods between other jobs, it really had very little cost and that it would be meaningless to develop its own specific cost.

Turning to accelerator 2, which emphasizes the importance of obtaining and understanding costs, it was decided to determine the cost. With this decision and the action that followed, the cost figure of $1.08 apiece became available. The effective use of technique 2 made it possible to follow up with other techniques, among them technique 7. The result was that a tool costing $1,100 was made, and an interchangeable part accomplishing the total function was then produced as a stamping for a total cost of 8 cents each.

It was only after emphasis was put on the proper use of technique 2 that the project opened up so that the remaining techniques could be used with a resultant return of $5,000 per year for an expenditure of $1,100.

A technique which often facilitates initiation of effective work is accelerator 3, "use information from only the best sources." Not uncommonly it happens that a source which may not be best for exactly the specific question proves best for a nearly related item or process.

EXAMPLE 3:   Weld supports ⅜ inch thick were cut from steel bar as shown in Figure 9-8. The quality was 3,000 per year and the cost $1.41 each. The irregular shape and the relatively small quantity

BEFORE   AFTER

Fig. 9-8   Weld supports at $1.00 less.

combined to necessitate considerable work on each. The part was used as a "weld segment" to fit into an opening in large equipment where it was welded in place as a part of a homogeneous mass.

The manager of tool design said that, although admittedly the part was of an irregular shape which was costly to make by individual processes, the quantity was so small and the material so heavy that it was out of the question to consider making dies and punching out usable parts. When he was asked for an approximate estimate of the costs of the tools and parts for the process of punching out the part, his reaction, after reflecting briefly, was that "it would be a waste of time to figure the dies because it is a foregone conclusion that they will be so costly as to make the alternative useless." This came from a highly skilled man in the field of dies, die construction, and die costs. It was difficult not to recognize him as the best authority on the question. The fact was, however, that his experience was generally with large quantities, and he did not have up-to-date knowledge of small-lot stamping technology.

When technique 3 brought this clearly into focus, an estimate was requested from a supplier of small-lot stampings. For him, who always operated in the small-lot field, the case presented no problem. His quotation was $75 for tools and thereafter 39 cents each for parts. This, then, was a case in which application of technique 3 led to a follow-through with succeeding techniques, specifically technique 11. The investment of $75 brought an annual return of $3,000.

SUMMARY

The progressive results that must be accomplished in the value analysis system are divided, by the type of work necessary to accomplish them, into three basic steps:

1. Make clear precisely what function the customer wants.
2. Evaluate that function or those functions by comparison.
3. Cause alternatives to be developed.

The "work" is accomplished in a step-by-step manner in a five-step job plan, which progressively uses four distinct and separate kinds of mental activity, or thinking. These five steps are (1) information searching, (2) analysis, (3) creativity, (4) judgment, and (5) development planning.

In accomplishing a suitable degree of results efficiently, all of the known knowledge and skills are used. Attention to a few dozen specific approaches or to the minimizing of specific retardants greatly accelerates results. The use of thirteen of these results-accelerating techniques is developed and illustrated in this chapter. They are:

1. End generalities.
2. Obtain and understand all available costs.
3. Obtain use information *only* from the best source.
4. Blast, create, and then refine.
5. Use real creativity.
6. Identify and overcome stoppers or roadblocks.
7. Use industry specialists to extend specialized knowledge.
8. Get a dollar sign on key tolerances and cost adders.
9. Find and utilize vendor's available functional products.
10. Utilize and pay for vendor's skills and knowledge.
11. Utilize specialty processes.
12. Utilize applicable standards.
13. Use the criterion "Would I spend my money this way?"

chapter 10

Special Knowledge Required

In practically all fields of human endeavor, the operator, to achieve the very best results, uses special tools in combination with special knowledge. The difference between one field and another lies in the nature of both the tools and the knowledge.

The tools may vary from the physical kinds that, for instance, the plumber needs to execute his work readily or the surgeon uses to perform his tasks expertly to the more figurative tools that the successful lawyer cannot do without.

As for the knowledge required, it ranges from the practical training and experience that the skillful plumber works with to the intricate medical knowledge needed by the surgeon or the intimate acquaintance with law, human behavior, and prior court decisions that the lawyer must have.

This basic situation also prevails as far as the value analyst is concerned. He too needs special tools combined with special knowledge to produce value alternatives which, by the process of comparison, identify unnecessary costs.

10-1   *Reach of Knowledge*

There is one basic difference, however, in the reach of knowledge required by the value analyst in comparison with the majority of other experts. Consider the income tax specialist, for example. He must have special knowledge in great depth pertaining to tax law, practice, and regulations involving a multitude of situations. Or consider the heat-transfer specialist who must possess accumulated knowledge in great volume pertaining to materials, heat conductivity, and practicable shapes and ideas for providing, preventing, or controlling the flow of heat. The need of both of these specialists is for comprehensive special knowledge, all pertaining to the relatively narrow bands of the applicable field.

In contrast, the special knowledge required for high-grade value work is extremely broad. It does not consist of knowledge in depth in any specific field. It is rather a matter of having the kind of broad knowledge that makes the holder recognize the multitude of technologies and product areas that he must explore to be assured of optimum performance and optimum cost in his product.

As we have seen in the foregoing discussions, the tools for professional-grade value work are the value analysis basic steps and techniques which are used to identify the problem, organize it into solvable integers, and bring a number of ideas to play upon each integer. By applying these tools in conjunction with appropriate special knowledge, alternatives are produced from which a choice can be made, either in the design stage or in subsequent design reviews, to accomplish the desired function reliably and at the same time to include less unnecessary cost.

10-2   *Nature of Knowledge*

The special knowledge required in value improvement work consists of information on materials, processes, functional products, sources of functional knowledge, approaches to function performance, and practical ideas for economical function solutions. In other words, the value analyst's requirement is for knowledge in moderate depth penetrating each of hundreds of widely diverse fields.

Only through the best combination of materials, processes, ideas, etc., is it possible, in any given instance, to arrive at the solution that secures reliable performance at the lowest cost, as represented by the "best value" alternative.

To achieve this result, it is not enough to have a library of appropriate knowledge, for the simple reason that, however comprehensive it be, the collection cannot be expected to include all information having a bearing on the sought solution. With the continual, rapid expansion of new knowledge, the latest information on materials, processes, and the like is hardly ever to be found recorded. Hence channels must be developed and recorded for ready access to such new information.

In consequence, it is important that the value analyst's library of special knowledge contain not only as comprehensive as possible a volume of trade knowledge backed by efficient means for quick recall of needed information but also well-organized references to a maximum number of sources of special skills that may be consulted in connection with each problem. Even then, 100 per cent performance can only be approached because no known system will scan the collection to ensure that the best information is brought into play.

Often the best alternatives for accomplishing desired functions reliably for small fractions of their expected costs are found by extracting from the fund of special value knowledge an overlooked material, process, or available functional product or some combination of them. The effective solution to a problem is quite commonly so simple as to almost produce embarrassment and frequently finds expression in saying such as, "Why couldn't I have thought of it before?"

Case Study

THE TIMER

Precision timers were used on precise electrical equipment. They accurately provided timing of from $\frac{1}{10}$ to 20 seconds. The quantity was 1,000 per year. The use of value analysis techniques brought into clear focus the unnecessary costs included in the following examples. The reader will note the importance of familiarity with the particular special knowledge which efficiently brought forth each of the alternatives listed.

An iron casting was purchased for 21 cents. It was very complicated and had a great amount of machining on it. By the time all the machining was done, its cost was $1.76. It was found that a rather heavy stamping could be purchased from small-lot vendors instead. Tool cost would be $100—10 cents each on a year's supply—and the part ready to use would cost 20 cents.

A special cam-operated electrical contact was assembled from specially fabricated pieces of plastic laminate, brass strip, and contacts. It cost 86 cents each. A specialty vendor provided a switch kit which contained all these parts as standard items. Parts could be taken from the kit, then purchased in the quantities desired and put together by him from his standard parts; this provided a finished switch which had the same operating characteristics and which could be used with a slight change in the mounting arrangement on the assembly, for 16 cents.

A timing lever assembly was made from metal strip cut, formed, drilled, welded, etc., and one screw-machined part which was welded in. It required a great amount of handwork and cost $6.56 each. It was found, in searching for a way to accomplish this function at more nearly its value, that, instead of the steel strip, a basic stamping which formed a principal part of the assembly was provided by a low-quantity stamping vendor for 20 cents each with $100 tool cost—again 10 cents each on a year's production. Adding the welding, the riveting, and an available commercial rivet instead of the special screw-machined part increased the cost 10 cents, so that the total now was 30 cents, or 40 cents for the first year, instead of $6.56.

An interesting assembly was a small pawl about 2 inches long which pivoted at one end and was pressed by a spring at the other end into notches on the edge of a dial. In this way it acted to hold the dial in exactly preferred positions which were exact fractions of a second or of a minute. It was made of $\frac{3}{32}$-inch-thick steel, suitably shaped. Riveted into it was a screw-machined part properly grooved to hold the end of the spring which pressed it against the dial edge. Its special shape, the making of the screw-machined part, the assembly, etc., brought its cost to $2. The value alternative which would most economically and reliably accomplish all the functions consisted of a stamping of the same size, again made by a small-lot stamping supplier. Instead of the screw-machined part, the metal sheet was blanked and a part of it about $\frac{1}{8}$ inch wide and $\frac{1}{4}$ inch long was turned up at right angles. In the punch-press operation, a small groove was placed on the top of this portion which, with the groove, served to receive the spring and make the screw-machined part and its assembly unnecessary. The cost of tooling was $50—5 cents each for the first year—and the cost of the part was then 7 cents, for a total of 12 cents instead of $2.

The foregoing are samples of thirty subassemblies or individual parts for which functions were examined and value alternatives were prepared.

The overall result was identification of enough unnecessary cost to allow production of the timer with costs reduced from $94 to $28.

The more extensive the accumulated special knowledge for value work, the faster and more efficiently the value work proceeds.

The special knowledge needed for explorations in the value phase is so broad that only its type can be illustrated in a discussion such as the present one, and the reader should realize that a hundred times more information than that which can be presented here is necessary for a high degree of value work. Whatever it is, the information must be in a form which, in so far as possible, can be referred back to for alternative means and ways of performing given functions.

To be most useful, the special information on materials and products must include data on the functions which the item will accomplish as well as on the types of new functions which it may accomplish. Also, the data must be associated with approximate costs or relative costs.

10-3   *Form and Constitution of Knowledge Fund*

In actual practice, persons engaged in value work have found it advantageous to accumulate the special knowledge needed in whatever form it usually can be obtained, such as handbooks, catalogues, charts, price lists, product and process descriptions, tables. But one factor that plays an important role in effective development of value alternatives is not commonly found in available technical or trade information, namely, the association between properties of materials and costs, as contrasted with the commonly indicated relationship between the material and its cost. In searches for alternatives to accomplish specified functions most economically, it is the relationship between properties and costs that is most useful.

Similarly, the most helpful process relationship is that between the properties of products produced by various processes and the cost of each process, including the material used. Again, this type of information is not normally incorporated in existing handbooks, catalogues, and trade information sources.

Were tables of relationships of functions to costs generally available, the required amount of special knowledge would be greatly reduced. However, to establish the relationship of function to cost, a chain procedure is necessary, starting with function and proceeding to a design concept, then going on into certain products and materials and advancing into certain processes appropriate for use with these products and materials in this design concept. At this end of the chain, costs can be determined.

For recognition of the magnitude of the job of securing the desired performance at lowest cost, the reader may well examine the chart in Figure 10-1 which shows the necessary process which must be completed, beginning with a desired function and culminating in a combination of design concepts, materials, products, and processes which will yield the required function and to which a definite cost can then be attached.

For purposes of simplicity, let us assume that for a typical function three design concepts or approaches must be considered and that, for each approach, three different combinations of materials, products, or modified products must be investigated; further, let us assume that for each subcombination three sets of processes are possibilities. It will be seen that twenty-seven alternatives result in this case. In many instances, the average would be nearer four of each kind, which would mean sixty-four alternative ways, many of which would accomplish the required performance and most of which would be associated with different costs. As a general yardstick, it may well be that, to accomplish the normal function in industry, between twenty-five and fifty deviations may justify investigation. The required performance and the lowest cost may appear in any one of them.

It will be obvious that it is necessary to have included in the special knowledge extensive information concerning relationships and interrelationships between functions, design concepts, materials, products, and processes. The problem of achieving functions reliably at lowest cost becomes the more complicated not only because the design concept influences and controls materials, products, and processes used, including the resulting cost, but also because the reverse is true; the resulting cost has an influence on the process selection, which in turn has its influence on materials and products, which again must influence the design concept. Continuous interrelationships must be cut and tried and changed, and

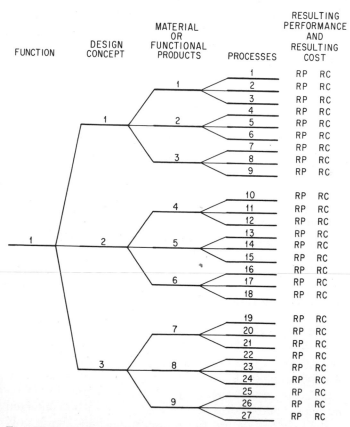

Fig. 10-1 Typical variety of combinations of design concepts, materials, and processes that will accomplish a specified function but at differing costs.

the problem cannot be reduced to one of starting at point A and proceeding to point B with assurance that the road followed will be the shortest.

In a variety of valuable handbooks, design guides, and other sources of information, there will be found tables and charts of the relationships of:

Functions to properties (e.g., current to conductivity)
Properties to materials (e.g., conductivity to aluminium)
Materials to costs (e.g., cost of aluminium)

Occasionally, helpful knowledge can be found covering narrow parts of the field and showing properties of materials or products that have had their functions related directly to costs. Such charts of properties related to functions and to costs provide a rather direct linkage between functions and costs. Although not listed above, some charts of relationships of functions to costs probably exist and more are likely to come, and they will constitute an invaluable part of the special knowledge serving the needs of value analysis.

The reader will do well to tie the process of bringing special knowledge to bear directly and efficiently upon a product to techniques 7, "use industry specialists to extend specialized knowledge"; 9, "utilize vendors' available functional products"; 10, "utilize and pay for vendors' skills and knowledge"; and 11, "utilize specialty processes." Often the special knowledge serves at best to identify the particular approach which is most likely to yield good results. Then suitable industry specialists must be brought into contact with a clearly defined function objective so that they, in turn, using their experience, can apply special knowledge, special materials, special products, and special processes with a degree of effectiveness which would be impossible for anyone less skilled in that particular field.

10-4   *Listing of Specialized Competence*

The special knowledge fund should also contain listings of specialists to be consulted, as the first step taken, after an approach to be explored has been indicated by application of the general special knowledge. Because of the vital importance of this part of the special knowledge fund, part of a listing that has served this purpose in actual practice is included. While the names and addresses of the persons to be contacted were included in the original listing, the transcription here shows only the activity involved. The tabulation is illustrative of the manner of developing sources of specialized competence on the products and functions being studied.

Value Analysis Special Knowledge
Sources of Specialized Competence

Item	*Source*[1]

Castings:
    Aluminum, bronze, brass sand
    Austenitic and stainless steel
    Carbon and alloy steel, sand cast
    Centrifugal castings, nonferrous
    Design and metallurgical assistance
    Die castings, nonferrous
    Ductile iron
    Gray iron, sand cast
    Malleable iron sand castings
    Pattern work
    Permanent molding, nonferrous
    Precision castings:
        Investment
        Centrifugal
    Shell molding, nonferrous
Chemistry and chemical engineering:
    Organic
    Physical and analytical
    Processes
Computational methods
Contracts
Cost accounting
Design and application engineering:
    Acoustics, vibration, and stress analysis
    Appearance design
    Engineering statistics
    Specialist applications
    Standards
    Technical data
    Technical systems
    Thermal systems
Electrical engineering laboratory investigations:
    Computer engineering
    Control systems engineering
Electronic engineering
Electronic data processing
Electron and radiation equipment engineering
Electron tubes

[1]Names and addresses of the sources listed in the original are deleted, as they were appropriate only to a particular work type. Each will fill in his own sources according to location, type of work, and experience for effectiveness.

Item	*Source*[1]

Equipment development:
  Coil design and manufacture
  Equipment engineering
  Equipment manufacturing
  Machinability
Information systems
Instrumentation
Insulation engineering
Laminated and insulating products:
  Mica products
  Varnished products
Magnetics and electromagnetic engineering
Manufacturing engineering:
  Manufacturing methods
  Plant engineering
  Plant layout
  Production control
  Purchasing factory equipment
  Purchasing ferrous materials
  Quality control
  Time standards
Metallurgy and welding
Nucleonics and radiation
Office procedures analysis
Patents
Porcelain products
Printing and related work:
  Addressograph
  Binders
  Composition
  Electrotyping
  Letterpress printing
  Mimeograph
  Multigraph
  Offset printing
  Photoengraving
  Planograph
Product planning
Product service
Punching, tool and die
Purchasing:
  Chemicals
  Fuels
  Ferrous and nonferrous materials
  Research

Item	*Source*[1]

Screw machine, cold heading, slotting, roll threading:
    All types of special
    Automatic, 0 to 3½ inches diameter
    Cold heading
    Hand, 0 to 17 inches diameter
    Screw-machined parts in any quantity
Semiconductor engineering
Specifications, Army and Navy
Tinsmith practice
Traffic knowledge
Training and education
Welded products
Woodworking

10-5 *Specific Product and Process Knowledge*

For the purpose of illustrating the types of resources on which data must be included and which must be available in some suitable form as special knowledge, the following abbreviated samples are presented. In each case there must be enough knowledge available to make a preliminary evaluation of the suitability of the material, the product, the modified product, or the process to effectively accomplish the type of function involved, together with a reasonable amount of comparative information concerning costs. In some of the lists offered here, only the item is named, while in others, somewhat more of the type of information required is provided.

MATERIALS

Adhesives
    Bonding
    Coating
    Glue-type
    Hot melts
    Rubber-base
    Sealing
    Synthetic-resin
    Thermoplastic
    Thermosetting
    Vegetable-resin

For value analysis work, as for various other purposes, the usefulness of the data file on adhesives, as on many other items, is enhanced by a cross-reference listing indicating the applications for which a particular type is especially suitable, together with characteristics of the bonds obtained.

Asbestos
  Cloth
  Cord
  Tape
  Thread
  Tubing
  Yarn

Asphalt
  Coverings
  Products
  Sheets

Ceramic
  Chemical-containing materials
  Extruded materials
  Guides
  Insulators
  Low-loss materials
  Metal-cutting tools
  Pressed materials
  Specialties

Fibers

Animal:
  Mohair
  Silk
  Wool
Mineral:
  Asbestos
  Metallic threads
  Tinsel
Trade-name:
  Vistex
  Vulcoid

Vegetable:
  Cotton
  Flax
  Hemp
  Jute
  Ramie
Synthetic:
  Nylon
  Orlon
  Rayon
  Spun glass

Glass
  Fabric
  Fibers
  Heat-resistant
  Insulation
  Shock-resistant
  Tapes

Paper
> Barrier
> Cohesive
> Electric-conducting
> Electric-shielding
> Fire-resistant
> Laminated
> Oil-resistant
> Water-resistant

Plastics

The rapidly developing and expanding spectrum of plastic material covering substantially all ranges of properties and prices is increasingly accomplishing functions reliably for the lowest cost. A clear understanding must be well in mind of the relative strengths and weaknesses, i.e., plus and minus properties, the relative costs, and also the limitations and opportunities of different fabricating methods of, say, at least twenty-five different plastic materials. This information can be obtained in different forms from the different companies providing the plastic products and materials. It is a "must" item in the value analysis special knowledge fund.

Aluminum

Special alloys for stamping, spinning, drawing, forming, shaping, brazing, welding, etc.

Special bonded material in which aluminum is bonded to various other metals

Special shapes for particular functions, extrusions, disks, etc.

Bonded Metals

A wide array of laminated, bonded, and overlaid materials including metals and nonmetallic materials; prebrazed and prewelded materials; and prefinished, preplated, preenameled, prepolished materials.

Metals, Embossed and Expanded

Available raw material with surface formed and deformed, textured, split and expanded, etc., to accomplish low-cost rigidity and/or appearance objectives.

While this listing is a highly abbreviated one, it should include enough to show the reader something of the proper penetration of information required in the special knowledge for value analysis.

Processes—Specialty

Specialty processes are listed here although in some form the necessary standard and common processes must also be included and considered.

Assemblies, Welded-wire

Welded assemblies of wire-formed parts are successfully replacing sheet-metal assemblies because of savings in material and make-up of low-cost wire-formed parts.

Bonding, Roll

Joining sheets of aluminum or copper by first silk-screening a desired pattern on one sheet, then hot-rolling two sheets together, thus creating a permanent bond outside of the applied pattern and allowing the portion inside the pattern to then be expanded by hydraulic fluid pressure. Tooling cost is extremely low.

Casting, Centrifugal Special

A lost-wax process in which molds are spun after metal is poured to flow metal to all sections uniformly.

Casting, Continuous

A process for forming a wide range of copper-base alloys into the equivalent of long mill rods, tubes, and shapes ready for machining or other fabricating operations.

Casting, Die

Produces low-cost castings, in multiple cavity molds, primarily of zinc, aluminum, and brass. Castings are of good surface finish. Dimensions can be maintained to ±0.002 inch.

Casting, Die, Miniature

Parts, up to an ounce in weight, of zinc or nylon can be cast automatically at a very low cost. An acorn nut that was formerly made on a screw machine at a cost of $12.24 per thousand is now made by this process for $5.76 per thousand.

Casting, Frozen Mercury

A precision investment casting process similar to lost wax except that mercury is used instead of wax for making molds. Produces castings to close tolerances.

Casting, Lost-wax

A precision casting process that produces parts to close tolerances. For example, a valve handle that was sand-cast and machined for $1.10 could be produced by the lost-wax process with the price reduced to 70 cents.

Casting, Plaster-mold

Precision casting made to ±0.005-inch tolerances in materials of aluminum, brass, and bronze with plaster molds. Cost of tools is low. Piece price usually lies between that of permanent-mold and die castings.

Casting, Shell-molding

A relatively newly developed casting process that produces parts with good surface finishes and tolerances within $\frac{1}{32}$ inch. Cuts down considerably on machining time.

Casting, Small-lot

Produces small zinc die castings in short-quantity runs. Owing to re-design of die-casting equipment, tool cost is kept to a minimum without sacrifice of quality or workmanship.

Chromizing or Chrome Diffusing

A heat-treating process which transforms the surface of iron, steel, and most ferrous metals into a chromium-rich alloy to resist corrosion, heat oxidation, and abrasive wear. A low-cost substitution for some types of stainless steel.

Circuitry, Mechanized

Etched circuits can be produced by either silk-screen or photographic processes. The photo process gives better definition but costs more than the silk-screen process.

Plated circuits can be plated on both sides of a Textolite board or its equivalent and connected by plating through holes in the board.

Printed circuits can be produced by printing on a suitable plastic board.

Stamped circuits are made by die stamping the basic circuit connec-tions out of a sheet of conducting material and attaching this circuit securely to a sheet of insulating material. The die construction is similar to a dinking die and is suitable for large quantities with costs often less than those for other processes.

Cleaning, Ultrasonic

Transmitting ultrasonic waves through cleaning solutions produces a violent action that literally blasts soil from intricate parts in a matter of seconds.

Connecting Wire, Solderless Wrapping

Developed by Western Electric and Bell Laboratories. Consists in wrapping wire around a rectangular terminal for electrical connections. Up to 40 per cent faster than soldering.

Extrusion, Impact

Drawn shapes or cans can be extruded from zinc, magnesium, and aluminum slugs at low cost. High tool costs limit this process to high-quantity runs.

Floturn

Cold-forming of metal blanks by applying pressure spirally with a roller over a mandrel. The blank diameter is exactly that of the finished part, but its thickness is greater. The machine flows the metal into the intended shape with dimensions held to ±0.002 inch.

Forging, Automatic Precision

Process for producing precision forgings in a fully automatic manner.

Forging, Cold-impact

Method of shaping high-strength aluminum alloys by direct compression. Can often produce in one operation parts which formerly required multiple machining or a number of smaller pieces.

Forging, Precision

Improved electrical upsetting and forging techniques that reduce costs over previously known forging methods.

Forming, Electro

An electroplating process that plates coatings of material on a formed matrix which is later removed to leave behind an intricate shape that it might have been impossible to produce by machining.

Forming, Hydro

Produces intricate and deep-drawn shapes by hydraulic pressure. Requires only a punch of low-cost material with a rubber pad as a die.

Forming, Roll

A process mainly for large quantities of low-cost parts with formed sides. For instance, a hinge could be roll-formed for 27 cents as compared with 37 cents by the former conventional method.

Forming, Stretch

Process of gripping a metal blank at its ends, applying a force sufficient to bring the material to its yield point, and then wrapping it around a die while it is held under this tension. After material has been formed around the die, the tension is increased and the material is permanently set.

Forming, Vacuum

Consists in clamping thermoplastic sheet in a frame, applying heat to soften the sheet, and then sucking the sheet over or into a mold by means of vacuum. When cool, the formed sheet is removed from the mold. Particularly useful for short runs since tool cost is low.

Grinding, Electrolytic

Removing stock by conventional grinding accompanied by electrochemical decomposition of the work material. Applicable on metals where grinding wheels quickly glaze and refuse to cut.

Heading, Cold

Forcing wire into a die under pressure to shape parts that normally are produced on screw machines. Adaptable mainly to medium- and high-production quantities. Very much lower in cost where applicable.

Lacing, Metal

With a patented punch and die that can be set up in conventional punch presses, sheet metals are joined together without rivets, welds, or solder. Metal is pushed downward from the top to become depressed sideways and make a permanent fastening wedge under the surface of the bottom sheet.

Machining, Electrical-discharge

A series of discharges occurring at the rate of 20,000 to millions per second between the electrode and the workpiece remove stock accurately on extremely hard metals that are othewise difficult to machine.

Metalizing, Vacuum

Metals and nonmetals can be coated with bright metallic finishes by evaporating the coating material in a vacuum and allowing the coating to condense on the objects to be finished.

Milling, Chemical Process

To remove stock from complex shapes and fragile parts, the metal to be removed is left exposed while the rest of the part is masked with a specially developed coating. The entire part is then submerged in an etching solution that removes the desired amount of metal to accuracies of 0.002 inch.

Molding, Small-lot

Process for producing small-lot plastic parts at a low piece price and a low mold cost.

Painting, Electrostatic Spray

An efficient, economical spray method of electrically applying paint to parts. Appreciable savings are often achieved in labor and material over other spray, dip, or flow-coat methods.

Polishing, Electro

The reverse of electroplating. Normally used to remove from 0.0003 to 0.001 inch of metal. Can provide savings in finishing wire forms and assemblies and on parts with tiny recesses or intricate designs. Often, burr removal and polishing, which normally require two separate operations, are performed simultaneously.

Powder-metal Process

Metal powders are formed in dies to desired shape, then hardened in baking ovens. Parts produced by this method are low in cost and close in tolerance.

Shaping, Cold

Billets of mild steel are formed by 3,000-ton presses into cylindrical shapes. Parts are made to close tolerances and with very smooth surfaces.

Shaping, Hot Extruded

Heated billets of metal are fed through dies set up in horizontal presses to produce many types of shapes. Extrusion dies cost approximately $300 to $500 depending on the complexity of the part.

Shaping, Small Parts Drawn on Eyelet Machines

Very low cost. Adaptable for high-quantity runs in view of high tool charges. Highly automatic.

Soldering, Ultrasonic or Fluxless

Special soldering iron sets up vibrations which remove tough oxide film from surfaces with resultant improved tinning and better joint properties. Used commercially, especially in England, on aluminum and its alloys.

Spinning, Automatic Metal

Automatic spinning, without expensive tooling, can produce parts which ordinarily take several drawing operations on draw presses.

Stamping, Chemical Etched

Intricate brass and aluminum sheet-metal parts, up to 0.020 inch thick, are produced by chemical etching without resorting to tools. Cost is approximately 3 cents per square inch.

Stamping, Multislide

Low-cost stampings are produced on a multiple head that eliminates secondary operations for forming, tapping, reaming, counterboring, and countersinking. Minimum quantity is 100,000 parts.

Stamping, Small-lot

Process for producing small-quantity stampings at low cost with low tooling cost.

Stamping, Squirt

Produces unusual stampings on conventional punch presses from developed lengths of bar stock.

Stitching, Metal

A low-cost method of fastening materials together. Without pre-punched holes, wire is pierced through the materials and formed over on the bottom side.

Swaging, Bar

Long tapers are produced on bars at low cost in special swaging machines. Tool cost is low. Piece prices by this method are considerably lower than parts machined on screw machines or centerless grinders.

Thread Rolling and Form Rolling

Low-cost method of threading round parts by feeding parts between two thread dies that move back and forth, forming the thread instead of cutting it. Knurling, grooving, and undercutting can also be done by special dies in the same manner. Cold-heading suppliers are fully equipped to perform this work.

Welding, Cold

Joining of two sheets of metal or wires by pressure without need of flux, solder, or heat.

Welding, Tip

Welding of wire joints without need of solder or flux.

The fund of special knowledge required must also include information on specialty products and specialty materials of which the following are typical examples.

PRODUCTS—SPECIALTY

Bumpers, Rubber

One-piece rubber parts with molded-in holding grooves that eliminate the need for additional fastening provisions.

Cans, Standard Drawn and Formed

Standard drawn and formed enclosures are available, with no extra tool cost, in more than 3,000 stock sizes, both round and rectangular. They are made from stock 0.019 to 0.025 inch thick and in sizes from $7/8$ inch in diameter by $1 1/16$ inch long to $6 \times 7 \times 7$ inches.

Fasteners, Special

A great variety of special fasteners, including self-tapping screws for steel and plastic materials, screws with preassembled lock washers, plastic rivets, nuts with preassembled lock washers, terminals, and precision-stamped gears.

Junction Boxes and Covers, Standard Aluminum

Over 500 different-size deep-drawn aluminum junction boxes and covers up to $17 \times 19 \times 7$ inches deep. Secondary operations on these boxes and covers are performed.

Pins, Roll

Rolled spring dowel pins that can be used in place of solid straight and tapered pins for one-half the cost with the elimination of hole reaming.

Spacers, Rolled

Rolled split bushings and spacer tubes from flat stock. Holes, slots, and cutouts are punched out before forming, thereby eliminating more costly machining operations after forming.

Terminal Blocks

Standard, molded, low-cost terminal blocks for appliances and other applications eliminate mold charges.

Terminals, Small

Solderless terminals for wire sizes 22 to 0. These terminals are supplied as individual terminals or on reels in strip form that can be attached to terminals automatically by machines which the producers also furnish. These producers also manufacture solderless terminals for special applications, such as relay tabs and plugs and receptacles. A push-on terminal recently developed is replacing the conventional terminal that is fastened with a screw.

Terminals, Tubular

Swaged from strip stock for use in place of more expensive, solid screw-machined terminals.

Tool, Wire-wrap

A tool for the wire-wrap method of making solderless electrical connections. The wire is automatically wrapped with a power tool so tightly around the terminal that it meets the exacting requirements of a permanent electrical and mechanical connection.

MATERIALS—SPECIALTY

Adhesive and Tapes

Electrical tapes with paper, plastic, glass, cotton, and acetate backings. A variety of pressure-sensitive tapes and adhesives.

Gaskets, Flow-on

Liquid-rubber material, flowed on with a gun, to replace die-cut and molded-rubber gaskets.

Insulating Products, Plain and Laminated

All types of conventional varnished cloth including silicone and other treated glass cloth. Mica and Mica-Mat tapes, sheets, tubes, and special shapes; also laminated sheets and tubes.

Materials, Electrical-contact

Thermometals, electrical contacts, precious metals, bimetallic products, and special alloys.

Metals, Rigidized

Sheet metal with rolled-in design patterns for rigidizing to yield increased strength and permit the use of thinner-gauge materials.

Nylon and Teflon

Nylon and Teflon slab, rod, strip, tubing, tape, and powders.

Paper, Fireproof Treated

Low-cost impregnated paper to replace more expensive asbestos paper and sheet for uses such as catching paint drippings.

Plastics, Reinforced

Glass-reinforced plastic giving added strength to plastic parts.

Rust Inhibitor, VPI

Chemical which is a slowly vaporizing corrosion inhibitor that preserves the surface of metal by forming a protective atmosphere. It is replacing grease and other protective coatings that take longer to apply and remove.

Rust Inhibitor, VPI Paper

Packaging material treated with vapor-phase inhibitor.

Shims, Laminated

Laminated material that peels off in 0.002-inch thicknesses. This material is stamped out to make shims that eliminate the grinding of solid shim material.

Steels, Coated

Electroplated with either zinc, copper, nickel, brass, or chromium or hot-dip-coated with lead alloy, tin, or lacquer.

Strip and Sheet, Prepainted

Prepainted steel supplied in coils ranging in width from $\frac{7}{32}$ inch to 30 inches and in thickness from 0.006 to 0.040 inch. Color coatings and lacquers in all shades on one or both sides are available in all types of synthetic enamels, as well as in chemical finishes such as acid and weatherproof materials.

10-6 *Relative Cost Knowledge*

Achieving value by generating appropriate alternatives is a task of preparation, study, and comparison. In this work it is obvious that relative costs are of the utmost importance. Therefore, included in the special knowledge of value analysis will be a large amount of accumulated relative-cost data to guide in the selection of materials, processes, and approaches which must be penetrated deeply in order to find the combination of ideas which reliably accomplish the function at lowered cost.

Securing maximum value is a difficult matter because the "basic rules" change during the act; that is, the actual costs of material and of processes change and so do the relative costs. However, the change in relative costs, which is of vital importance in making comparisons and in selecting alternatives that bring the best value, is far less than the change in actual costs. Inflation factors often increase all costs, be they of steel, aluminum, copper, brass, or other material. Hence it is valuable in this work to prepare and accumulate special tables and charts of relative costs as efficient direction indicators in preliminary examinations for the selection of alternative materials, products, and processes. Such tables are useful general guides which provide suggestions for possibilities to be the bases of subsequent specific examinations.

Tables 10-1 to 10-9, providing relative-cost data, are examples of this class of special knowledge.

TABLE 10-1   Machine Speeds*

Machine	Operations per minute	Average per 1,000
Punch press, high-speed auto., 4 tons...................	250–400	$ 0.35
Cold header, ⅛-in. stock..............................	100–500	0.50
Punch press, high-speed auto., 15 tons..................	150–550	0.50
Punch press, high-speed auto., 25 tons..................	125–200	0.65
Cold header, ¼-in. stock..............................	90–450	0.80
4-slide machine, light................................	75–175	0.80
Punch press, 60 tons.................................	75–150	0.85
Cold header, heavy 1-in. stock........................	80–400	1.00
4-slide machine, heavy................................	50–125	1.00
Punch press, hand feed (blanking), 75 tons..............	50–125	1.00
Punch press, hand feed (blanking), 300 tons.............	40–80	1.60
Thread roller..	40–80	1.60
Screw-head slotter...................................	30–60	2.00
Automatic wire cutter and stripper.....................	30–60	2.00
Dial tapper..	30–50	2.50
Punch press, forming, slide feed.......................	30–40	3.00
Punch press, forming, hand feed.......................	15–30	4.00
Tapping machine, foot-operated........................	15–25	5.00
Tubular riveting machine.............................	8–15	7.00
Resistance welding machine...........................	5–10	13.00
Centerless grinding machine...........................	2–8	16.00
Molding machine, thermoplastic.......................	1–4	30.00
Brazing machine.....................................	1–2	50.00
Molding machine, thermosetting.......................	½–1	125.00

* These are average figures and are based upon one operator and one machine.

TABLE 10-2 Operation Speeds

Operation	Operations per minute	Average shop cost per 1,000
Take micrometer reading	5–8	$16.00
Use GO and NOGO snap gauge	10–15	8.00
Stamp part with hammer	15–20	6.00
Stamp part with rubber stamp	20–30	4.00
Drill small hole, drill press	4–8	20.00
Pierce small hole, punch	20–30	4.00
Wrap part in tissue and seal in carton	2–5	35.00
Position part in "egg-crate" carton	10–15	8.00
Pick up and position part in fixture	15–30	5.00
Pick up and drop part in fixture	30–50	3.00
Pick up, start, and hand-drive small screw	3–6	30.00
Pick up, start, and air-drive small screw	10–12	9.00
Power-drive small screw, hopper feed	10–20	5.00
Rivet with high-speed hammer 2 parts	4–8	20.00
Resistance-weld 2 parts	5–10	13.00
Tubular-rivet 2 parts	8–15	7.00
Cut off small tubing, screw machine	5–10	13.00
Cut off small tubing, abrasive wheel	30–60	2.00
Count parts visibly	60–120	1.00
Sort handful of parts 2 stacks	60–100	1.50
Deburr small screw-machine parts	7–12	13.00
Polish head of chrome-plated screw	5–12	20.00
Draw arc and hand-weld 1-in. pass	3–6	25.00
Ream hole, drill press	2–10	25.00

TABLE 10–3　Steel: Miscellaneous Forms
(Relative costs: Hot-rolled 0.2 carbon = $1.00)

Name	Relative price			
	Bar	Sheet	Strip	Plate
Hot rolled, 0.2 carbon	$1.00	$0.99	$0.99	
Hot rolled, special quality	1.07			
Cold drawn	1.36			
Cold drawn, sulfurized carbon	1.55			
Cold drawn, screw stock	1.60			
Cold drawn, 0.4 to 0.8 carbon	1.36			
Cold rolled, 0.2 carbon	....	1.11		
Galvanized sheet steel	....	1.20		
Enameling sheet steel	....	1.19		
Aluminum coated	....	1.51		
Aluminum killed strip, cold rolled	....	....	1.42	
Cold rolled, carbon steel strip	....	....	1.31	
Plate, copper bearing	....	....	....	$1.00
Plate, boiler quality	....	....	....	1.05
Plate, 0.35 to 0.45 carbon, under 1½ in. thick, silicon killed	....	....	....	1.09
Plate, structural quality, under ¾ in.	....	....	....	.97
Plate, chrome-silicon flange quality under 1½ in. thick	....	....	....	1.66
Plate, carbon-silicon, flange quality under 1½ in. thick	....	....	....	1.17

TABLE 10–4　Stainless Steel
(Relative costs with steel = $1.00; base price includes chemical extras only)

AISI type	Relative price	
	Sheet and strip	CF wire
201, Low nickel	$ 6.85	$ 7.84
302, 18–8, General purpose	8.13	9.56
304, 18–8, Excellent weldability	8.13	9.56
309, 23–13, Heat resisting	15.09	14.40
310, 25–20, Heat resisting	18.94	19.45
316, 18–12, Heat resisting	12.49	13.04
321, 18–10, Titanium stabilized	10.99	11.72
347, 18–10, Columbian stabilized	13.26	12.78
403, Turbine quality	6.23	5.16
409, Muffler grade	3.85	
430, Decorative	6.04	5.93
446, 27% chrome, heat resistant	10.77	8.05

TABLE 10–5   Brass and Bronze Rod
(Relative costs with steel = $1.00; base price does not include extras)

Name	Relative price
Free-cutting brass	$ 8.80
Yellow brass	11.74
Best-quality brass	12.23
Muntz metal	11.30
Naval brass	11.43
Admiralty brass	12.95
Low brass	12.72
Red brass	13.04
Commercial bronze	13.45
Gilding bronze	13.77
Everdur	14.49
Cupronickel, 20%	17.97
Nickel silver, 18%	16.33
Phosphor bronze, grade B (leaded)	17.24
Phosphor bronze, grade A	17.30
Phosphor bronze, grade C (8% tin)	17.94
Phosphor bronze, grade D (10% tin)	18.52
Ambraloy	15.61
Beryllium copper (Berylco 25S)	42.64

TABLE 10–6   Brass and Bronze Sheet
(Relative costs with steel = $1.00; base price does not include extras)

Name	Relative price
Muntz metal	$11.78
Naval brass	12.21
Yellow brass	11.77
Leaded brass	12.06
Best-quality brass	12.03
Low brass	12.52
Red brass	12.85
Commercial bronze	13.25
Gilding brass	13.58
Manganese bronze	12.79
Admiralty	13.05
Ambronze	14.11
Everdur	14.48
Nickel silver, 18%	15.39
Cupro nickel	16.66
Phosphor bronze, grade E (1% tin)	16.33
Ambraloy (aluminum bronze)	15.52
Phosphor bronze, grade A (4% tin)	17.28
Phosphor bronze, grade C (8% tin)	17.92
Phosphor bronze, grade D (10% tin)	18.51
Optical brass	17.38
Platers metal	15.67
Trodoloy (Berylco 10)	37.80
Beryllium copper (Berylco 25S)	42.64

TABLE 10–7   Brass and Bronze Wire
(Relative costs with steel = $1.00; base price does not include extras)

Name	Relative price
Yellow brass	$11.83
Low brass	12.51
Red brass	12.95
Commercial bronze	13.35
Gilding brass	13.68
Everdur	14.50
Ambraloy	16.60
Phosphor bronze, grade A (5% tin)	17.19
Phosphor bronze, grade C (8% tin)	17.83
Phosphor bronze, grade D (10% tin)	18.41
Nickel silver, 18%	17.94
Cupro nickel, 20%	19.13
Beryllium bronze (Berylco 25S)	42.64

TABLE 10–8   Copper
(Relative costs with steel = $1.00; base price does not include extras)

Name	Relative price Bar and rod	Relative price Sheet and strip
Hot-rolled rods, tough pitch	$13.73	
Hot-rolled rods, tough pitch (hot forging)	13.73	
Hot-rolled rods, tough pitch (cold forging)	13.73	
Drawn rods, tough pitch	13.73	
Drawn rods, tough pitch (bus bars)	13.73	
Hot-rolled rods, tough pitch (switch blades)	15.16	
Commutator copper (scalped)	14.16	
Commutator copper (high silver bearing, 25 to 30 oz.)	14.58	
Strip tough pitch, rolls	.....	$13.85
Sheet and plate, hot-rolled, tough pitch	.....	13.96
Sheet and plate, cold-worked, tough pitch	.....	14.98
Strip, silver bearing (10 to 15 oz. per ton)	.....	14.36
Spring and brush copper	.....	13.85

TABLE 10-9 **Aluminum**

(Relative costs with steel = $1.00)

Type	Description and usage	Relative price				
		Sheet	Rod	Plate	Foil	Extru-sion
1100 3003	General purpose, coils	$5.93				
1100 3003	General purpose, circles	7.27				
3005	Siding (bare)	5.13				
3005	Mobile home, type 2 (painted)	6.10				
E C	0.375-in.-diameter electrical conductors	. . . .	$4.26			
5005	0.375-in.-diameter appliance and architectural	. . . .	4.56			
7075	Structural for aircraft	. . . .	. . . .	$7.62		
1100 3003	0.0035-in.-thick conversion type	. . . .	. . . .	. . . .	$7.03	
1100 3003	0.00035-in.-thick lamination type	. . . .	. . . .	. . . .	9.16	
1100 3003 5005	0.004, 0.0055-in.-thick finished stock	. . . .	. . . .	. . . .	6.02	
6061	Structural, pipe, furniture, etc.	. . . .	. . . .	. . . .	. . . .	$6.96

SUMMARY

In accomplishing any task well it is necessary to have the required knowledge and techniques and to develop the required skill. In order to succeed better than competition in value work, much knowledge suitable for comparisons must be available. If the work is product oriented, it should include extensive collections of:

Materials, with emphasis on newer or lesser known materials

Functional products, with much emphasis on the lesser known and constant additions of the newer

Processes, again with much emphasis on the lesser known and much attention to proper addition and understanding of the new

Sources of specialized competence—names, phone numbers, and addresses that can be used to maximize the advantages in any specific use of a material or functional product or process

Relative cost information, appropriate to the particular needs, suitably developed and indexed, should be kept.

Each design approach for the purpose of accomplishing a function, each material, and each process introduce their own order of magnitude of costs. Costs of each, i.e., design approach to design approach, material to material, process to process, related to others in its class become included in the special value analysis knowledge.

Records are gradually built up in the most used areas of relationships of function to cost. These form superior guides and economize greatly on time. The following three-relationship statement shows that basically function-cost relationships can be established for many functions directly from available data and are valid, subject only to slight modification as price of material changes.

First relationship—functions to properties—engineering handbook
Second relationship—properties to materials—engineering handbook
Third relationship—materials to cost—catalogues

Therefore the relationship of functions to costs, or, as it is often expressed, the cost-function relationship, can be established for needed items at any time.

Since there is often so much choice of material and process, it is essential to have for ready use much *comparative* information on both materials and processes. Tables 10-1 to 10-9 show relative costs for examples based upon steel = $1, for stainless steels varying between $3.85 and $19.45 depending upon the type and form of the stainless. The various copper-based materials listed vary between $8.8 and $42.64 × the cost of basic steel.

Value analysis knowledge differs somewhat from most technical and engineering knowledge in that costs are absolutely essential in addition to the usual performance data.

chapter 11

Understanding
the Decision Environment

By now, the reader will be well aware that two separate types of work must be done well in the important task of eliminating substantial amounts of cost which do not contribute in any way to the customer's use or satisfaction.

First, identification of unnecessary cost through the generation of value alternatives

Second, decision making to effect implementation of the work on appropriate value alternatives and bring its benefits into the product

The value analysis techniques and special knowledge serve for the execution of the first phase, but the dollar payoff comes only with appropriate actions in the second phase. It is deemed both desirable and necessary, therefore, that the reader of this text attain an understanding of the problems that almost always prevail in the decision-making area.

The matter of securing good value alternatives is a straightforward proposition. Qualified and value-trained people can be hired and assigned to the task, and, given the proper working tools, they will invariably produce good alternatives. An organization for the generation of good value alternatives can normally be set up and made to function well within a period of a year.

11-1   *Decision Environment Requires Vast Consideration*

In contrast, it is well to expect that it may take several years to effect sufficient changes in the thinking of the decision makers to approach the same efficiency in the implementation as that attained in the development of good alternatives. Thomas Edison, in a letter to one of his managers in the 1920s, said, "Remember, on the average, it takes 7 years for men to accept a different proven solution to a problem."

The matter of implementing this work is very much more difficult because the people who must do the implementing are normally already in place, often will not receive additional training, and are operating according to plans and schedules based on established thinking and practice. This means that they must be taught to accept different thoughts, different types of ideas, and different technologies, all of which may seem to conflict with their endeavor to maintain established reputation of success in their field of operation. Besides, they may have had unfortunate prior experiences with poorly conceived or incompletely developed attempts to lower cost and hence may be wary of efforts in that direction.

A business or service consists of a group of people each doing various things that they are interested in and do well and that the particular business or service needs. As competition or its equivalent in some form makes it desirable or necessary to help each of these people to increase their yield and benefit to the business or service, it is profitable to examine the actions and interactions of these people, with the hope of providing them with some helpful tools, understandings, procedures, or systems that will enhance the accomplishment of each. It is being accomplished in this text by examining the task, establishing some aids therein, and examining the human environment in which each individual accomplishes his part of the task.

It has been aptly said that if no changes are required, i.e., each action in a business can be made today as it was successfully yesterday, then no decision-making people are needed and there should be none. Each needed task was performed well before and will continue to be performed well as it is repeatedly needed.

11-2   *Decision Makers Must Cause Change and Accept Personal Risk*

It is basic that a competitive product or service must change. The life of the business or service is often determined, not by the repetition of tasks, but by the quality of changes developed and considered and the quality (call it what you will—skill, art, ability, or luck) of the decision makers who make changes. Volumes of experience attest to some real need for assistance in the work area of the decision makers.

Just as in a baseball game—when the fielder may catch thirty flies during the season, making outs in each case, then make a bad miss on one, allowing three runs, and find that all that is remembered of him that evening and in years to come is the *one* he missed—so it is in decisions affecting change in products or services. Wherever there is change, there is risk. A manager or engineer may make thirty decisions bringing great benefit to the business and then make one that is costly, embarrassing, and damaging. He will often receive so much negative recognition from the one bad decision that the thirty good ones are entirely forgotten, his reputation *is* damaged, and he may lose promotions and, in some cases, his job. Therefore, it often becomes a simple matter of enlightened self-interest for a manager to make an absolute minimum of significant changes and to make them only when the combination of circumstances is precisely right to minimize the harm to himself if the results are not as expected.

Sacrificial behavior is not unknown, especially among the young, but a program built upon the premise of individuals making self-injuring decisions continuously for the good of the project or business will not thrive. It then becomes the opportunity of management to become so constituted that decisions and actions of their people will be beneficial to the business and at the same time will not risk injury to the decision makers. Every decision, small and large, should be makable on the basis of enlightened self-interest.

This book develops an understanding of and appreciation for enlightened self-interest and provides techniques and approaches that combine the self-interest and self-protection of men with the best interests of the product or service.

Injury to Decision Makers Is Real

The danger in change is not a myth. It is a fact recorded thousands of times in history. The well-known and well-used path is the surest and the safest.

While going west in search of gold, one covered-wagon train came to a decision point. Should they go by the well-marked and well-traveled trail, which is a long, long way around, or should they take a path directly across the valley to their objective, solving the difficulties of the short path as they make themselves known? The party divided. Some went the well-known longer route. Some took the changed route, and all of that group perished. As a result, the beautiful valley that they attempted to cross is now known as "Death Valley." The people who took the unchanged course reached their destination. It is one thing to favor change; it is another and far more risky one to make changes.

Embarrassment Injures Decision Makers

To learn constructive essentials from the examination of the force of fear of embarrassment, it must be fully accepted by the reader that this is not a perverse characteristic or a personality weakness of managers. Instead, fear of embarrassment is a real, ever present, cause-and-effect factor that exerts its force on both logic and feelings. Embarrassment in one's profession *is* a significant factor that may retard both satisfaction at the job and advancement. Therefore, the imminence of it must and does always influence decision-making criteria.

11-3   Unwelcome Decisions Required or Extra Cost Results

Decisions Based on "Sound General Criteria" That Do Not Fit the Specific

For example,

- The requisition on a *one-shot* order for screw-machine parts called for 5,000. They cost 10 cents each, total, $500.
- The parts could also be made by cold heading; 15,000 was the minimum order. They cost 2 cents each; total, $300.
- The sound general criterion "Buy as required—do not accumulate excess inventory" added $200, or 66 per cent extra cost.

Decisions Based on "Traditional Criteria for the Area" That Do Not Fit the Specific

For example,

- Small motors were billed to one plant "on the parts list basis" at 28 cents each extra ($2,800 extra for each 10,000 order) because coil assemblies were on one order and rotor assemblies on another.
- The criterion traditional to the area was, "Write separate orders when ordering materials from different drawing lists so that incoming

packages will be marked with the correct drawing list and accumulation for assembly will be facilitated." This traditional decision added $2,800 of extra cost per order.

Decisions Based on What the Decision Maker in Error Believes to Be the "Policy, Practice, or Wish" of Superiors

For example,

■ The practice in one plant was to allow twenty weeks for tool changes.

■ An approved change in one part reduced costs $50,000 per year, or $1,000 per week.

■ Four man-days of tooling work costing $350 were required. Work on the tools was scheduled to start in sixteen weeks so that it would comfortably be ready in the established twenty. Twenty-thousand dollars in excess cost was to be accepted so that the $350 tool change would "wait its turn" according to "practice." Fortunately, this plan was discovered by a value consultant after eight weeks. When brought to the attention of the manufacturing manager, the tool was made at once, saving $11,000 of the "normal" extra cost.

A surprising observation is that in nearly all cases the criterion that prevented decision making, keeping extra cost, was in itself a good generality.

Decisions That Become Routine Because They Seem to Be in Harmony with Similar Actions in That Area

For example,

■ A plant had the practice of bringing every job into the factory that the factory could do. Several parts were purchased from a supplier at 84 cents per set. After assembly, the manufacturing cost became $1.33. When a profitability and market-loss crisis developed, the vendor was asked to quote on the assembled parts instead of the "loose" parts. He quoted 86 cents. The total manufacturing cost then became 86 cents rather than $1.33.

Often, objective value criteria are in conflict with the "way of thinking" in an area. Overcoming the subjective thinking is very difficult.

Lack of a System to Secure Available Pertinent Information before Certain Classes of Decisions Are Made

These are the situations associated with subjective feeling. One example is the "let's make it ourselves" area. Being for this is like being for "motherhood" and "virtue." To develop objective criteria that might show large amounts of excess cost is emotionally interpreted as being against "what's good"; hence, often no provision is made to rigorously develop meaningful supplier alternatives for use as effective value criteria.

Decisions Based on "What We Normally Want to Do"

An engineer faces a design problem by thinking, designing, and testing and then thinking, designing, and testing; finally he has something that works. He then naturally wants to do it that way. He does not want to change it.

A manufacturing man may have space and machines and know how to plan and use them. He wants to use them—he does not want to change plans for available functional products or different processes or materials. He does not want uncertainty introduced.

A buyer wants to buy from a man who has earned his confidence through the years and who has become a fine friend. He does not want to take the business away from him although his people may have become complacent and outdated.

However, management must often make unpopular decisions to the contrary if the competitive value of leadership is to be achieved.

11-4   Environment Is Always Subjective, but Objective Decisions Are Needed

Subjective Coloring Obscures the Objective Situation

Coloring other than by the objective facts of the situation, in a decision involving value, results in lowered value—extra cost—in that product or service. These "shades of gray" are established by

1. Known or assumed attitudes of higher executives
2. The prior experiences of the decision maker that have established his "attitudes"
3. The known objective facts of the situation

For example,

Men vary	1. Attitudes of superiors, %	2. Prior established attitudes, %	3. Objective situation, %
One man............................	0	75	25
Another............................	75	15	10
Still another.......................	50	25	25
Possibly ideal......................	10	0	90

Often the objective situation in decisions involving value has insufficient weighting to be either a controlling or a heavily influencing factor in the decision. For example, in one factory, it was shown that casting some special parts of available scrap chips would reduce costs to less than half and make better shapes practicable. However, this was not done. The prime attitude was that the factory should be a *machine shop* not a *foundry*.

Decisions Vital to Profitability Are Often Made by Those Accountable for Quantities or Performance but Not for Profitability

There are scores of value-decision cases that exemplify this situation. The following are representative:

Shop cost	Shop cost after value criteria were developed
$12.50	$1.82
4.95	0.55
11.33	2.28
7.00	2.00
8.76	1.67
7.05	1.10

Obscure Cause-and-Effect Relationship Allows Decisions Injuring Value

Although decisions affecting most other aspects of the product are based on cause-and-effect criteria, such as

For quantities, count them
For performance, test them

value decisions are often based on criteria far removed from the specific situation, weighted too heavily on the subjective side and too lightly on objective facts of the specific value situation. As a result, the flow of instructions that injure only value do not bring their own correction. Their effect is to generate sales-volume and profitability problems in the business. They are not recognized as the cause and accordingly are not forthrightly dealt with.

For example, automatic equipment was installed to make $50,000 per year worth of parts. The market-volume and profitability problems that developed were assumed to be normal. Years later, under critical market pressure, a value study was made, which showed that functional products of equal reliability and convenience could have been purchased for $10,000 per year during the entire period, which would have left $40,000 of additional earnings each year.

Feelings Always Influence and Often Control Decisions

For example, consider the following sequence of events:

1. A product has failed in the field repeatedly, and the company has been embarrassed. It needs a different switch.

2. An engineer creatively develops one, using a new principle.

3. Manufacturing works out the way of making it, and $10,000 in temporary tools are approved by management to try it.

4. It works. All feel pride before peers for successful accomplishment. Managers and immediate superiors feel and act in a commending manner. All are very pleased with job and themselves; both logic and feelings are in total harmony.

5. Later (perhaps a year, perhaps five), competitive pressures require switch functions for lower cost, and the engineer is assigned the task because of his "experience" in the area. He knows more about it.

6. He attacks the problem with vigor. Keeping the main operating principles of his former approach, he can change a few parts, improve some tooling, and eliminate a few obvious uncontributing costs. He gets 20 per cent out.

7. His logic says the changes are good. His feelings say the changes are fair. He has even now made some slight inroads into his earlier model, which was a proven success in the eyes of himself and his peers. His feelings don't like it. He is uncomfortable about it. He wishes it could have been left alone.

8. Now it becomes necessary to remove much more cost from the total product. He is asked, "How much more can we, by pulling all the stops,

get out?" His logic says, "A little." His feelings say, "None." He says, "Possibly a hard maximum of 5 per cent."

If this engineer is to benefit the company's sales and earnings by a 50 per cent reduction, he needs the help of a new strategy and some new tactics. Since the deterrent is his feelings, which by now have stopped aggressive search by his logic, the solution must come through an approach that deals with his feelings.

Dr. Ralph Graves, eminent psychologist at Union College, Schenectady, N.Y., tells us that logic does not change feelings but that feelings, being emotions, can be communicated with only in emotional terms. Therefore the approach created must emotionally communicate in order to release the man from his past publicly proved work and allow his feelings to become reorganized in a new situation that may remove one-half to three-fourths of the cost. This emotional approach must be based upon logic drawn from the task at hand so that the new adjustment of feelings will be such that the cost objectives are reached. A strategy of approaches and techniques must be created that will allow men to change their own feelings.

Environment Is Hazardous to the "New"

The word *environment,* as used here, includes a man's managers and his peers. Of course, few environments exist that would not accept a fully developed, fully debugged, fully tested, and fully service-proved change that would keep all customer factors at half the cost. But, significant improvements, like people, are not born full grown. Resources, money, and men must be committed without assurance of results. Creative ideation, knowledge searches, exploration, and basic tests precede results. Of the creative ideation, 99 per cent are worthless; 90 per cent of the knowledge searches are useless; and 75 per cent of the basic tests fail. Meanwhile the designs and practices of the past are working perfectly.

Hence there develops, to some extent, in most environments a "feeling" that men who press hard toward vastly better ways for accomplishing functions at lower cost are dreamers who, in fact, have lost essential touch with reality and have their feet in the clouds and their heads out beyond thin air. This takes the tangible form of occasional derision of the newest idea creations, especially the continual stream of worthless ideas, useless knowledge, and failing tests.

The environment is often "unsafe" mentally and socially for activity that would produce large accomplishment. Only small, traditional-type cost-reduction activities can live comfortably. The following are some pronouncements heard from management. All communicate to the feelings of men. What do they say?

"Get out today's production; improve the process if you have time."

"Lick that engineering performance problem on the production line; develop a new approach later, if you have time."

"We made this change to save $8,000; it has already cost us $25,000 in field failures." (But the ten changes that worked out well in the field, saving $300,000, didn't become conversation.)

To the extent that the "environment" in which men work is unsafe for the creative and hazardous for the new, all work in decreasing costs is retarded or stopped. An efficient system for preventing or reducing cost must, then, deal effectively with this environment and with the "feelings" of the individuals involved.

11-5   *An Environment Abhors Change*

Men are accustomed to holding certain beliefs about their associates and expecting certain things from them. Any environment may be likened to a network of piping. All the valves in the system have, by experience, belief, habit, and tradition, been set in a certain manner. As long as the flow is entirely according to this accustomed pattern, all actions are smooth and few frustrations are created. However, if more value alternatives are to be implemented, actions must be taken which differ from the habitual. Familiar "do it our way" patterns must be disturbed. Some valves in the system must be further opened, some further closed. This causes a complete readjustment of the flow in the system. The change from that which was expected is apt to be resisted at every turn.

Only with a realistic recognition of these actions and interactions in the decision environment will the value consultant and value engineer be able to understand and take a mature viewpoint toward the long delays and the multitudinous objections which are commonly raised prior to the implementation of good value alternatives.

Now, with this recognition of the situation, thought may well be directed to the questions: What can be done about it? and What are the first steps to take for improvement in this decision environment? Unless the reader stops here to make a searching study of himself, he will be inclined to discount the relevance of this chapter. By analyzing himself, however, he will find that he fits into the same type of pattern. To be useful, this particular discussion must be extremely realistic and must deal with situations as they are, not as they appear on organization charts or in reports or in statements made by people operating in the outlined environment.

It Is Comfortable to Avoid
Embarrassment

Each man in an organization (or social or cultural group) must *do what is expected of him* or be prepared to face embarrassment. Avoiding embarrassment seems to motivate his minute-by-minute thought and action more than almost any other factor. If he does more, or less, or differently, some of the many forms of criticism or ridicule or embarrassment will come from his superiors, his peers, or his "friends."

As long as he operates in the "expected" range—in *all* of his activities and relationships—he is relatively free of embarrassment. What his "environment" believes is "good practice" he must believe. What his environment believes is bad practice, he must believe. He must largely accept what, in his environment, is considered "facts" as facts. He must largely accept the assumptions which are believed by his environment to be valid.

He must not "reach out" in thinking or searching further than the pattern set by his environment. All change involves some risk—but he must not take more risk than the pattern of the environment permits. Often he may not even investigate a method which has been condemned by his environment without high risk of embarrassment. Furthermore, he must not start or take part in any action which might embarrass his boss.

11-6 Minimizing the Risk of
Personal Loss

A series of research studies brought forth the surprising information that most decisions are made on a basis of avoiding or minimizing personal losses such as reduction of authority, demotion, dismissal, or embarrassment. This finding seemed so improbable and so startling that it caused the writer to think back through several of his most difficult decision-making experiences, especially a considerable number which he knew were wrong but which "had" to be made in a certain way. Surprisingly, every one of these decisions was made to avoid or minimize personal loss. Again it is suggested that the reader stop to reflect on and analyze some of his own decision experiences before proceeding on to the following pages.

A few examples of situations in which the danger of suffering personal loss occurs may further illustrate the point in question:

A purchasing agent may for years have purchased a product from one supplier, even though this supplier may not have kept pace with either technical progress or value innovation. A decision by the purchasing agent to change over to what seems to be a better product at a lower price brings immediate danger of personal loss. Every change brings risk.

The engineer who traditionally used a certain type of assembly for accomplishing a certain function and has decided to change to the use of what he believes to be a simpler, more reliable, and certainly much more economical assembly is certainly taking a chance of personal loss.

As for the manufacturing manager, he is apt to be operating with machines of certain types, with people of certain experience, with buildings of certain area, and with patterns of so-called "overhead liquidation" accruing when chips fall from the machines. For him to decide on a value alternative which might temporarily use a fraction of the machines, a fraction of the people, and a fraction of the building and which might provide little "liquidation" places him in a position of immediate personal loss.

Any business manager knows that there are few things that rate as "sure." However, a thing which has been done over and over in the past is more sure than something new. Therefore, any different decision runs the chance of bringing personal loss to the decision maker.

Experience has shown that merely securing good value alternatives—even before implementation—may bring personal loss to engineering people, manufacturing people, purchasing people, in fact everyone connected with the present mode of doing the job. This is especially true if the particular value alternative appears to be so straightforward that important people in the management and decision-making area see at a glance that it will probably work.

The normal pattern in any decision-making area is to "sound" progressive in speech and writing and to have great plans for big new things, for big changes, etc. This minimizes the chances for personal loss. If the higher levels of management did not hear and read such pronouncements, they would become concerned and might think in terms of making changes that bring about personal loss. When it comes to making decisions and taking actions, that is something different. Here most people concerned with making decisions "stick to the channel," rationalizing each decision on the basis of some nearly related data or experience. In this manner, they again minimize the chances of personal loss. For very much the same reason, there is often a very strong and very understandable resistance on the part of management to the establishment, in any organization, of a really competent value group which could effectively produce good value alternatives.

A further point to be borne in mind is that in the average run of cases in which the results of good value-improvement work identify value alternatives which will bring very much lower costs, reactions are invariably uncomplimentary to those responsible for the present practice.

For instance, in a case cited in an earlier example, a value alternative developed by the use of value analysis techniques showed that the functions of a spacer stud costing 8 cents could be provided for eight-tenths of a cent. The manager said, "What do we have on our methods engineering staff, men or boys?" Did the men who first accomplished this job suffer personal loss? Surely. Did they suffer embarrassment? Certainly.

In another case, after the use of value analysis techniques provided a value alternative at $2\frac{1}{2}$ cents which reliably accomplished the total function of a $15\frac{1}{2}$-cent item made on a special installation of $30,000 worth of automatic equipment, the manager said, "Why didn't you think of doing it this way before we spent the $30,000 for tooling?" Did the men who previously worked on that job suffer personal loss and painful embarrassment?

Quite normally, when, as a result of the use of value techniques, an effective alternative is brought into view which will reliably accomplish the entire function for a small fraction of the cost, the comment is made, "That was done wrong in the first place!" Do the men who previously worked on the item suffer personal loss and embarrassment? Most certainly.

Anyone who wishes to become expert in the area of identifying unnecessary cost and stimulating corrective action may well follow a two-step approach:

1. Recognize this behavior pattern as *the* big problem.
2. Take every step possible to minimize fear of embarrassment or personal loss which comes, or may come, to those in the decision area supporting changes.

An estimate of where the fountainhead, or source, of this personal-loss obstruction lies indicates this general situation:

Managers and bosses	90%
Peers	10%

This clearly shows the problem to be that of creating the required action environment, i.e., decreasing the fear of embarrassment or personal-loss risk. To decrease it effectively, work must be done on changing the attitudes, pronouncements, and actions of managers and bosses. The crux of the problem is:

What are their real beliefs?
What are their pronouncements?
What are their actions?

It is coming into indelibly clear focus that in the matter of achieving a much higher degree of value, i.e., faster implementation of more good value alternatives, the personal loss to the men in the environment must be reduced or eliminated and that action must start at the top.

One example of the type of communication that is necessary with top men and bosses at their present stage of recognition of this problem may be recounted here. Steel J bolts, threaded on one end, were used in large quantities for a holding function. They cost 11½ cents each, $92,000 per year. Use of the value techniques produced an interchangeable alternative which accomplished the total function with the same reliability at a cost of 1½ cents each or $12,000 per year, a saving of $80,000 per year in purchase cost. As already indicated, the important question always is how to convey this type of information to a manager or a boss in a way that will allow him to see the merit of the value system that produced the suggestion rather than to follow the normal pattern of depreciating the men who previously worked on the job. In this case, it was handled by the following dialogue (see Figure 8-17, page 147):

"Mr. Smith, would you like to see what your men are accomplishing by the use of these value analysis techniques?"

"I certainly would."

"You use large quantities of this J bolt in this application [showing him the product using it]. Now, if you had the assignment of removing large amounts of cost from this without in the slightest reducing its quality or safety factor, how would you go about it?

"Is it made of steel?"

"Yes."

"A piece of standard steel with a hook on one end and a thread on the other. How can you make it any simpler?"

"That's right, Mr. Smith, that's where your men started. Now let's see what they produced using the value analysis techniques. This part [showing the value alternative] accomplishes the total function with the same reliability, but instead of costing 11½ cents, this costs 1½ cents."

Mr. Smith, startled, said, "How much difference did that make in our yearly cost?"

"Eighty thousand dollars per year reduction in purchase cost."

And now, for his final comment, "How many men do we now have doing this type of work?"

Did this mean that men in the organization suffered personal loss? Of course not, because the manager was put in the same position as they were in before he answered.

11-7   *The Incredible Reality*

Unseen and unrecognized, the fear of embarrassment sits with the decision maker at his desk and is the overpowering factor in the decision making.

Case Study

DANGER OF EMBARRASSMENT IS MORE FORCEFUL
THAN RESTORED MARKET VOLUME

A high-volume control device lost two-thirds of its market because, due to high costs, marketing people did not quote competitive prices. Management organized three cost-reduction teams—one in engineering, one in manufacturing, and one in purchasing. After a few months, they had found small cost benefits, but these were by no means sufficient to restore competitive profitability to the product. The marketing manager brought the problem to a value analysis group.

Function-based value analysis system was started on the product. It was soon found that costs on the order of 25 per cent could be removed with no quality deterioration. When this was learned by one of the managers, he went to the vice-president, who had authorized the work, and asked that *the work be stopped*. Why? Danger of practically assured "embarrassment." All responsible management people knew that this control was in "trouble" and that full-time management lead committees had completed cost studies and "found nothing significant could be done." If a different problem-solving approach and thinking system were now to show large earnings improvement, it would communicate (rightly or wrongly) to all that "the men on the job are not effective thinkers and leaders." It is the most embarrassing and perhaps the most injurious thing that can happen to a professional man.

Case Study

FEAR OF EMBARRASSMENT IS MORE FORCEFUL
IN DECISION MAKING THAN ENDING COMPANY
LOSS

When a company with about $5 million business per year lost its profit position, the vice-president of engineering asked this author for help in finding a value engineer. He obtained a good one and then a second man. A seminar was held, which considered one purchased item, a large forging, which cost $500,000 per year. The result was that five changes in this item were put into effect immediately, keeping all quality and reducing the cost by $160,000 yearly. Result? The vice-president of engineering prevented the value engineers from obtaining any increase in salary for two years, let it be well known that they were unwelcome in the vice-president's office; ultimately he had them report to someone lower in the organization, and then ended the activity completely.

What caused this reaction? The reality of some embarrassment and fear of more. All management and peers knew that the large forging was the sole responsibility of the vice-president of engineering. Before the seminar, he had said, "I've handled that myself; nothing whatsoever that could be done has been left undone. It is really a waste of time to include it in the studies." When $160,000 of cost was eliminated, he was embarrassed and probably hurt. Until then, the president had thought he was brilliant in the matter of reducing costs. Naturally he did not like to be embarrassed and hurt in his profession even if it meant hundreds of thousands of dollars to his company.

This case study and others are presented, not to bring discredit ω the managers involved, but to illustrate the role embarrassment may play in decision making. A manager *must* make decisions that avoid embarrassment for himself, or he may be badly injured in his professional career.

Case Study

**FEAR OF EMBARRASSMENT IS MORE FORCEFUL
IN DECISION MAKING THAN A PROFIT ON THE
JOB**

A 1,500-foot-long copper conducting bus was required for the winding of large electrical equipment. As the maximum length available was 300 feet, it was necessary to braze five pieces together, using four joints. These joints were very costly, had to have very high quality, and, of course, were right in the electric circuit. Worldwide competition for this type of equipment set very competitive selling prices. However, a low-enough price was quoted to secure an order for several pieces of this equipment.

Then came the task of maintaining quality and specification, still avoiding a loss and if possible making a profit. A man who had learned the value analysis system was asked to help. He helped on six items. (One will be reported here.) He reasoned, "Those brazed joints are adding a lot of cost and providing no customer-wanted function." He placed the value of the function secured by all of the brazing at nil and started work.

The value analyst asked engineering if there was any engineering reason why a one-piece bus would be disadvantageous. They said, "No, but the material is only available in 300-foot lengths." He asked manufacturing if it would make any problems in insulating and winding if the material were all in one 1,500-foot piece. They said, "No, but the maximum length obtainable is 300 feet." He asked purchasing how they might go about it to buy 1,500-foot lengths. They said, "We cannot buy it in 1,500-foot lengths, and 300 feet is the maximum obtainable," showing him the copper materials book, which said so.

The value analyst reasoned that the copper bus must be made in long lengths and cut off. Why not coil it up, put it on a skid, and ship it? He asked purchasing to make an appointment for the buyer and himself to visit the mill of the copper company to further determine if there were basic reasons for cutting it off in 300-foot lengths. They went to the supplier's mill. The supplier said that shipping the copper bus in longer lengths presented no problem. Orders were placed for 1,500-foot lengths. This proved so convenient to the supplier that he lowered the price of the copper. Operations were simplified in every area, saving much cost. Problems of quality control, inspection, etc., were eliminated in the factory, adding to the large dollar saving.

What was the result? Just as could be forecast. Since the decision-making managers in engineering, manufacturing, and purchasing had all taken and supported the position that it was available only in a maximum length of 300 feet, they were embarrassed. The longer lengths had probably been discussed before in the presence of the company president. Rightly or wrongly, the president's appraisal of their thinking ability, resourcefulness, and effectiveness on the job was lowered. They probably could be injured professionally. Consequently the *scope* of the value analysis and engineering function in that company was reduced and their budget further limited. This would prevent future embarrassment.

11-8 *"What Managers Believe" Is the Master Key*

What managers believe is extremely important in that it governs what they say, and what they say controls the extent of personal loss to men who face situations and effect changes. Experienced men in industry know that changes invariably involve risk. The manner in which management handles cases which "temporarily go wrong" as a result of changes for the improvement of value is a positive indication of what beliefs they hold about value and what importance they place on removing unnecessary cost and meeting other assumed commitments, such as those pertaining to performance and shipment. Management's reaction in these circumstances determines the amount of personal loss which individuals in the decision environment must risk if they make decisions that involve change for the purpose of implementing good value alternatives.

Instructions from the boss to "keep it working but get the cost out," "keep the daily shipments on schedule but get the cost out," or any similarly worded operating "dogma" clearly indicate that management inwardly believes the elimination of unnecessary cost to be very much secondary in relation to the overall benefit to the business. They signal that to embark on a change for the purpose of substantial elimination of unnecessary cost is to choose a course of great personal risk.

In general, today's management and managers are sufficiently well accustomed to technological advancement to realize and inwardly feel or believe that they must make sacrifices, effect changes, and take risks to secure essential performance improvement in their products. To date, however, they have not been long enough subjected to the hard economic pressure which results from the maturing of products, coupled with the growing resourcefulness of a widening number of competitors, to develop the same sense of urgency and necessity in matters relating to the elimination of unnecessary cost.

Persons choosing value work as a career will be wise to investigate and determine, before accepting any assignment, whether there are enough positive factors in the particular decision environment into which they will feed their value alternatives to make their work rewarding to the company and, in the long run, to themselves.

Finally, management people or value consultation specialists who want to delve deeper into these normal human reactions which delay and minify the realization of dollar benefits from good value engineering work will find valuable guidance by studying some good psychological literature on the subject of human behavior in situations involving change (see the Appendix, section A-2).

Management Beliefs that Support Competitive Value Decisions

1. What your people believe you think they are determines what they must do and say.

2. Decisions are very personal. Each is based mainly on minimizing the risk of embarrassment or personal loss.

3. Feelings control plans and limit decisions.

4. We cannot communicate to men's feelings by logic.

5. What men believe heavily influences their decisions.

6. Most popular beliefs are partly wrong.

7. Men discredit what they do not understand.

8. An idea "unthought of" is as absent and as totally unusable as a new metal undiscovered.

9. Any new thought or idea or a determined search for new ideas attacks the feeling of security.

10. Creative people are felt to be hazardous by noncreative or judicial people.

11. There is no "right" design; rather it is satisfactory for this time.

12. Profit is not added to *price*. It is taken from *cost*.

13. Selling prices should be established by market levels as a policy not an expedient.

14. Costs are determined by our own decisions and actions. Each decision has been the result of the knowledge, thoughts, feelings, and logic of the various decision makers.

15. Men must be made to feel that it is *good* to make their own product or services obsolete rather than "cling with pride" until a competitor does it and takes some of the market with him.

16. Experience shows that management normally cannot make significant decisions to change, based upon observed results alone. The risk of embarrassment is too great. To cause decisions bringing significant change, either

    a. The need must be intense and severe (in which case risk of embarrassment is probably greater if no change is made than if a change is risked) or

    b. They must *understand* in considerable detail, just how the re-
sults are accomplished (which allows them to make value judgments to implement significant change with a minimum of fear
of resulting embarrassment)

17. Top management's job is to set a climate and create some attitudes
that will allow a higher order of results to grow, without embarrassment
to decision-making people.

SUMMARY

Value analysis or engineering is a promoter of change. Change always
brings risk. Whenever a change does not develop the expected results,
the "cause-and-effect" relationship immediately points the finger of *error*
at the responsible decision maker. Everyone knows he did it. He is uncomfortable and embarrassed, and his reputation is downgraded. His
opportunities for advancement are diminished. As a result, for very valid
realities, a manager learns to avoid embarrassment and to fear it. The
fear of embarrassment becomes an important factor in his decision values
system.

The tragedy is that when the disciplined thinking system produces
large cost savings with no new technology and with small or no additional investment in equipment, the decision maker is often downgraded
on the basis of "You are not as smart as I thought you were or you
would have done that long before now!" The unstated question that
colors his decision system and becomes a decisive factor in decision
making becomes "Might it be embarrassing to me?" As a result, great
understanding of this situation must be possessed by the decision maker
and others, such as the value analysis specialist, the man's boss, and his
peers, if objective data are to bring prompt profitable actions from good
value analysis change proposals.

The source of the primary injury to a man, which comes from the
embarrassment resulting from a decision to make a good change "that
could have been made years earlier" or an erroneous change "that should
not have been made at all," is his boss or the management group above
him. The boss, unfortunately, all too often makes direct statements that
reveal his critical attitude.

Experience has shown that the fear of possible embarrassment is so
strong that management personnel will not normally make an affirmative
decision for substantial change based on observed and proved results.
They require for prompt decision either severe need or a detailed and
complete understanding of how the benefits are created by the change.

We are faced with a stern reality: *The manager is the key man. By his
attitudes and actions he can treble the profit results from the value
analysis system, or he can cut them in half.*

chapter 12

Effect on Other Work in the Business

A number of very vital interrelationships come into play in the effective use of value analysis techniques. Some of the most important of these are the relationship of value analysis to:

Accounting   Management
Appearance design   Purchasing
Cost reduction   Quality control
Engineering   Sales
Manufacturing

In the simplest language, the objective of value analysis and value engineering is to develop practical value alternatives to the end that all decision making will achieve an improved degree of value in the final product or process.

12-1 Accounting

In the same simple terms—perhaps too simple for the accountant—the principal objectives of accounting activity are twofold.

1. Accumulate suitable after-the-fact figures so that period-end profit and loss accounting will be proper both for tax purposes and for business owners' purposes.

2. Suitably apportion costs and incomes to guide before-the-fact decision making.

Value analysis bears no relationship to the first objective but a very significant relationship to the second. More general acceptance of this fact is needed.

It is only rarely that the situation is assessed as it was by an accounting manager who said: "As in engineering, where a product developed for a particular purpose can be made to accomplish that purpose efficiently and well, so it is in accounting. Systems can be developed to accomplish particular purposes. The serious problem, however, is that accounting systems often are used either as they are or in some amended form for other than the originally intended purposes and then are not as effective. Give us a clear understanding of an exact purpose, give us time and resources, and we can develop an efficient system which will accomplish that purpose."

As in the physical sciences, where men often endeavor to accomplish several purposes with the same product and seldom accomplish divergent ones efficiently, so it often is with accounting systems.

In the past, as an analogy, the horse was employed to pull the plow and then also to pull the buggy. If he was heavy enough for an efficient draft job, he was far too slow and inefficient with the buggy. Conversely, if he was light enough and fast enough to be an efficient buggy horse, then he was far too weak and inefficient as a draft horse. In four respects this use scheme bears a striking resemblance in its accomplishment to the accounting systems commonly in use.

1. A horse suitable for the draft job is used also on the buggy. The owner rationalizes by saying, and by learning to believe, that "he is also pretty good on the buggy."

2. A horse suitable for the buggy job is used also in the field. Again, compromises are accepted, but the owner gets used to the level of performance of the buggy horse in the field. He rationalizes for himself that "the horse is also a pretty good field horse."

3. A compromise horse is used. Though the horse is not capable of the heavy loads in the field or of fast work on the buggy, the owner gets accustomed to its degree of performance in both respects and rationalizes, "He is a good buggy horse and also a good draft horse."

4. Two different horses are used. The importance of the draft work and the importance of the buggy work cause the owner to acquire two distinct types of horses. He now gets efficient draft work and efficient

buggy work, but he has two horses to own and to feed. From a business-man's point of view, he must decide whether the increased efficiency justifies the extra feed.

Although, as the accounting manager stated, accounting systems can probably be developed to efficiently accomplish almost any purpose, there is quite naturally and properly a great reluctance on the part of management to provide more than one basic system. Since tax and earn-ings accounting are considered absolutely vital, compromises are usually made and inefficiency is allowed in the second area, which covers useful and meaningful cost data for making before-the-fact decisions. Usually modifications, sometimes at great expense, are made in the tax and earn-ings accounting systems, and the over-all system then is considered "pretty good" and is used extensively in decision making. In effect, those interested in costs for decision making usually find that they must use the "draft horse" or attempt to work with a modification.

As emphasized in section 8-2, the quality of value alternatives and the quality of the resultant decision making, which affects the degree of value in the product, are very deeply affected by the degree of mean-ingfulness of the costs with respect to the specific purpose of making a proper selection of the engineering, manufacturing, and other alternatives to accomplish the functions the customer desires.

Decisions affecting value can be no better than the information which enters into the comparisons, and this information cannot be better than the meaningfulness of the cost figures derived from accounting. When a better degree of value is required, the payoff to the company of mean-ingful costs created for the purpose of comparing value alternatives will become very large.

The use of effective value analysis is both troublesome and rewarding to the accounting activity. It is troublesome because:

Meaningful costs are required. To interpret costs meaningfully, analysts must inquire into and learn how they are determined.

It may show that much of the detailed work of breaking down costs by parts and assemblies does not really make a contribution but provides misleading information instead. If so, accounting must face up to the shortcomings of traditionally done accounting work and cost compiling.

It may show that many of the costs traditionally used do not precisely reveal how the business is affected when individual decisions are made one by one.

It may become necessary for accounting and cost people to learn and develop some very new practices, procedures, and systems to convert one system to another.

The rewarding aspects are:

Accounting work can now make real additional contributions to earnings.

Accounting will face real challenges in providing meaningful information for the necessary decision making.

Satisfaction will be derived from seeing that the work of accounting is put to good use and forms the basis of decision making that results in better decisions and improved earnings.

Two of the important classes of decisions that we are concerned with here are:

Make-versus-make decisions
Make-versus-buy decisions

At first glance, it may appear to be of vital importance to learn how the business is really affected only in the case of make versus buy. However, further thought will show that this is not at all true. The class of make-versus-make decisions may involve hundreds of different alternatives, some of which will be tabulated here. The cost may very well vary by a factor of 10 to 1 between different methods for individual items or individual functional assemblies. The lack of meaningfulness of the costs can easily lead to support of decisions which cause the product to contain so much unnecessary cost that orders are lost or perhaps the total business is lost.

Some of the kinds of make-versus-make alternatives that may be involved are as follows:

Casting versus stamping
Wire form versus sheet metal
One part versus several parts
One type of machine versus another type of machine
One shift versus another shift
Varying degrees of automation
Totally in-plant versus partly in-plant parts and partly purchased parts or assembly (the border line or "gray" area between a make-versus-make and a make-versus-buy decision)
Make as needed versus make periodically and hold in inventory

It is readily seen that although no decisions to make versus buy are involved in these cases, wide ranges of applicable costs are controlled by the decisions made on the basis of the costs provided by the accounting activity for the decision making.

In make-or-buy decisions—or, more correctly stated, in the area of determining at which stage in the cycle from the rawest form of raw material to the finished product is it advantageous for the factory to bring the material into the plant and perform the necessary operations on it—it is both exceedingly difficult to develop and exceedingly vital to have meaningful cost information. It is a relatively easy matter to make make-or-buy decisions pertaining to large groups of activities, but to be realistic in operating a business, even where over-all looks are taken periodically, important decisions must of necessity be made one by one. Unless the over-all decision arrived at is one in which decisions made one by one provide for the right value, the cost information used is inadequate and unsatisfactory.

While at first glance it would seem simple to determine how the business would be affected by making a part, this cannot be done by merely determining the material used, the labor required, the indirect expenses in the form of maintenance and liquidation of machines and equipment employed, and the amount of consumed supplies. Buildings are involved which might, or might not, exist regardless of the decision on a particular item. The entire supervisory and management staff of the organization will probably exist regardless of the decision on the item, and the same amount of space may be required regardless of the decision; likewise, the same amount of maintenance may be required. The question of determining precisely how the business will be affected if a particular decision is made to buy rather than to make is a most difficult one.

Often, with traditional systems of accounting, it is more straightforward to determine how the business will be affected by a change from buy to make if the change is comprehensive enough so that new buildings and new machines will be required. In this case, definite costs can be assigned as an increase to be computed in the decision-making formula. The sticky problem results when serious consideration is given to taking the decision in the opposite direction, i.e., from make to buy, because now many facilities already on hand and already being paid for in various accounts may not be needed.

A further reason for the need of particularly objective and meaningful comparative costs in this particular connection is that make-or-buy decisions lie in the emotional area. A strong emotional pull toward decisions to "do it ourselves" usually exists. Often, this pull is so strong that neither the accounting specialist nor anyone else is requested to develop really meaningful alternatives which could lead to decisions contrary to the do-it-ourselves practice.

Finally, it should also be noted that the techniques of value analysis apply to any action which costs money. Each activity of the accounting unit can be analyzed by the use of these techniques to determine precisely what function is accomplished by each act, by each piece of paper, by each file, by each person each minute of the day. Such evaluation by accounting people, who have first learned to use the value analysis techniques and then applied them to their accounting practice, has brought important yields.

12-2 *Appearance Design*

Those not engaged in value work often believe that decisions prompted by value analysis techniques will tend to decrease the appearance and attractiveness of a product. Not precisely understanding the value analysis techniques or approach, they expect that the procedure is to eliminate all except the use functions. Nothing could be further from the truth. Value analysis techniques in the very basic approach recognize two classes of functions, namely, those functions which cause the product to work and those functions which cause the product to sell.

The latter class is comprised mainly of features of appearance and convenience. More often than not, the application of value analysis techniques results in an improvement in the appearance of the product by opening up opportunity for effective work in the appearance-design activity.

One of the phases of the study of a product consists in determining precisely what, from the viewpoint of appropriate volume of sales at appropriate prices, constitutes the major areas of opportunity. These opportunities may fall in one or more of three categories:

Improved performance
Improved appearance and/or features
Lower cost

With the factors of appropriate performance and appropriate cost under control, attention is then sharply focused in the areas of improved appearance and features in order to build up the appropriate sales volume.

Value analysis studies have shown that great opportunity exists in the appearance-design area. Technical people, however, who are expert in development of performance, often do not realize the magnitude of the contribution which can be made by those especially skilled and trained in appearance design. In many cases, they make decisions affecting the appearance as "best they can." This usually results in added cost and only a moderate degree of appearance improvement. Because of such experience, there is a rather widespread belief among technical people that improved appearance requires increased cost. This is seldom the case.

Being specifically oriented toward identifying the problem and developing better solutions to it, the value analysis techniques promote the use of specialized skills and knowledge in all fields, including that of appearance design. With appearance-design aptitude brought to bear on design problems very much better appearance at substantially lower cost usually results.

The application of value analysis techniques to a product contributes materially to the separation of the work functions from the sell functions and brings appearance design directly into focus to gain from management the emphasis and support that it deserves.

12-3 *Cost-reduction Activities*

Where emphasis is put, accomplishments result. Traditionally, performance-oriented work is a scheduled, measured, and integrated activity in the business. Planned resources are spent, and planned results are normally achieved. The work is taken in stride by the business. Thus, in the absence of temporary performance problems, suitable performance of the product is the result of long-term and regular activities.

As for cost, the situation is almost directly the opposite. It is everyone's job. How a good degree of value is obtained is not too well known, nor is the degree of value obtained readily measurable. Each person involved does as well as he knows how. The normal measurement of the suitability of value work is based on an appraisal or a guess of how well it is done as compared with how competition does it.

Since performance work is basically "right-hand" work and value work is traditionally "left-hand" work, it is normal that costs often become too high. Short-range activities of a fire-fighting nature must then be established and must be given enough emphasis to prevent results that are intolerable.

Often, in a particular business, the extent of this problem can be predicted, so it is planned well in advance to impose, by a number of expediencies, a certain amount of cost-reduction effort, together with the resultant measurable reports throughout each regular period of a year.

The work involved competes with the regular work of most technical men who believe their principal job is one of accomplishing other objectives—usually performance objectives, new-product objectives, or similar ends. Quite commonly, the manager or boss is more oriented toward, and more comfortable with, performance work, and so his best supervising effort goes in the direction of helping and measuring his subordinates on the performance parts of their jobs. To him, cost-reduction work then becomes an added or "thrust-in" burden which he must, to some extent, do something about.

In these circumstances, a certain amount of pressure may be necessary to compete with the motivation of a man for the regular phases of his job, and he is often told that it is intended that he shall spend part of his time, perhaps one-half day a week, on the cost-reduction activity. In order to strengthen the pressure which will cause him to do this, he is given a budget of savings which he is expected to accomplish in a certain period.

Cost-reduction work, as a rule, is after-the-fact work. The tooling has been provided and the product has been standardized; changes spell deviation. In many cases, replacement parts must be continuously stocked, and when changes are made, other items must be added to the catalogue. Likewise, drawings must be changed. Indeed, these and many other deterrents to good cost-reduction work often diminish substantially the valuable results of the activity.

Nonetheless, what is known as cost reduction is a vital activity. As most businesses are organized, they could not long endure without it. A first step, when instituting a value analysis program, is to make sure that those who are working on cost reduction continue to do at least as much of it as they have been doing. A great deal of effective cost-reduction activity will be necessary until a planned and integrated activity, professional skills, techniques, and knowledge are provided to the business so that value work can be taken in stride, the same as performance-oriented work is.

As a business begins to apply value analysis techniques to cost reduction, two changes will be observed.

The results per man-hour of cost-reduction work will be greatly increased.

More satisfaction will be derived from the work because it will be seen to be effectively done with the achievement of a larger yield.

Cost Reduction versus Value Analysis

In contrast, value analysis is a long-range planned activity. It has set objectives, and it operates to always keep the costs right.

Similarly, just as long-range integrated performance work uses good tools, long-range integrated value work uses good tools to accomplish the set objectives.

Suitable value work is done in the product-conception stage, in the engineering-design stage, in the manufacturing-engineering stage, in the purchasing stage, and in the production stage.

By doing this work on a planned basis as the product "grows" and is developed, it becomes practicable to take many actions not possible in after-the-fact cost-reduction work, which is not a part of the normal pattern and which is hampered by problems of existing tooling, standardization, servicing, replacement, etc.

The reader must not, however, overlook the fact that the value analysis techniques are often also used on products in the after-the-fact stage, especially when the particular industry has progressed to the point where substantial redesign is imminent or when a competitive degree of value work has not been done during the earlier product stages.

Case Study

INCREASED DOLLAR YIELD PER MAN-HOUR
FOR COST-REDUCTION WORK

When fabricated, 2½ cents worth of steel in this back plate, Figure 12-1, became 10½ cents of cost. The part was in a high-volume appliance. With a quantity of 1 million, each penny becomes $10,000. Therefore, each penny of unnecessary cost *is* important. The function of the back plate was evaluated at considerably less than 10½ cents.

Cost analysis and value analysis study showed that far too much of this cost was for the operations of suitably smoothing and deburring the top edge of the plate. Investigation was made of alternative materials, products, and processes which would accomplish the needed functions. It was found that adding ½ cent per pound to the cost of the steel, which ensured providing it with a mill edge, completely eliminated the burring and smoothing expense. The result was an identical part from a use and appearance viewpoint—probably a somewhat neater part—with cost reduced from 10½ cents to 4½ cents. This study was motivated by the cost-reduction coordinator and netted him a $60,000 credit to his budget.

12-4   Engineering

The enormity of the engineering activity in most organizations is largely underestimated. Greatly oversimplified, it may be said that the engineering function has two responsibilities.

Design and development of new products
Constant reduction in cost of existing products

A somewhat closer view will show the complexity of the responsibility normally carried by engineering. While in years past its job was deemed satisfactorily done if the product performed its functions reliably, in more

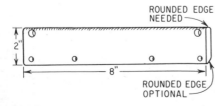

Fig. 12-1   Back plate.

recent times a great many complicating requirements have been included in the engineer's responsibility. Some of these—aside from determining a way to accomplish a function and providing a design which will do it—are:

Design to size
Design to weight
Design to special conditions of vibration, temperature, corrosive environments, etc.
Design to appearance
Design to cost
Design to new manufacturing processes
Design to time schedules
Design to utilize new materials

A realistic appraisal shows that the engineer must keep in mind so many factors that he usually has to be satisfied with compromises in some areas of his responsibility. Quite naturally, the areas in which he can prove his attainments readily by tests are the ones that get his best attention. In other areas, such as that of value, where definite measurements are largely nonexistent, he must often, under the pressure of time schedules and other commitments, consider that he has "done well enough" and jell up his designs.

It is in the areas affecting cost that value analysis has an intimate relationship to engineering and can contribute greatly to the value content of technical work. The relationship of value analysis to engineering may well be compared to the relationship of, say, metallurgy or heat transfer to engineering. In these two fields, information vital to engineering decision making is recognized to exist, and the engineer is accustomed to drawing on these techniques, and the knowledge therein, before he makes his decisions. As the metallurgists act to assist the engineer in identifying appropriate metals for use in accomplishing a specified function, so the value analyst acts to provide the engineer with information which will allow him to identify unnecessary costs.

The engineer must draw his conclusions and make his decisions based on the best facts he can lay his hands on. The value analyst must be prepared to provide more facts about value alternatives for the engineer to use at the point and time of engineering decisions.

It may help the reader to review here some of the types of situations that every experienced engineer has faced and that have often been the cause of unnecessary costs in designs. Frequently, costs are lacking. In theory, the engineer might be said to have cost figures to use in choosing his alternatives. In actual practice, however, very many vital decisions must be made with exceedingly poor cost estimates, if indeed cost estimates are at all available. It is not unusual to find an engineering manager saying, "I had no reasonable idea of what the costs would be until after the first production run." *A part of the kit of tools of the value analyst will serve to provide useful and meaningful costs at the time of decision.*

Commonly, in any particular plant, there is considerable pressure and habit directed at designing for the machines already owned. The engineer knows that the machines will make suitable parts, and especially if he is short of time, he might be open to criticism if he produced a design that could not be made on the local equipment. In consequence he takes the normal way out and designs for the available equipment. One of the functions of the value analyst is to search out the very best process for a functional part or assembly, regardless of what the process may be or where the equipment may be located, and to determine what the cost of the found alternative will be. Again, the engineer is provided with sound value information at the time of his decision making.

Some applicable methods of manufacture are unknown to the particular manufacturing and engineering people in any one location at some time or another. It is again the task of the value analyst to reach out and cause the corresponding value alternatives to be developed and brought into focus for the engineer's decision.

Certain materials are thought to be unsuitable. Every person tends to draw upon his experience and his knowledge, thinking that it is applicable when it is not. As a result, excellent value alternatives are not considered. The search techniques in the value analysis kit of tools, combined with the special knowledge of value analysis, must be applied to develop objective information for the engineer to use in his decisions. The same is true when certain methods and processes are thought to be unsuitable. Objective information will show that they are suitable and represent good alternatives. Every human being accumulates a certain number of misconceptions as he proceeds in his business career. The use of the value analysis techniques illuminates whole families of misconceptions with fact and brings out into the open good value alternatives which otherwise would be rejected without even being considered.

Wide ranges of functional products can be furnished by specialty suppliers to be used, either as they are or with some modification, to accomplish the needed function. Once again, the search techniques and the special knowledge of value analysis bring much more of this sort of information into clear view for the engineer's consideration in his decision making.

The field of new materials is expanding so rapidly that it provides a wide area of opportunity for the value analyst to search out and identify new applicable materials for the engineer's functions and then to bring them to his attention with complete, appropriate costs.

One of today's normal methods of securing business in many industries consists in providing an engineering service. The engineers of suppliers are anxious to become acquainted with needed functions and to endeavor to adapt their products, materials, or processes to them. Value analysis includes action to search out such supplier engineering competence, to clearly convey to capable representatives the functional problems in question, and to bring back their solutions for the responsible engineer's decision.

Engineers working on a design often realize that more time and resources would provide better value in their solutions, but at the same time, they may be hard pressed by a management to end their work and make the product as it stands. Utilization of the special knowledge and techniques of value analysis helps to bring useful alternatives into view within time periods allowable. Any individual can use only those ideas which he is able to think of at the specific time. The value analyst, by application of his techniques, can often assist the engineer in thinking up more applicable value ideas.

Experience indicates that it is not an unusual thing for engineers to find themselves bogged down in clerical work. Taking a leaf out of value analysis teachings and proceeding to analyze the function of such clerical activity have, on numerous occasions, helped the engineer to rid himself of much clerical effort and have thus enabled him to proceed with his creative work faster.

One extensive area in which value analysis can be of great importance to the engineer may be well identified as the "warm-blood" area. After a person has been confronted with a situation, studied it, collected information on it, thought it through, and reached a decision, this decision becomes his "warm blood." Psychological studies show that it is very difficult for him to start again with the same problem and not be pulled into the same preformed channels of thinking. Value analysis can assist him greatly in such situations by bringing up new objective alternatives for his consideration and decision making.

It is well to recognize again that the engineer has one of the most difficult of all jobs to perform. He must first search for and develop his own evidence. He must then be the judge and make his decision on his own evidence. Experience shows that when more and better evidence is developed through value analysis, decision making by engineers results in very much improved value.

Case Study

CAN WE SCRAP THE SCRAP?

In order to secure advantageous operating characteristics, it was necessary to provide a silicon-steel transformer core of a specific configuration with relation to the coils which went on it. As the steel laminations were stamped to make this core, 42 per cent of the steel became scrap while the remaining 58 per cent was used in the product. It appeared that, without sacrificing efficiency or operating characteristics, this was the way to do it.

A value consultant brought into contact with the job went to the silicon-steel specialist and also to the transformer specialist in a large research organization and confronted them with the problem. It just didn't seem right to him to live with the enormous amount of unworking cost involved in throwing away 42 per cent of the silicon steel. The silicon-steel specialist brought forth a change which resulted in reducing the scrap from 42 per cent to 25 per cent by working out a new stamping pattern. Two months later, after careful study and test, changes were put into effect which eliminated 5 cents apiece of the cost on 3 million transformers per year, a difference of $150,000.

Then two interesting things occurred. The engineers were startled and intrigued that this could be done, and both the transformer-circuit specialist and the silicon-steel specialist became intrigued by the problem. In about a year, another suggested improvement was made and tested. This involved changes both in the silicon-steel core and in the coils. Improved performance was found to be provided without adding to the coil cost, and the silicon-steel loss was reduced to 5 per cent.

In conclusion, the relationship of value analysis to engineering is one of generating greatly expanded information for the use of engineers and of identifying value alternatives for the engineer's inclusion in his decision making. It is little wonder that the first vice-president of engineering of a well-known company to examine the operation of these techniques stated, "Value analysis is the best method yet found to help engineers remove unnecessary costs from their products."

12-5   *Manufacturing*

Basically, the job of manufacturing is to use machines, processes, and people to change the form of material to conform to the designs of engineers.

The basic function of value analysis is to identify each element of function provided by each element of cost. Accordingly, the consultation provided by the value analyst to manufacturing will start always with a clear identification of the contribution to function furnished by each activity in manufacturing which adds cost. Creative study of the increments of function and of the increment of cost brings expanded information into the decision-making area and makes practicable a still further elimination of unnecessary cost.

For example, more information is provided by observations of rather difficult or time-consuming operations throughout manufacturing.

What contribution is made by the hardened steel?

What contribution is made by having holes slightly different instead of the same size?

What contribution is made by heat-treatment between operations?

What contribution is made by a tapered instead of a straight screw?

What contribution is made by an operation that is causing quality difficulties?

The functions and contributions required of the process and the related difficulties having been brought into view, the search techniques of value analysis, together with the special knowledge, elicit alternatives for the responsible manufacturing man to use in his decision making and in his discussions with the engineers.

Studies of manufacturing work often show that unprofitable items are being produced. The reason for this lies in the nonexistence of clearly crystallized and developed alternatives. When information of that character is developed, unprofitable work may be removed from the factory.

Case Study

DID THE VENDOR CONTRIBUTE?

No operation should be performed by manufacturing people unless it contributes to the enterprise; in fact, if many are performed which do not contribute, the vitality of the business is sapped. This case reports one study to determine the realities of manufacturing contribution.

In one phase of value work on an assembly of a few hundred parts, quotations were obtained from appropriate vendors on machine parts which were actually being made in the plant. The quotations showed that, on a considerable number of the specialized parts, vendors' prices were lower than the comparable in-plant manufacturing cost, which consisted of labor, material, and overhead.

In this particular plant, it was the custom for the manager of manufacturing engineering to make make-or-buy decisions. He was considerably challenged by these lower competitive costs and arranged for a study of his own manufacturing operations on the items in question. In all but one of a dozen cases, he was able to lower his costs comparably, and hence he allowed only the one part to be placed with a supplier. This was protested by the purchasing people who had been instrumental in helping select the vendors who provided the lower quotations. As a result, the case was resolved in the higher manager's office. There, after the facts were developed, the question was asked: What is the right action for us to take in cases of this type? It was quickly decided and accepted that the right action was, whenever suppliers had made contributions, to compensate them in some suitable form.

The manufacturing engineer, however, felt that the suppliers had not contributed. "They didn't show us how to speed up our machines, how to use different types of cutting tools, how to plan some of the parts more effectively. All of this we did ourselves."

The manager's response was, "Whenever anyone comes here and takes any action that causes us to eliminate substantial amounts of unnecessary costs from our products, he has made a contribution regardless of all other circumstances." Again he raised a question: What is the appropriate action to take in this case?

After discussing the issues involved, he instructed that at least one-third of the jobs on which suppliers had developed effective bids and made constructive quotations should be awarded to them regardless of other factors and that they should continue to enjoy the business for approximately a year, even though the factory now had improved its own processing to meet the lower costs.

Good value work will help rid manufacturing areas of "busy work" which does not contribute, so that their efforts may be used on operations which make important contributions to the business.

Often manufacturing work proceeds along rather habitual lines involving the particular products being made on orders placed with the factory for quantities according to specific schedules. More complete information on expected quantity requirements, inventory-carrying costs, types of tooling for the resultant volume, and applicable specialized vendor knowledge often allows the manufacturing decision makers to eliminate important amounts of unnecessary cost.

Whenever a change is to be made, there is much work to be done in connection with obtaining the new and complete information, analyzing and evaluating it, and persuading those involved that the path to better value lies in a different direction. In all these activities, the value analysis tools and special knowledge are very helpful to manufacturing.

Misunderstanding is often eliminated by the application of value analysis tools. Too often costly specifications are continued, and in effect, needless and costly operations are performed which do not, if the whole story were known, add in the slightest to value. In one instance a stamped steel bracket was carefully "sized" in an expensive operation so that it would fit perfectly into a mating part. Study to ascertain precisely the value that came from the mating operation showed that a lead mallet was always used at assembly and so, of course, the sizing operation made no contribution whatsoever to value.

The process of associating precisely the contribution to function of each addition to cost identifies the area in which the relationship of value analysis to manufacturing allows manufacturing men to make different decisions that help solve their problems, speed production along, prevent quality problems, and lower costs.

12-6   *Management*

Basically, the objectives of management with relation to the business are to provide the proper organization, including facilities, and to make the proper decisions to operate on a profitable basis. If not profitable, all the tragedies of bankruptcy will soon occur.

The method is to use the resources of capital, men, materials, equipment, and time to make and sell products (or services) as skillfully as competitors do. Competition is the measure. The need is for answers as good as, or a little better than, competition, in order for the business to endure.

Case Study

THE CONTACTS THAT WERE LOST

Large benefits to management result from the new information which they can now have as a result of knowing the value of the various functions in the products they manufacture. Often normally undiscovered opportunities to increase these values will result.

In the design of new products or in major redesigns, accumulated experience is studied, new information believed to be applicable is searched, and models are prepared for test. In the case of electrical equipment, certain types are also sent to the Underwriters' Laboratories for its inspection and test. The value audit of a product which had been in production two years indicated that it contained considerable "waste," that is, cost which made no contribution to life, safety factor, or use of the product. The contacts used cost $26,000 per year more than seemed appropriate, and an investigation was made. It was found that during the design work reasonable and appropriate contacts had been developed by test, and they had been selected. However, it was also found that, during the assembly process for preparation of samples to be sent to the Underwriters', something had gone wrong and the supply of the appropriate contacts had been exhausted. In order to avoid delay at the time, the engineer had furnished another, more expensive contact to the assemblers. This had solved the assembly problems and the samples had been made and sent to Underwriters' Laboratories where they had received approval. Two years later, with this information in hand, the appropriate contacts were submitted to the Underwriters', and of course, approval came forth with the result that the unnecessary, noncontributing cost was eliminated. *Searches often disclose the unexpected.*

The work of a business is twofold: to provide something which the public wants and to provide it for low-enough cost. The business will succeed or fail according to the effectiveness with which management makes decisions in these two areas.

The relationship of value analysis to management, of course, falls in the second category. In the past, there have been severe organizational shortcomings. High among them is the fact that most important responsibilities can be effectively delegated and the degree of their accomplishment measured so as to be known. For example, the president or general manager delegates:

To his engineering head responsibility for performance and design quality

To his manufacturing head responsibility for production quality and shipments to a predetermined schedule

To his industrial designers, or the engineering head, responsibility for competitive appearance and features

To the manager of inventory control responsibility for keeping inventory within certain established ranges

To each of these men, that which is delegated is the prime job. Success or failure depends upon accomplishment in the assigned area.

When it comes to value, this is everyone's business. Each party is told to coordinate and cooperate with the others to secure good value. Attainment of good value is a "second job" with unclear delegation and indefinite evaluation.

Experienced managers have often said that one of their major problems is that they have had little choice, no matter how much they were in need of lower costs, but to have the same people reexamine their work of the past. The result has been that a very negative, unrewarding, and inefficient job has been done.

With the advent of value analysis techniques, this vital problem of management is being corrected. The manager may now arrange for a suitable number of competent men to learn how to handle value. He may delegate directly to them responsibility for achieving certain value objectives. This becomes their job and they succeed or fail according to their performance on this one objective. Accordingly, the magnitude of results is of a different order.

The best managers agree that where management places emphasis, there they secure results. This they are enabled to do with the help of the value analysis suggestion sheet written in managers' language. The reader will recall that the suggestion sheet is a clear-cut presentation of unveiled solutions uncluttered by supporting data which are needed only by the engineer or other on-the-job decision maker. With the value information oriented to specifics, the manager may now apply effective emphasis to achieve the degree of value results which he feels the business needs.

Another important way in which the use of value analysis techniques can greatly assist the manager is in identifying, and helping to compensate for, the costly disadvantages of honest errors. In any field of activity, responsible people accumulate honest wrong impressions and, accordingly, make entire patterns of decisions incurring more costs than necessary. Experience has shown that the costs in such instances can often be from two to five times as high as is necessary to reliably accomplish the desired functions.

In this respect, any manager can do much good by having his subordinates know he understands that a portion of their decisions will be in error and that they will not be criticized for what is a normal occurrence. He must also recognize that the same is true for a percentage of his own decisions, and since these may vitally affect the earnings position of his company, he would do well to use value analysis techniques to illuminate wrong beliefs with objective value data, so that decisions in the future may be more in harmony with best alternatives.

An important phase of the relationship of value analysis to management can be emphasized by the question: What is a most important responsibility of management to value analysis? In Chapter 11, the importance of the decision-making environment, which is largely under the control of the manager, was discussed. As a prime requisite, a manager, to enchance his earnings results, must provide an environment in which men can make decisions to obtain better value without the risk of personal loss. Full recognition and proper implementation of this situation by the manager can more than double the rate at which good value alternatives that deviate from past practice are put into use to retain product reliability and quality and to provide increased earnings.

12-7   *Purchasing*

A significant part of the responsibility of the value analyst, after the functions required have been determined, is to locate in the vendor market the particular product, process, or know-how which will bring the best answer at the lowest price. Therefore, close and extensive relationships must exist between purchasing and value analysis.

Fortunately for both operations, effective value analysis greatly improves the grade and degree of purchasing work, and efficient execution of certain purchasing activities greatly improves the degree and amount of value analysis accomplishment.

Case Study

IT'S PATENTED

A large quantity of special metal dials were being purchased. They cost 90 cents each, which seemed high, but purchasing had been able to get no other bids.

A value consultant studied the functions. They were found to be very simple, certainly not worth 90 cents. Discussions were arranged with the supplier, whose attention was called to the large increase in the quantities purchased and to the simple function of the dial, as well as to the fact that cost analysis showed it was not worth 90 cents.

When the chips were down during the negotiation, he acknowledged these statements but said, "The dial is patented." It was such a simple product, however, that the patentability of it seemed very much in question. The patent attorney was consulted, and when he got in touch with the patent people of the supplier company, he received information on what was patented. It proved to be only an extremely minor detail which was relatively unimportant in the use to which the dial was being put. The result was that the supplier proposed a price of 40 cents instead of 90 cents. He stated that, although a quotation of 30 cents might be expected, he felt that his pioneering work in the field of dials had been important and that even though the precise item he had patented was of little value, it seemed reasonable to him to receive a 10-cent payment for it. This was a well-founded contention.

The matter was concluded by deciding to continue buying the dials from him, but for 40 cents rather than 90 cents. This resulted in saving a large amount of the cost of the military product involved. *Investigation of questionable patent situations, as well as of any other situation which might add cost, is a part of value analysis.*

To those using the value analysis techniques, purchasing can supply valuable information about specialty-vendor knowledge and precise data regarding individual companies' personnel, products, or processes. The following value analysis techniques can be most efficiently used only with continuous purchasing support.

Use industry specialists to extend specialized knowledge.
Utilize vendor's available functional products.
Utilize and pay for vendor's skill and knowledge.
Utilize specialty processes.
Utilize applicable standards.

Purchasing men, situated as they are at the point of transfer of the company's money for materials, products, and services, often have reason to suspect that good value is not being obtained on particular items. In such circumstances, their invitations to value consultants to study the items, combined with their suggestions as to where to turn and how to obtain efficient work, almost always prove highly profitable.

The inducement to such action by purchasing men lies in the added job satisfaction—over and above the day's pay—derived from feeling that extra contributions are being made to improve company earnings. Basically, purchasing personnel are dedicated to getting their money's worth.

In the atmosphere of competition, however, they must also be constantly aware of the fact that their expenditures have a bearing on the profit picture. They can ill afford to let this point be overshadowed in the execution of the diverse, and often laborious, aspects of their responsibilities, such as ensuring that needed materials and supplies of satisfactory quality are obtained on time and that emergencies of supply, of transportation, etc., are resolved promptly.

The work of obtaining full value for expenditures, which is in keeping with the attainment of higher earnings, can be inestimably enhanced by the effective use of value analysis techniques by competent persons trained and skilled in applying them. As functions are studied and further clarified, value alternatives come to light. Discussions with technical people crystallize the alternatives that are practical, usable, and acceptable from the technical viewpoint. This allows purchasing people to buy a material or a product which may be entirely different from that originally intended but which is obtainable at very much lower cost and still is functionally useful. The result is satisfaction in a job well done.

It should be observed at this point that full recognition of certain basic premises is necessary for the effective interplay of the relationships in question. These premises are:

1. *The value analyst will not do the buyer's job.* Unless the value analyst has a complete prior understanding with the buyer, the interest that he takes in vendors and his communications with them will be questioned. As the buyer sees it, this is his corner of the ball diamond, and now the value analyst is on it. Quite naturally he wonders: "What is he doing in there? What is the effect going to be on my job? How will the efficiency and effectiveness of my work be affected? In the past I have enjoyed contacts even with the technical people of the vendors and have progressively learned from them. Will the value analyst's work now reverse this trend and steadily weaken me in the area?"

These and allied questions will interfere with the buyer's performance, and it is imperative for him to know that the value analyst will not do his job and also just what the value analyst will do. With a precise understanding of the relationship of value analysis to his job, the buyer will recognize that it will extend his range, increase his competence, promote his growth, and enhance his contributions to the company's earnings. The value analyst will not be making decisions which were formerly the buyer's, but he will be providing more information for the buyer to work on so that he can make more rewarding decisions.

2. *The buyer must be kept advised.* If the buyer, as well as the company, is to benefit from the value analyst's activities, the buyer must be protected from any embarrassment that could result. Therefore, he must

be a party to whatever work is being done in his area. This does not mean that he personally needs to expend time sitting in on all discussions. It does mean, however, that the value analyst will let him know what is going on and will give him the opportunity to take part, to the extent he wishes, in discussions leading to later purchases. It is very common for technical people to work with competent vendors on projects involving considerable complication and to arrive thoughtlessly at the answers to the various problems so that the purchasing decision is in reality being made step by step by others than the buyers. This is contrary to the philosophy of good management under which a specific person is assigned responsibility for each major activity, such as engineering, manufacturing, sales, purchasing.

Thus management expects the purchasing manager and his organization to be responsible for properly purchasing any particular product. When, during the cooperative development of a purchasing decision, the purchasing people are not properly advised of the steps along the way, but are told only of the final answer, they become, in effect, rubber-stamp manipulators who blindly place orders and abdicate their responsibility to make sure that their purchases represent value. If they refuse to follow the decision and open the project to bidders who have not had time either to learn all of the intricacies of the job or to make substantial financial and technical contributions to its development, their action may result in injury to the competent vendor who originally worked with the technical people as well as harm to their company. The product thus selected will probably not be up to standards when it arrives from the new vendor; and the result will be additional injury to the purchasing department, which becomes subject to criticism by management, and, in the final analysis, to the customer, who may not receive on time the product he had a right to expect.

A few simple ground rules and a reasonable amount of mutual understanding provide for a very rewarding cooperation between purchasing people and value consultants. For anyone who expects to be using value analysis techniques, it will be profitable to examine some of the purchasing practices which would be affected, adversely or favorably, by his work. The following extracts are offered from a set of guides which have stood the test of usage.

PURCHASING PRACTICES PERTINENT TO THE PROPER RELATIONSHIP BETWEEN VALUE ANALYSIS, THE PURCHASING FUNCTION, AND THE PURCHASING MAN

These statements and purchasing practices are guides to be used with intelligence and with consideration of the other fellow and his job.

1. *Sources of Supply*

   The purchasing department will select sources of supply. They will endeavor to do so in the best interests of the company and with a view to creating and maintaining good vendor relationships. *If vendors are asked to bid, they must know that the source has not already been decided.*

   Strong and enduring relationships with tested suppliers are to be maintained. To do this, frankness and fair dealing, with maintenance of quality, delivery, and fair price, will have a great weight. It is the intention of the company to conduct purchasing so that suppliers will value business sufficiently to make every effort to meet legitimate competition.

   a. Buyers will buy from sources with good reputation and sufficient financial standing to meet the job requirements.

   b. The best bid on the combined bases of price, quality, and service will be accepted.

2. *Commitments*

   a. The purchasing department conducts and concludes all negotiations affecting purchaser, selection of vendor, prices, terms, delivery, adjustments, etc.

   b. Commitments and orders, to be valid, are to be stated by a letter, a purchase order, or a contract which sets forth appropriate details and which is signed by the purchasing agent or by a person duly authorized to sign in his stead.

   c. Negotiations leading up to, or apt to conclude in, contract arrangements should not be undertaken without the knowledge and authorization of the interested buyer in the purchasing department.

   d. No one who is not a member of the purchasing department should commit himself to any vendor on preference for any product or source of supply for any product or give any information regarding competitive performance, final approval, or price.

3. *Vendor Relations*

   The purchasing department, realizing that good vendor relations is a company asset, must be alert to promote a program of equity and friendship with sources of supply.

   a. Salesmen will be received in the purchasing department and in other departments after arrangements have been made by the purchasing department.

   b. In addition, the purchasing department will arrange interviews between vendor representatives and company production, engineering, research, and maintenance personnel when it appears to be to the advantage of the company or when the buyer is in doubt as to the merits of the proposal or when such an interview has been requested by an appropriate employee of another department.

   c. All suppliers' representatives are to have a complete hearing for their sales arguments the first time they call. Subsequent policy will depend on the particular circumstances. Courtesy and prompt reception of salesmen are part of the code; if the interview is to be denied, there should be a prompt acknowledgment of the call, together with a reason for not granting the interview. A buyer, or any other company person, is not required to put his time absolutely and indiscriminately at the disposal of any and all comers, however frequent at whatever time, or on what mission they may be calling. Some matters are not appropriate to the department's needs or are not timely at the moment the salesman elects to press them. The buyer must necessarily be the judge, but he is not relieved of his obligation of courtesy.

d. The purchasing department will handle all correspondence with suppliers except when technical details make it desirable to secure technical or other assistance.

e. Requests for prices, trial lots, etc., should be made by the purchasing department.

f. When a free sample is accepted for test, an obligation is assumed by the company to make a fair trial and to inform the vendor of the outcome of the test. However, as a preferred practice, the company may *buy* sample lots, thus incurring no obligation but establishing the interest of the company in completing the trial and making a fair evaluation.

g. In fairness to all concerned, prices and other specific information received from vendors are considered confidential. The quotations of one supplier may not be divulged to another, and such information should not be circulated indiscriminately within the company.

h. Buyers should be reasonable in requesting supplier's technicians to call, unless volume of business justifies such expense. Information can ordinarily be obtained by letter, telephone, or telegraph.

4. *Interdepartment Relations*

The success of the purchasing department depends on the kind of job it does in procuring materials, equipment, facilities, ideas, and supplies. The most effective functioning of the purchasing department is possible only when other departments perform well their functions of engineering, planning, receiving, testing, and storing. Therefore, intelligent, constant, and harmonious contact between purchasing and other departments relative to their needs and the procurement of their needs is a "must."

a. The purchasing department has the duty and authority to ask reconsideration of specifications or quantity of material if, in the opinion of a buyer, it appears that the interests of the company may be better served. However, the final determination of quality and quantity are the prerogative of the engineering and requisitioning departments.

(1) Purchasing specifications, while written by engineering, should be checked by the purchasing department before being issued to be sure material is obtainable and practical.

(2) It is desirable that the drawings for new-purchase parts be submitted to purchasing, as much in advance of the required date as possible, to allow purchasing to develop the best possible source of supply.

b. Buyers must be alert to pass on to potentially interested individuals information derived from salesmen's interviews and direct mail or other advertisements and deemed useful. In a similar manner, members of other departments are expected to reciprocate by drawing items deemed to be of value to the attention of the purchasing department. If the purchasing department does not have a record of, or experience with, the items, suitable inquiry will be made by its personnel.

12-8   *Quality Control*

While value analysis is not as directly related to quality control as it is to purchasing or engineering, one specific relationship exists with extensive opportunity for mutually beneficial activity. Before dealing with it, it will be well to identify two important areas of possible misconception about the relationship of value analysis to quality control.

These two misconceptions, which are entirely too general, are:

1. "The function of value analysis is to identify and cause to be removed all costs which provide extra safety, extra quality, and extra life beyond the minimum needs. It is the aim of value analysis to remove all of the quality which can be eliminated without having the product fall apart in its customary use."

This statement is totally false in every degree of its implication. The use of the value analysis techniques identifies unnecessary cost, i.e., cost which does *not* add to safety, to performance, to life, or to the appearance desired by the customer and which, in fact, adds nothing whatsoever to the product under any condition.

2. "Lower cost means lower quality." This common belief, which is often inherited from early childhood and which normally persists to control vital decisions, is also entirely false. Cost and quality have no direct relationship. Indeed, it frequently occurs that the highest cost gives the lowest quality. The reader will add greatly to his value competence if, at this point, he frees himself of any remaining tie to his childhood experience of buying small oranges for 25 cents a dozen and larger ones for 50 cents a dozen.

The reason for the existence of any product is that it accomplishes a certain function or a certain group of functions. Good quality comes with the selection of good answers to the question of how to use materials, processes, parts, and human efforts to accomplish these functions. Poor quality results from having poor answers to the question. It is as simple as that. Cost is not part of quality determination.

Now, to introduce cost in its proper perspective:

Good-quality products result whenever the answers chosen are good answers whether they be high-cost answers or low-cost answers.

Poor-quality products result whenever the answers selected are unreliable answers, whether they be high in cost or low in cost.

Case Study

LOWER COSTS MAY MEAN DOING IT THE RIGHT WAY

Precision gear sleeves, about 2 inches in diameter and 5 inches long, were used on a precision product with expanding volume. They were manufactured in the plant at a cost of $15.75 each. Extensive inspection was required, as this was both a high-temperature and a high-speed gear on which even minute imperfections had to be eliminated.

As the volume increased faster than the production facilities for manufacture, it became necessary to locate another source. Considerable purchasing effort produced a source which made suitable gears. However, the cost was $17 each.

During this search for suppliers, a specialist who had achieved considerable success in some of the branches of the gear field had also been located, and he had quoted a price of $6. But the consequences of the failure of the job were great, and thus a feeling prevailed that, "He is so new in the business that he doesn't know what he is up against, and to do business with him will bring trouble."

Nevertheless, after the $17 supplier was located, discussions proceeded in an orderly fashion with the one who had quoted $6. A tool maker and an inspector from the factory visited this vendor and brought back word that his facilities, processes, and equipment were excellent. The buyer then revisited the supplier and went through each detail of the drawings and specifications, encircling in red the tolerances, requirements, and specifications which it was feared the vendor might have overlooked. The vendor advised that, in each case, he had noted the requirements and had expected to make the sleeves according to the specifications. He did, however, sense that concern was caused by the lowness of his quotation, and so he increased his price to $6.75 to provide a contingent amount for any possible unforeseen factor for which he had not planned.

A production order was then placed with him subject to the strict limitation of individual-lot release. Thereafter, when the first ten were released and arrived at the plant, they were found to be the smoothest and best gears of this type which had ever been seen. Still, a normal cautiousness and concern existed. The inspector said, "I doubt that these were built on the production facilities the vendor expects to use. Every one is perfect. They seem to have been built on gauge machines instead."

After being assured that the ten gears were built on the equipment which was put in place for the production order, a release of one hundred was issued. These hundred were also of the same hitherto unexperienced high quality. This was followed by a release of a thousand, also of the same high grade.

Two interesting results followed. First, the inspection department, after days of making inspections and never finding any flaws, began to feel that inspection was superfluous, and a simple checking routine was established which eliminated 95 per cent of the inspection of the gears from this supplier. Second, inspection personnel started putting strong pressure on the procurement department and on the factory to discontinue buying from the $17 supplier and also to discontinue in-plant manufacture of the item so that the extensive inspection required on gears received from these two sources could be permanently and totally discontinued.

The outcome was that the $17 supplier was dropped. But, in order to have a second source of supply for the vital part should a serious problem of any nature end production temporarily in the plant of the $6.75 supplier, 25 per cent in-plant production was continued.

Scores of cases of this type prove to the experienced that good quality is the result of "doing it the right way." So is good value.

As stated repeatedly in the foregoing discussions, the operation of value analysis is to identify the functions clearly and then to search out and develop, by using value analysis techniques and special knowledge, good answers for the lowest cost. No quality reduction is involved. However, if quality problems are present at the start of the value study, quality improvement will result.

With the factual situation in clear focus, it will be recognized that value analysis and quality control have joint opportunities. Value analysis techniques can have an important impact on the solving of quality problems, and in turn, the quality control activity is an important means of identifying the areas in which contributions can be made by the use of value techniques. Whenever quality problems exist, it means that the functions involved are not being secured in a suitable manner. This provides a clear start for the effective application of value analysis.

12-9 *Marketing*

It will be found that beneficial relationships exist between value analysis and sales work. Products in general may be divided into three classes:

Existing products
New products
Products adapted to customers' special requirements

With regard to existing products, the sales department must provide to customers the performance features and attractiveness they want at competitive prices. Often, costs in comparison to competition are too high, and the sales department is unable to sell until lower costs are established. Lowering of costs by the required amount is invited and supported by the use of value analysis techniques in important areas of the product.

In the development of new products, it is incumbent upon the sales department to determine what functions, or what combinations of functions, the customer desires and, further, to determine at about what market price these functions can be sold. It is at once apparent that the sales department is here dealing in functions and costs, which are the stock in trade of value analysis. The opportunity exists for value consultants to apply the special techniques and the special knowledge toward the development of value alternatives which will provide a sound basis for investment, planning, advertising, staffing, etc., to provide the new products.

In connection with customers' special requirements, the value analysis techniques are tools for studying with them precisely what their needs are. With a clear understanding of the function, or functions, a customer needs, sales people are enabled, by providing the precise new functional components required, to effectively adapt their products to accomplish most economically the full need of the customer.

Viewing the relationship from the opposite end, it will be seen that sales provides to value consultants important areas of opportunity. With regard to established products, they know precisely where to work to meet the company's emergencies. In connection with new products, they know the considerations which should receive top priority in the new product line and can make contributions that will have long-standing high value. As for special products, they have the extra opportunity of using their techniques to help secure specific additional orders.

SUMMARY

Properly organized, instructed, and integrated value analysis people do not make the work of anyone more confused or difficult. Instead, they increase the effectiveness of the work of most of the other administrative or professional groups.

In the area of accounting, value analysis encourages the use of meaningful costs. Meaningful costs bear the same relationship to good decisions among "cost" alternatives that meaningful tests do among "performance" alternatives. A value analysis organization helps accounting people contribute to better decisions by encouraging use of costs that are meaningful for the purpose of comparisons.

Appearance design people are assisted by the separation of the aesthetic from the use function, the separation of the costs that go into aesthetic functions, and the emphasis value analysis places upon providing an opportunity for them to use their special abilities and skills on the product.

Every technique of value analysis is so constituted that when utilized by cost-reduction people, a far greater yield per man-hour results. Cost reduction is a part-time activity of everyone. It is essential to normal operation. Value analysis is a full-time activity of a few with special training, techniques, and skills. Both have the objective of minimizing unnecessary costs.

Engineering people are assisted at every turn by the operation of the value analysis system. Essential information is gathered for them. Functions that they must provide are made clearer. Costs that they need are developed for their decision making.

Manufacturing people find that the functions provided by the operations they must perform are often evaluated, and less troublesome or less costly means for achieving the required purpose are brought into view. They find that alternative means for accomplishing functions help them to remove unsatisfactory operations from the factory. Value analysis search techniques often uncover materials or processes that they can examine and include.

Furthermore, value analysis brings a good answer to a vital dilemma of management people. Nearly all essential work, excepting that of securing good costs, can be assigned to a competent group: performance of the product to engineering, quantities of production to manufacturing, volume of sales to marketing. The results are measured—they are suitable or they are not—and proper corrective measures can be taken. However, the vital factor of proper costs, in a competitive business, is a matter of conversation and harangue. It is "everybody's" job and hence it is nobody's job. It is not assigned, and performance is not measured as are other vital factors. Properly staffed and assigned, value analysis people will accept the assignment of assuring proper costs. They have the tools to accomplish it, and it can be measured by the competitive cost results.

The possible contribution of purchasing people to earnings is increased because every value analysis operation assists them to more nearly buy "function." The search system finds suppliers of specialty components, materials, skills, and information, which purchasing people can thereafter use to bring greater value into their company.

Those responsible for the control of quality are assisted by the problem-solving system of value analysis, which finds better answers to engineering, manufacturing, and purchasing problems. Good quality is the result of "doing it the right way," which results from the use of the value analysis system.

The vital sales responsibility to know "for sure" what functions the customer wants and is willing to pay for is emphasized as the very start of high-grade value work. Help is provided when needed. Sales people are provided with clear statements of the functions the engineering and manufacturing departments are striving to provide and with the "value" (lowest known cost) of producing each of the functions. They are supplied with alternatives that provide various benefits for their discussions with customers and for their evaluations.

chapter 13

Effective Organization
for Value Work

Appropriate organization for the attainment of the best benefits of value analysis will be discussed first from a viewpoint of the overall business, second from the viewpoint of the interrelations among the men performing the work, and third from the viewpoint of the relationship between the men doing the work and the management of the business.

Performance orientation having been of maximum importance in the industrial development of the United States, normal management people have learned quite precisely how to effectively accomplish performance-oriented assignments. In these endeavors, cost has been recognized to be important to the extent that each person has given thought to value and has constantly taken certain actions with reference to value. It has been expected that such actions will normally be taken in addition to carrying out the performance-oriented assignment.

This means that getting good costs has been and is generally considered by most managers to be somewhat similar to breathing. As the individual takes his bath, has his breakfast, and drives his car to work, he just continues breathing, and he does a reasonable job of it at all times without paying much special attention to it. Care is taken by the employer that air is provided for breathing, and care is taken by the employee that nothing obstructs his ability to breathe. Otherwise, each continues the especially identified activities for which he has acquired certain training or skill.

Similarly, normal management believes that value is everyone's business, whether his specific assignment is to design the product, to handle its drafting, to engineer its tooling, to lay out the factory, or to do anything else. Periodically, emphasis is placed upon the importance of achieving value, i.e., periodic drives are made, during which men are relieved of other work in order to place more emphasis, for a time, on value. It is expected that an acceptable degree of value will be achieved in the product by this "everyone-does-it" approach.

That method of handling value is, in fact, satisfactory as long as everyone else uses the same method. In the final analysis, the only real measure of value is a comparison, on the basis of functions provided versus cost, with the same functions and costs of competition.

However, when competition takes a different approach and provides better value, the traditional system is no longer satisfactory. The situation parallels that which has taken place in accounting practice through a certain development in the past few decades. Not long ago, it was normal practice to expect the bookkeeping and accounting staff of a company to be sufficiently informed to prepare any necessary reports for income taxes or any other purpose. As the years went by and tax matters assumed more importance, it was recognized that the amount of tax experience and knowledge a good accountant could have in addition to keeping up with his other fields of endeavor differed widely from the penetration of knowledge required by a tax specialist—a man who dealt with tax matters every day of the year. This caused a change in thinking. It became recognized that the well-informed general accountant could not possibly know enough about tax matters to identify even a reasonable amount of unnecessary taxes and that the extra expense to the company of making it "everybody's business" to know all the intricacies of tax matters was prohibitive. The management situation and the management attitude changed. It became standard practice to expect from regular accountants a basic understanding of tax law and practice but to utilize tax specialists and consultants, specially trained and experienced in income tax practice, to identify important amounts of unnecessary tax at the proper time and to the proper extent.

Likewise, in a number of the fields of performance engineering, it is well recognized that it would be both inefficient from a viewpoint of cost and ineffective from a viewpoint of performance to undertake to teach every engineer all of the knowledge necessary to advance design work in areas where, for example, extra-high-temperature metals are required or high efficiency of heat transfer is needed. Hence, specialists who have a depth of penetration of knowledge and experience in those areas are called in at the right time and to the right extent in order to provide information which will bring better decisions and achieve better performance.

Thus industry is learning that there is a vast difference between the everyone-does-it result and the result which is achieved by specially trained men using an appropriate set of techniques and a specialized universe of knowledge. And so managements of competitive businesses—businesses in which value is important—are learning that it is efficient to provide value consultation to aid their decision makers at the right times and to the right extent.

It is not the intention in this chapter to suggest that the use of value techniques is exclusively a matter for full-time specialists. That would be like taking the stand that all sections on tax accounting should be removed from textbooks on general accounting. It is rather the intent to point out clearly that while much can be gained in achieving good value by everyday use of certain of the value analysis techniques large amounts of unnecessary cost will still be unidentified. Further, if value really is important to the business, the benefits from value activities must be enhanced by the use of specialized skill and knowledge.

Obviously, the prevailing philosophy of management and the size and scope of the particular business will determine the appropriate provision for value analysis effort. Hence the discussion which follows merely outlines basic patterns that should help to orient the reader.

13-1 *Smallest and Smaller Businesses*

It is useful to understand clearly that while in the smaller businesses organization is not a problem, the lack of large expenditures of the hardware and process type obscures opportunity. To accomplish important results, a clear focus on the fundamentals of all business—even the smallest business—is necessary.

1. What is money spent for?
2. What precisely is the performance or service or benefit which is to come to the business as a result of the expenditure?
3. What is the value of that performance or service or benefit?
4. What are the alternative ways of securing the same performance or service or benefit and what are the associated costs?
5. The value then becomes the lowest-cost alternative which will reliably accomplish it.
6. Regardless of the size of business, the number and status of individuals involved, the type of business, and the type of alternative, whenever change is involved there will be resistance at every step.

7. Typical of the nonproduct type of expense, i.e., items for which money is spent, are the following:

Paper work: Precisely what necessary function or service does each item of expenditure serve? What are the alternatives and their costs?

People's time: Precisely what necessary function or service does each item of expenditure serve? What are the alternatives and their costs?

Maintenance: Precisely what necessary function or service does each item of expenditure buy? What are the alternatives and their costs?

In businesses of below $200,000 sales per year, the owner or manager will benefit his business very profitably by securing training in value techniques. In businesses of $200,000 to $2 million, one competent and dependable man from among the top three is usually given training in value techniques. This man will himself evaluate functions, services, and benefits secured in important expenditure areas. He will promote suitable group work and action in appropriate areas. He will constantly teach the functional approach and lead activities which bring benefits from it.

Depending upon the size and nature of the business and the emphasis at the time, he will devote more or less of his attention to this responsibility and activity.

13-2   One-man Setup

Businesses with $2 million or more of annual sales will start with one or more carefully selected and trained value consultants. The selection of personnel for the one-man setup is most important. This man must rank high in competence, must have a proven record of high accomplishment, must be respected by his peers and management alike. His background must be exceedingly broad. The qualifications set forth in Chapter 14 are a *must* for him.

Even so, it must be recognized by management that, since he will be constantly calling for change, his will be a most frustrating job. Experience shows that when one good man works in an atmosphere of frustration long enough, he often decides that it is not worth it and asks for reassignment to more traditional work which will make him more acceptable to his associates.

Real attention must be given by management to this new work until it becomes understood by, integrated into, and accepted by every phase of the business.

13-3   Two-man Setup

Two men can provide a much more satisfactory penetration of the necessary knowledge and experience. Combined in the two, if the work is product oriented, should be skill in (1) engineering ideas, (2) manufacturing methods and processes, and (3) the very extensive field of using vendor and specialty-vendor competence. While the two men work together, they do not work as an interlaced team. Rather, they work as consultants to each other on any particular job. In every instance, each project or activity is the responsibility of one of the two. That individual, in turn, to the right extent and at the right time, consults with the other man on the job. One of the two may be the senior man and carry certain responsibility for assigning work to the other. Care must be taken, however, that neither of the two works as an assistant to the other but rather that each accepts responsibility for a particular activity in the plant and consults with the other as needed.

13-4   *Three-man Setup*

Normally and practically, three men constitute the smallest efficient operating unit for wide-range value work. It is then usually possible to have the necessary penetration in the three required areas of skill named above. The three men again act as individual value consultants, each taking responsibility for particular value work and calling on the others as consultants to improve the degree of accomplishment. Again, one man may be a senior member who organizes and assigns work to the others, or else the three may report to one and the same manager who, in that case, must have a real grasp of value work, its problems, and its opportunities, and must be capable of performing the management function skillfully. Three men often aid one another during the creative phases of their work studies, and having enough in common, they do not readily become frustrated and discouraged.

13-5   *Four or More Consultants*

As the business begins to see the benefit of the activity, additional value consultants will be added. This will provide more penetration in the three identified areas, and besides, additional abilities will be secured. For example, with groups of four persons or more, an individual who has special abilities in teaching and communicating will be very valuable in that education is an important part of the work of value consultants and specialists, as further outlined in Chapter 15.

With four or more individuals assigned to the value work, it will be of definite advantage to have the managerial functions delegated to one of them. He, then, will be the one to:

Set objectives
Establish plans and programs

Provide for proper staffing of the group, augmented by provisions for continued development and growth in the individuals' competence

Motivate appropriate actions

Support each specialist in his work with other segments of the business

Administer work assignments, schedules, compensation, facilities, etc.

13-6   *Structuring*

In setting up a specific value work activity, first attention must be given to how this work fits into the overall organization of the business. The objectives to keep in mind here are:

Accomplishing the value work in the most efficient manner

Securing the fullest support of the effort

Constantly improving the competence in execution

Coming continuously into prompt contact with those vital areas of the business in which the best contributions can be made

As will be even more clearly understood after studying Chapter 15, value work begins in the sales function of the business and continues into, and through, design engineering, manufacturing engineering, purchasing, and production. It is important to note that here sales is at the beginning instead of the end of the series. This is so because it is normally the responsibility of the sales department to determine what products and functions the customer wants. Hence the product cycle starts, in effect, with the sales activity.

Since specific actions must be taken in each of these areas in the development of the product, it follows that certain benefits are secured and certain risks must be accepted if the activity is made to report to any one of them.

Unlike the tax consultant who will clearly report to the accounting manager or the high-temperature-metals consultant who will clearly report to the engineering manager because the respective contributions of these specialists fall within specific functions, the value specialist's point of reporting in the organization is not precisely defined since his contributions go into all areas.

The benefits of having the reporting point in the sales area are that the value consultants, through close contact with sales and marketing-planning people, get to know early in the cycle the functions desired and the approximate price for which the functions will probably sell on the market. Thus they become especially well conditioned to study these functions, evaluate them, establish value alternatives, and help carry on proper value activities throughout the business for maximum contributions to the excellence of the final product. On the other hand, as the reader will readily see, a drawback exists in that the value specialist's work will suffer because these people are so far removed from a depth of knowledge of such things as who the specialty vendors are and where specialized skills are available from vendors.

Similarly, if the reporting point is engineering, the value personnel are likely to be too closely identified with the engineering phase of the product cycle. Although they will bring great benefits by clearly identifying and evaluating functions and by providing value alternatives, experience shows that they tend to become more and more like engineers. Their penetration of knowledge in the vendor field and of specialized products and specialized skills, especially outside the company, becomes arrested to the detriment of their competence as value consultants.

Further, if the materials procurement or the purchasing area is the reporting point, great benefits are derived because the value specialists are in constant and normal contact with the almost unbelievable supply of functional products, functional ideas, and specialized skills that the vendor area offers. However, they are now isolated in some degree from what is going on in sales, engineering, and, to an extent, manufacturing, and much care must be taken to avoid losing a balance in competence and developing skill only in the vendor field.

When the reporting point lies in any of the above segments of the business, it has been found necessary to provide periodic and arbitrary pressure, measurement, emphasis, and motivation to make sure that both a balanced activity and a balanced growth in all necessary areas continue.

Effective long-range organization for proper value is most likely to result when the activity is structured into the area of the business that is accountable for earnings and profits.

The Company President's Quotation

The president, general manager or project manager may be the lowest-level man who must face accountability for value, yet decisions that can either halve or double profits are made without his knowledge.

Engineering management may believe manufacturing is inefficient. Manufacturing management may believe that design is too costly to manufacture. Marketing management may believe that selling work is efficient but product costs are too high.

Lack of value is possibly the only major problem for which accountability below the general manager level is unfixed. By contrast, the responsibility for other aspects of the product are clear-cut:

If performance is not suitable, it's engineering.
If quantities are wrong, it's manufacturing.
If inventories are too high, it's materials.
If customers don't buy, it's marketing.

But, if value is poor, it may be

Poor engineering
Poor manufacturing
Poor purchasing
Poor product planning
Poor management

Poor work results of any business function adversely affect value. As contrasted, poor work results of many work functions do not necessarily adversely affect performance of the product. A product with limited engineering may accomplish its functions reliably. The only sure casualty will be value.

A poorly manufactured product, i.e., one made in slow, inefficient machines, may accomplish its function reliably, and, if enough machines are running, quantities will be correct. The only sure casualty again will be value.

A product including purchased elements "bought" in a clerical fashion may accomplish its function reliably. The only sure casualty will be value.

The direct and full purpose of all value work is to improve earnings and profits by making it possible both to sell adequate volume in competition and to have costs lie sufficiently below the selling price. Therefore, understanding, emphasis, and support flow normally from a management area which is accountable for earnings.

A well-organized business will have definite plans reaching at least five years ahead and will be implementing those plans. Some of these will involve new products or improved performance of existing ones, others will involve expanded manufacturing capacities, and still others will involve increased ability for sales. The first plan is the primary responsibility of the engineering department, the second that of the manufacturing department, the third that of the sales department. To the extent that there are definite plans for identifying and minimizing unnecessary costs to provide increased earnings and definite implementation of these plans by a suitable number of people with direct skills in the area of increasing earnings, this important objective is likely to be secured.

13-7 *Integration of Research and Development with Emphasis on Military Contracts*

Benefits from Available Knowledge Sooner

Most research work is goal oriented. The purpose is either to learn new truths of nature or to combine and extend what is known in a certain manner to accomplish a specific purpose. In either case, there are problems to solve. The disciplined thinking processes of the problem-solving system, described in Chapters 1 and 4 to 6, are being used to accelerate good solutions to problems in which, not cost, but some other parameter is the basic need. As one manager of rather "pure" research put it, "We are quite accustomed to the practice of buying knowledge (through consultants) which we do not have in house, but it was a new approach to us to buy the ability to get more benefit from the knowledge which we have."

Whenever cost of the research work, cost of the end product, or time to achieve a research objective is of prime importance, the procedures of value engineering are especially productive.

A top challenge to everyone engaged in work on products for the military agencies is making research and development work yield products of required performance in sufficient quantities. This is a difficult task, but it is also a fascinating opportunity promising very high rewards.

It is the purpose of the following discussion to help the reader recognize his opportunities to make contributions toward significant advances in dealing with this problem.

Some very pertinent questions here are:

To what extent does the present output of research and development result in products which can be economically manufactured in the large quantities needed for the available expenditure?

Can this extent be drastically improved?

If so, what are some of the steps to take in going about the task?

Will not the research and development period be prolonged?

For the moment, research and development work, which has as its objective the important job of producing lower costs for weapons which already have satisfactory performance capabilities, will be bypassed. Instead, consideration will be given to the greater challenge of applying value engineering techniques to research and development work concerned with providing weapons of new capabilities desirable from new technologies and to doing so in a minimum of time.

Decision Criteria—Performance and Time

The matter of securing better problem solutions depends, first of all, upon providing a clear and exact view of the problems. In research and development work, two factors are commonly given overwhelming and overpowering status and emphasis: performance and time.

Decision Criteria—Performance, Time, and Cost

In order to meet the challenge of providing adequate new weapons, three factors must receive equivalent emphasis: performance, time, and cost (quantity capability).

Understanding the Research and Development Problem

Certain basic factors seem to decree the creation of designs and specifications which are suited to single- or small-lot manufacture. In making test samples in lots of one or two, processes which will produce such samples at minimum time and cost, with minimum tooling, and with minimum search into outside special production technology are quite naturally used. For example, weldments, sand castings, specially made machine parts, and the like are often unquestionably best for quickly constructing experimental models, but they are often decidedly the worst solutions for economical production later.

It is natural that this fact tends to be overlooked by the people whose prime obligation is to get their mental creations into hardware, to test them against natural law, and to press harder into the fringe of human knowledge as quickly as possible. Technical people in this type of activity do not at any time intentionally use a material or process which is more costly than another which they feel confident will accomplish the function as well. As they press their objective of expanding performance capabilities, they turn in each case to the most economical combinations coming within their sphere of knowledge and confidence. And when a design is tested and proven, they feel that it represents, in general, the lowest reasonably achievable cost and that performance results would be retarded if they were to accept the additional design criterion of cost.

Two factors make the problem even more complex.

First, at this stage of the development, with a design proven and tested, time has usually run out, so the only acceptable procedure seems to be to go into the market to buy, however fantastically costly this may be, these "near breadboard" designs with all their complexity, with all the design experience based upon the single or small quantities made during development, and with attendant loss of reliability in operation.

Second, manufacturing engineers delegated the job of producing the design-in quantities are extremely reluctant to change even small details of a proven design for the purpose of making large reductions in cost. Their only safe course is to make it like the proven design and specifications and to perhaps limit suggestions to only relatively minor deviations. This plan is extensively followed.

On the foregoing bases, it appears that to bleed in the skills of quantity manufacture by searching out the best technology, materials, processes, and manufacturing procedures during the research and development stage would prolong development and that by doing so just prior to his first production order, the contractor would subject his organization to delays, uncertainties, and possible losses which it is beyond the realm of reason for him to accept.

Unless a new approach is found, all of the above considerations make it appear that in critical military work it is necessary to continue to force through the research and development on a *time* and *performance* basis, to proceed to buy the first production lot or two, and then, perhaps with established experience and with some of the particular weapons on hand, to go after the job of applying the value techniques in order to provide simpler, more reliable weapons for, say, one-half to one-third the cost.

This will be at a time when drawings and specifications are complete, spare parts lists have been prepared, spare parts are in stock, all of the tooling has been paid for, and instruction books have been written and when, not unlikely, the weapon is obsolete.

The obvious conclusion from this review of the situation is that it behooves government and industry to provide a better answer.

Research and Development Problem Solution

In essence, the problem is how to add work to accomplish the new objective of attaining better cost value and, at the same time, promote the established objectives with respect to performance and time. One good type of organization for this purpose is shown in Figure 13-1. Competence in value technology is injected to work along with other needed competence at all stages of the research and development.

The value engineering techniques being specifically developed out of day-to-day encounters with constant roadblocks represent means for breaking through these roadblocks, whether they be against better costs or better performance. Actually, experience has shown that as much as 25 per cent can be cut from expected research and development time when challenging cost objectives have been added to previous performance-time objectives and when value technology has been brought into play along with the cost objective.

Commonly in research and development work, 95 to 98 per cent of the product falls in areas of known technology, and 90 per cent or more of the product cost is ascribable to the provision of known functions. Often it is desired to provide these functions in the new product in a manner which makes them simpler, more reliable, smaller in size, or lower in weight, i.e., with qualities which are the normal direct result of the use of the value technology.

Better Research and Development Answers Sooner

Illustrations by the score are to be found in military work areas. Study of some of them will provide the reader with guidance in establishing the use of value technology in his research and development activities.

An example, documented by the Navy in a film available for showing to qualified groups, is the Bureau of Ships' application of after-the-fact value engineering to a procurement of 1,000 landing craft. One included item was a 200-gallon gasoline tank which was completely drawn and specified to require very costly metal, much custom welding, and other cost-consuming factors. It was quoted at $520 each, $520,000 for the lot.

As the value technology was applied, the function of reliably containing 200 gallons of gasoline was evaluated at approximately $50. The

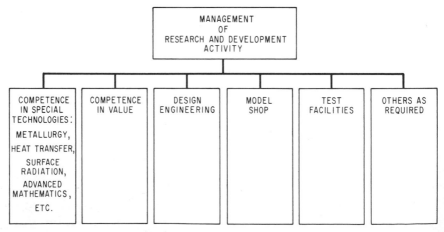

Fig. 13-1   Practical organization for securing both value and performance objectives.

result was that four 55-gallon steel drums, treated for gasoline and other environmental conditions, were used at a cost of $80 each or $80,000 for the whole procurement. (See example, Chapter 3, section 3-2, for a more complete discussion of this case.)

In retrospect, it can be seen that if the value technology had been available and had been used during original research and development on the product, it would have been totally unnecessary to design and draw up the tank and to prepare specifications on the welding, testing, etc. Instead, standard steel drums treated with available environmental finishes would have been specified, probably on one 8 × 11-inch page, with no design work and no drawing preparation. Engineering time would have been conserved and devoted to the acceleration of other research and development work on the craft, with the end result of shortening the time for the total project.

It follows that better solutions are attainable sooner by:

1. Utilizing the value techniques to overcome stoppers against either improved performance objectives or improved cost objectives.

2. Expanding the technological competence addressed to both the performance aspects and the value aspects of the product throughout the development by drawing upon the huge supply of top-grade knowledge, technology, and creativity which exists in diverse government and industrial circles. Organizing for the task of bringing good alternative solutions into clear focus in a minimum of time and with the utilization of best know-how wherever it exists is a part of executing sound value engineering.

In these ways, the research and development process for better means of accomplishing functions becomes substantially one of blending together the twin needs of extending the range of performance on the one hand and lowering the cost on the other. Technology oriented toward the performance field will be utilized to the fullest, while at the same time, equal competence in people trained in the techniques for accomplishing functions at lowest cost will be working hand in hand to produce more reliable, lower cost (higher quantity) research and development work in less time.

It would be gross oversimplification to contend that the suggested change in approach is an easy one to bring about. The conflict with past human concepts, thoughts, behavior, and procedure is too great. However, it seems indisputable that the day is here when the technologies for obtaining very much better cost must take their place beside the technologies for obtaining better performance. Only in this way will each weapon have quantity capabilities as well as performance capabilities.

SUMMARY

The task of value analysis people is to assure that in every part of the business actions are accomplished that will allow the achievement of competitive costs. Often, in normal operation of good business, decisions and actions that seem quite proper are taken in one company area, such as management, sales, or engineering, and do indeed produce no extra costs there. However, they may and often do cause large amounts of unnecessary costs to develop in manufacturing, procurement, or elsewhere.

Experience has been gained with the value analysis group reporting to sales, engineering, manufacturing, procurement, accounting, and general management. Reporting to each has certain advantages, and reporting to the first five has a common disadvantage. In order to operate successfully and assure the business of proper costs of present and new lines alike, work must be done in, with, and for each of the decision-making areas named. The tendency is to develop the habit of doing much more thorough work in the area of reporting, using an important amount of time in so doing, while leaving other business areas without the assistance required to secure assured overall company results.

Often, after need becomes overcritical and assured results are essential, reporting is done to the man accountable in measured terms for earnings. This has proved very effective.

chapter 14

Essential Qualifications and Training for Value Analysts and Engineers

14-1 Qualifications

Successful accomplishment of some types of work requires logic and experience. Examples are the work of the plumber and the electrician. Other types of work require logic and experience supplemented by the development of certain skills. Examples are the work of the surgeon, the typist, the telegraph operator, and others. Then there are types of work whose successful accomplishment depends on experience and extreme creativity. Examples are certain types of art and some types of music production. Probably most other types of work activity fall in the range between these extremes.

As wider experience is gained, the specific qualifications for the relatively new vocation of value specialist or consultant will become more clear, more tangible, and more reliable. The indications of experience to date are that for the successful accomplishment of value work, the requirements are logic, experience, and great creativity, plus the development of certain mental skills such as ability to:

Make rapid and effective searches
Recall

Sort out useful information from what is not useful

Put together new, different, and useful combinations of ideas, materials, products, and processes to accomplish functions

Promptly select those combinations which are most apt to be good ones

All these abilities and skills, it will be seen, have a close tie-in with creativity and thus actually become the means through which creativity operates. It will also be noted that the special information and knowledge of value analysis operate directly to support the development and use of this skill.

14-2   *Traits, Characteristics, and Experience*

The necessary traits, characteristics, and experience, as spelled out and defined below, constitute essential qualifications for men engaged in value work.

Knowledge

For product work, a practical understanding of the properties of materials and their uses and of manufacturing processes, their potentialities, and their limitations is needed. For service work, the equivalent knowledge in that field is necessary.

Imagination

A good practical creative imagination commonly includes ability to retain extensive amounts of information concerning ideas for approaches and solutions to product problems, types of materials, properties of materials, processes, costs, and so forth, all arranged in a suitable order so that differing combinations may be creatively brought together and examined for applicability to problems at hand.

High Degree of Initiative

In value work, there are no definite beginning and ending points, and specific instructions on how and where to proceed are usually nonexistent. Further, this type of work is not well enough comprehended by general management for a rate at which it should be accomplished to be spelled out. For these reasons, it is essential that men in value work have a high degree of initiative, which must include what might be called self-drive, so that work activities will be started and carried through to completion with little if any supervision.

Self-organization

Initiative and drive are not enough; work must be effectively organized. Because of the lack of precedent and the lack of knowledge of organization for value work, conventional management supervision provides no experience for effectively instituting and executing the work. Therefore, the individual doing the work requires the ability to organize his activity effectively, as well as enough initiative to carry it out.

Personality

The work requires a mature, stable personality which is not easily discouraged. The entire field of activity in value work comes within the area of change. The amount of opposition to change usually prevailing cannot be conceived by anyone who has not attempted to operate in this area. The individual doing value work will be confronted with negative attitudes and delays of all sorts, with belittlement, and even with ridicule. The basic nature of anything new and the inherent attitude of the people with whom he will be dealing decree this. As Charles Kettering said, "The consensus of any group of people concerning something new in their field is always wrong." Or, as Thomas Edison said in 1926, "It requires about seven years for the average individual to accept a new proven solution to a problem." Because of this very exhausting aspect of value work, it is strongly recommended that it be performed by two or more persons working together. Each can then have an emotional environment of support, at least part of the time, which helps him feel that his work is a satisfactory and worthwhile endeavor.

Cooperative Attitude

A desire to work with others and a general knowledge of how to do it are other requirements, since the work is largely an endeavor based on working with others. It begins with acquiring an understanding of the job and proceeds by developing information which is often not available in ready form but which must be obtained if good value alternatives are to be produced. Knowledge concerning desired functions and methods for accomplishing them must be collected. Significant information must be communicated to competent commercial and technical people, and their wholehearted support (often with quotations) must be enlisted in expanding the area of knowledge in the direction of their skills through the preparation of value alternatives. In many instances, the work includes the difficult assignment of getting information without giving offense.

Experience

All indications to date suggest that some five years of industrial experience in engineering, in manufacturing, or in special procurement dealing with particular specifications, opportunities, arrangements, and negotiations between buyer and seller (or equivalent experience) is essential. It seems also that actual experience in working with the normal situations that affect the development of value alternatives is required. These situations involve decisions between varying ways of accomplishing a function, between varying sources of supply, between differing systems of make versus buy, etc. Without experience along this line, there is a lack of background for efficient and effective search of possible combinations and for presentation of new and good value alternatives.

Belief in the Importance of Value

Starting with certain native inclinations and modified by childhood and business experience, any person develops interest in certain lines and disinterest in others. In essentially all cases, human beings are interested in food, although in some cases of unusually unfortunate environments, even loss of interest in food is developed by people. Some individuals are interested in flying, while others vow that they will resist it to the death. Similarly, some people develop an interest in providing new products through the development of new functions which their ingenuity can translate into a practical product. Other individuals develop an interest in making products more economical so that distribution may be widened with resultant benefits, not only to the company involved in selling the products, but to mankind in general, through more universal use. At the present stage of experience with value work, it appears that there exist marked degrees of difference in the beliefs of various individuals in the importance of low cost—or its equivalent, high value—in the general sense. Experience has shown that men who have strong belief in the importance of value are much more likely to be sufficiently motivated to develop the initiative, self-drive, and enthusiasm necessary to accomplish their work well. Such strong belief also seems to be an important factor in creating emotional stability in this very frustrating type of work. Hence the conclusion that "belief in the importance of value" is a significant trait.

An Understanding of the Management and Decision Process

It is also important to have a reasonable comprehension of the management and decision process. A host of good books provide this knowledge in depth. Management processes are not always optimum. For years, up to and including the present, decisions have not always been the best ones, but they are very real and very "controlling." Removing unnecessary costs often means patient, persistent, effective work for improvement in these areas.

14-3   Training

Five Essentials of Training

With the following training essentials, men will be prepared with understanding, with procedures and the experience of using them in disciplined thinking and acting, and with the confidence that grows only from a self-done task.

1. It must allow and cause each trainee to develop his own disciplined thinking.

2. It must provide understanding of reasons for excess costs.

3. It must provide disciplined procedures for identification and removal of unnecessary costs.

4. It must provide some new knowledge and much technique to be used in determining what knowledge to get, how to get it, and how to use it.

5. It must cause and allow each man to actually use the system and to secure better results than he thought he could.

How Much Training?

One week of training followed by six months of good on-the-job value work (preferably with other trained and experienced men), another week of training of a more advanced nature, often including the teaching of beginners), and then six months of additional value work are good.

A general conclusion is that with this year of alternating between on-the-job work and periods of training, men who have the proper characteristics, qualifications, and traits for the type of work involved can acquire a sufficient degree of knowledge and skill to be considered competent to start on a career of work as value consultants.

It is significant to understand that training is mandatory because value work is based on the use of different sets of techniques in a special way and on the use of special knowledge. Without suitable training, the quality of the value work will degrade the profession for those competent qualified people who can accomplish results of the highest order.

An Effective 40-hour Training Seminar

Sessions can run continuously for a week or can be spaced.

Hours 1 to 4:	*Minutes*
Why the training?	15
What are we trying to do?	15
What is the value analysis and engineering system?	30
Why is the value analysis and engineering system needed?	30
Case studies	60
The vitalness of the right complete system	30
What must the system do?	30
Hours 5 to 8:	
All cost is for function	30
Case study	30
Identify, classify, and name the functions	30
Project work—get started, understand it	30
Identify, classify, name functions of project	90
Hours 9 to 12:	
Evaluate the function	30
Case study	30
Evaluate the functions of the project	60
Problem setting—function grouping and dividing	30
Case study	30
Problem setting on the project	30
Hours 13 to 16:	
Specific knowledge	30
Problem setting on the project	60
Problem solving—job plan	60
Project work—"What are we trying to do?"	15
"Information" step on project	45
Hours 17 to 20:	
Problem solving—job plan continued	60
Case study	30
Finish "information" step and get into "analysis" step of project	60
Decide and precisely define what problems are to be solved	30
Case study	30
Hours 21 to 24:	
Specialized knowledge	30
Group creativity	30
Creativity on project problems	60
More "information, analysis, and creativity" on project problems	60
Case study	30

Hours 25 to 28:
    Specialized knowledge   30
    "Judgment" step of job plan   30
    Project work—information, analysis, creative, judgment 120
    "Development" step   30

Hours 29 to 32:
    Specialized knowledge   30
    "Decision environment"   60
    Case studies   30
    Project work   90

Hours 33 to 36:
    Using the system to solve the hard ones   30
    Overcoming roadblocks   30
    Finish project work—get into shape for reporting 120
    Examples of good reporting form   15
    Questions and answers on reporting   15

Hours 37 to 40:
    Finalize results and suggestions and prepare charts, reports, presentations 120
    Present reports   60
    Discussion   30

SUMMARY

Value analysis is a system for use when better than normal results are needed. It is readily understandable that before an individual can be expected to achieve better than normal results, he needs the experience that enables him to produce normal results under the usual conditions. Five years or more of experience dealing with product or service factors of similar types are usually essential.

Broad knowledge in the field, a good practical creative imagination, a high degree of initiative, the habit of good self-organization, a mature personality, a very cooperative attitude, a belief in and "feeling for" the importance of low costs, and an understanding of the management decision process—all are essential for the optimum value analysis person.

An initial training period of 40 hours, of which about half is actual work, using the system, starts the use of the techniques. Six months of experience followed by another period of training usually results in enough familiarity with the system so that the individual can develop skill in value analysis.

chapter 15

Work Content
for the Value Analyst,
Engineer, and Consultant

In this chapter, as throughout the book, the names value analyst, special-ist, engineer, and consultant are considered synonymous. Not unlikely, as the profession grows, differentiated meanings will develop for these four terms.

The principal work content falls into four basic classes:

Integration
Value appraisal and product evaluation
Value consultation
Value training

A suitable proportion of work from each of these classes must be achieved in each of the product-cycle stages, beginning in sales and progressing through engineering, manufacturing engineering, purchas-ing, and production.

15-1 Indoctrination of Management

Allied to the training of the "doers," along the lines discussed in the following paragraphs, is the matter of indoctrinating management. A full comprehension by management at all levels of the aims and workings of value analysis is a prerequisite to the attainment of the fullest measure of benefit from coordinated value activity. It falls within the scope of the work content of the value consultant to arrange and conduct indoctrination sessions as the conditions may warrant. Well-proportioned attention to this phase of cultivation invariably brings substantial "payoff" both to the company and to the individual. Management understanding, confidence, and active support are essential to high achievement.

15-2 *Integration*

It is normal human nature to discredit that which we do not understand. Thus, if a new system appears in the industrial or other business setup, it will be subject to suspicion, doubt, discredit, and disfavor by all who do not understand it. It is self-evident, therefore, that what comes first is to integrate the work into the activities of every individual in the work area. Each person must know what the work of this new activity is; how it will be done; how it will affect him; in what respects it will make his work more difficult or simpler; what benefits that he has been getting he will now have to divide with value personnel; that this activity is not the boss's "pet" brought in under disguise for a period of time and later to be changed into something that will affect him badly.

The responsibility for answering all these questions before they have had time to arise to any significant extent becomes the first part of the work content of newly established value consultants.

Experience proves that it is a safe rule to devote as much as half of the entire resources for a period of many months to correctly accomplish this part of the work. Obviously, as understanding grows, the time devoted to it diminishes. However, with new situations continually developing and new people often coming in, care must be taken not to overlook this part of the work even in a going operation. It must be clearly understood that the purpose of the value consultants is to assist each individual who makes decisions affecting value to have at hand more information at the time of decision making so that he will make better decisions. Unless this is well known and unless working understandings are developed which include all of the relations, the results of the value activity will be greatly diminished.

15-3 *Value Appraisal and Product or Service Evaluation*

This is after-the-fact value work. It consists in starting with the product, or process, in its present form, studying its functions intensely, applying the value analysis techniques and special knowledge, and producing improved value alternatives which are then presented, in suitable form, to the decision-making people involved. This is probably the part of the activity which is best known and which is most apt to be overdone.

It is very important to periodically provide a value appraisal for typical products and services of a particular area. This not only brings possibilities for greatly improved value of the specific item but also serves as a measurement of the degree of value work which is being effectuated on other, unstudied products. Results in this class of value analysis activity are limited in that it represents after-the-fact work. Often the outcome is embarrassing to the people who had to make operating decisions at an earlier stage, perhaps when they had important performance problems to solve and were possibly short of time and help. Work in this area brings much antagonism unless it is handled with extreme care. Besides, changes here are more costly and often more slowly made because drawings have been made, instruction books have been printed, replacement parts have been standardized, etc.

Nevertheless, sight must not be lost of the tremendous benefit to increased earnings which may come from doing a proper amount of work in this direction. As one engineering manager said, "When a product is designed, the entire field is at risk, and lacking time to make minute studies of every detail, all decisions must be made on the safe side even though it is well known that some of them are locking into the product considerable excess cost." After the product is in operation and has proved itself, work can then proceed on studying these various phases of the product one at a time. Unnecessary cost should be identified and should be made subject to removal as promptly as practicable.

Experience has shown that much more satisfactory results are accomplished if value consultants study products of this class on the invitation of whichever department—sales, engineering, manufacturing, or purchasing—is involved in the later decision making. When thus invited in, their findings are sought and do not come as an embarrassment to the original decision makers.

15-4   *Value Consultation*

It is, of course, normally very much more desirable, and in actuality very practical, to provide value alternatives before the fact. This results from consultation, a direct parallel to the work performed by the tax consultant. Sales, engineering, manufacturing, or other people, faced with a product to design and produce or with a manufacturing system to develop or with a function to evaluate, quite naturally invite value consultants to make their contributions.

The process starts, then, by learning thoroughly the functions needed.

This can be done almost as well from a drawing or specification as from a model. Next the consultants proceed to apply the value analysis techniques and special knowledge to establish the values of these functions and provide tangible information on value alternatives. The information thus derived is used by the decision makers in their original decisions so that the product will have the intended performance or features and will offer a better degree of value as well. As value people have worked successfully along this line in an operation, they have been accepted, and more and more of their time has been requested for before-the-fact consultation work.

15-5   *Value Training*

An important segment of the work content lies in constantly training substantially all individuals in the business to recognize and use certain of the value analysis concepts and techniques which they need and can take in stride in their daily work. In some cases, it is also desirable to provide training which will provide for replacements in the full-time professional value work.

Experience has proved that many of the value analysis techniques are useful not only for the purpose of helping sales, engineering, manufacturing, and purchasing people to secure better value while they execute their other essential assignments, but also, in many cases, for enabling these people to better accomplish their basic assignments.

The value analysis techniques are means for recognizing what is basic in the product or service, i.e., what the required functions are. They are also means for efficiently developing alternative answers which often will provide better quality, increased performance, lighter weight, improved appearance, and other added values to the product in addition to lower cost.

As a consequence, it is obviously desirable to establish courses to provide basic value analysis training to substantially all design engineers, draftsmen, manufacturing engineers, methods experts, production leaders, materials specialists, buyers, and others whose decisions affect the value of the product.

From practice it has appeared that training of people throughout the business environment will produce about half of the gain which can be accomplished by the effective use of the value analysis techniques and special knowledge. These people then take the work in stride, and it improves their value on the job. It also improves their yield to the company as well as their own job satisfaction. It is therefore important that value consultants recognize this area of responsibility and opportunity and effectively organize appropriate training.

As to the amount of training, this will vary with the individual, the individual's work, and the prevailing situation. Between forty and eighty hours of combined training and "do-it" work for each of these people is likely to result in substantial accomplishment. One afternoon of training each week for ten to twenty weeks is a good plan.

The training should consist of indoctrination in the value analysis techniques and in the special knowledge, concurrent with the study of actual products from an area which provides opportunity for the application of the techniques. It will include suitable contact with experts from outside the specific area whose knowledge penetration is of vital concern to the trainees in providing better answers to the projects under study. It will also include dealing with representatives of vendors of available specialty functional products to make the learners realize that large numbers of functions can be readily accomplished by using what already exists on the market, usually at the most economical cost.

It is apparent that when others in the business environment have had this basic training the task of integration is practically completed. In consequence, the consultants will be called upon to make their contribution to value at the right time, before decisions are made, and much more challenging value objectives for the business can be reached in a straightforward manner.

15-6   *Application to Various Business Activities*

Sales

INTEGRATION: Make sure that each salesman, each sales engineer, and each development engineer working in sales is fully advised on what the value consultant's work is and how he will work with them.

VALUE APPRAISAL AND PRODUCT EVALUATION: The first indication that a product has become comparatively overpriced often comes from experiences in the sales department. When this happens, the sales people are in a position either to turn the product over to the value consultants for value study and appraisal or to initiate action which will result in this being done by the design engineers or by other proper decision-making personnel.

CONSULTATION: With reference to both new products and existing products, sales people are directly oriented toward providing the desired function to their customers at competitive prices. On the invitation of sales people, the value consultant proceeds to study the functions involved. He applies the value analysis techniques to develop values for the functions, value alternatives, and alternative courses so that the sales people may make, or promote, decisions which will meet their objectives.

VALUE TRAINING: In order that sales people may bring the benefits of many of the value techniques into their daily work, a liberal number of them need value training. They will be benefited by increased abilities to identify the functions which the customers really want and to help provide the customer with what he really wants at the most reasonable cost. They will recognize these benefits and will want to be included in suitable value training programs.

Engineering

INTEGRATION: The availability of value consultants in a business lengthens the reach of all engineers as far as value is concerned. Before this contribution can be made, engineering people must know that the value consultant, starting out with the functions desired, will be capable of developing tangible value alternatives, thus saving them time and aiding them in their decisions. They must also know in what respects the value consultant needs their assistance in order to bring benefit to the common enterprise.

VALUE APPRAISAL: The engineering activity is faced with continual demands for lower costs of existing products. Alerted to the effectiveness of the value analysis techniques as used by the value consultant, the engineering people will invite the consultants to study the existing work and provide practical value alternatives for their decision. The same thing occurs in many instances when quality problems arise; the value consultant then will seek to provide value alternatives from which one may be chosen to yield a lower cost and also to eliminate the quality problem.

VALUE CONSULTATION: Perhaps one of the greatest opportunities for contribution by the value consultant comes when he is invited by the design engineers to acquire an understanding of their new products, to study the functions which are to be designed into them, and to present value alternatives for engineering decision. On new products, design engineers often have other objectives, besides function, which can be promoted by the use of the value techniques. Objectives such as smaller size, lighter weight, increased reliability, and better appearance are automatically furthered as the value consultant develops alternatives for reliably accomplishing the function. From these alternatives, the engineer can then choose the one which most nearly achieves his major objectives.

EDUCATION: Engineers, designers, and draftsmen—in fact all personnel in an engineering department—are busy at the basic tasks of determining the best ways to accomplish functions and of suitably drawing up the solutions and specifying them. Day-to-day use of some of the value analysis techniques will allow them to attain a much higher degree of value in their work, and in addition, it will often help them to reach other objectives more efficiently and economically. An effective training program for these people is of great significance.

Manufacturing

INTEGRATION: Basically, all manufacturing people are engaged in some part of the activity of endeavoring to manufacture and ship reliable high-grade products economically. This involves the choice of machines and processes, the development of methods, and the planning of patterns by which manufacturing operations will be performed and manufacturing costs will be expended on the product. Whether the product will be made or purchased is of great significance to them. Likewise, the alternative methods of purchasing materials at various stages of completion and the economies and costs involved are of great interest and must affect their decision making when high value is a prime objective. It is thus apparent that the manufacturing people must be at once advised of the work which is to be done by the value consultant and of the method he will use in doing it. They will also need to learn how their particular activity integrates with the consultant's activity and what responsibilities and opportunities they have in making his value work effective. Finally, they will want to know when to call on the value consultant for information that he can prepare for them for better decision making.

VALUE APPRAISAL AND PRODUCT EVALUATION: Normally, little of this type of work is done for manufacturing people, although in many cases, they are manufacturing functional components in certain ways and will request value studies to determine alternative means by which they may provide all functions desired by the engineers and still simplify their own manufacturing.

The reader must be cautioned here to note that it is not intended that value consultants should know more about manufacturing than the manufacturing people. They do not act as consultants to the manufacturing people on manufacturing methods or processes unless these are of such a highly specialized nature that the value consultant is in a better position than others in the organization to determine the sources of the required specialized knowledge.

CONSULTATION: A part of the stock in trade of the value consultant is knowledge of where to turn to find specialized knowledge of great depth. Therefore, he attends special exhibits and special shows where he can learn of the sources of such knowledge. From these sources, he will be able to derive specialized manufacturing knowledge or functional product knowledge of special interest in manufacturing considerations. For that reason, manufacturing people will, on occasion, call on the consultant for studies and suggestions.

VALUE TRAINING: It is no doubt now readily understood that men in manufacturing who are making decisions on processes, shapes, exact arrangements, and similar factors which will commit costs and which are needed to provide the functions expected by the engineers can derive large benefits from having a basic understanding of the use of the value analysis techniques. Accordingly, such men should be included in suitable training programs.

Purchasing

INTEGRATION: An important part of the contribution of the value consultant is to bring into the sales, engineering, and manufacturing areas new information concerning specialty functional products and specialized skills which vendors can provide if they are searched out and found at the right times. It is clear that unless purchasing people understand the exact nature of the work of the value consultant they will look askance at his contact with vendors and will rightly fear complications in connection with future purchases. Establishment of complete understanding and integration on the basis of practical working relationships is a vital first step.

VALUE APPRAISAL AND PRODUCT EVALUATION: Purchasing people often buy functional products or material which is made into functional products. They are at the point of transfer of the company's cash, and they are, by tradition, very much concerned about protecting this cash and bringing equivalent value to the company. Experience has shown that they continually ask for and want product evaluation work, the results of which may be intended to influence decisions made by the home-plant engineers or specification writers, in the vendor's plants, or by themselves. Good product evaluation work brings great benefits to purchasing people. Caution should be taken, of course, that when the decisions to be made by purchasing involve engineering, manufacturing, or sales people, these individuals are brought into the picture early so that they will have the same desire to have the product evaluation made. Only in this manner is embarrassment avoided and results accelerated. As for items which will have a bearing on decisions to be made by the vendors and vendors' technical people, each is a case unto itself. Competent purchasing people, faced with alternatives involving vendors' decisions, normally know how to carry out negotiations advantageous to both the buyer and the seller.

CONSULTATION: In relation to the purchasing activity, product evaluation and consultation become substantially one and the same activity because purchasing will call in assistance at any rate before they make the purchases.

VALUE TRAINING: It has been found that when buyers are made acquainted with the techniques and with the use of the techniques and the special knowledge several important results occur. First, buyers develop the practice of thinking in terms of buying a function or functions, and their minds are directed into very profitable channels in a high percentage of cases. Second, they recognize the high value to the company derivable from specialized vendors to whom they have ready access. They become more willing to make searches. They learn how to search better for any type of specialized competence which will make contributions to the company's products. They learn also the great importance of providing for proper communication between the company's technical people and the vendor's technical people. They become catalysts to bring the right competence outside the company into immediate contact with the proper competence within the company. Increased benefits result for both performance programs and value programs.

SUMMARY

The indoctrination, both original and continuing, of management is the first essential work. Since the system is new, they do not understand what it is, how it works, how others are affected, what results are to be expected, or how they should manage it.

The essential work content of the operating value analysts is fourfold:

1. *Integration.* Making sure that everyone in the "environment" knows, in general, what it is, what it proposes to do, how it is to be done, how it affects them, how it can assist them to reach higher accomplishment in their work, and what other effect it will or will not have on them.

2. *Value appraisal and product or service evaluation.* Examining the existing product or service, using the system to remove costs and update the product or service.

3. *Value consultation.* Assisting others who are in the process of creating a new product or service.

4. *Value analysis technique and system training.* Conducting a suitable number of appropriate courses for others so that the earnings competence of their company will constantly increase or, if they are a service, the functions secured per dollar will constantly and permanently increase.

chapter 16

Motivation, Measurement, and Tests

16-1   Motivation

Achievement of significant objectives in any activity requires motivation in some form or another. What constitutes appropriate motivation in the area of substantially decreased cost, and thus increased value, will be discussed next.

Motivation will be considered in four categories:

The business
Managers
Value consultants and others using value analysis techniques
Decision makers

The Business

No business has sufficient competent personnel to pursue all desirable objectives with high emphasis. The general situation in business may be likened to that faced by a baseball team, which has only nine men to cover the entire field. Depending on the score, the pitcher, the batter, and the phase of the game, these men will be placed somewhat differently and will play under instructions to put emphasis on particular activities. Much the same occurs in business. The organization must possess an appropriate amount of competence, or else it will fail. But the men who make up this competence must vary their activities to meet the greatest pressures and thus produce results in those areas in which action is most needed. To motivate a business to organize for high value content in its products, a "force of necessity" is normally required. It must be vital to the business to accomplish value objectives in addition to performance objectives, shipment objectives, and other goals.

A corresponding force is often created by a forward-planning management which, when it sees a threatening situation developing, proceeds to generate emphasis for effective actions to prepare the business to meet the situation when, perhaps years hence, the time arrives.

In the absence of either of these two forces, motivation is usually inadequate to cause steps to be taken to establish and execute a program which will provide for leadership in value.

Managers

Experience has shown that motivation in four forms provides satisfactory results.

NECESSITY: This may be the necessity imposed by the immediate situation or the necessity created by forward planning by the top management of a business. Either of these forces makes it vital to efficiently identify unnecessary costs, and they dispel all doubt about the importance to the business of assigning sufficient resources to accomplish significant results in the area of value.

BOSS PRESSURE: This force must, of necessity, be clearly promoted by the managers' superiors so that there can be no question in managers' minds as to whether they should strive for significant progress in the value area or merely continue to give attention to the traditional areas to which they have been accustomed. Each manager must know that, to an important extent, he will be measured and appraised according to his accomplishment, i.e., the accomplishment of the group he manages, in this activity.

MINIMUM-PERSONAL-LOSS ENVIRONMENT: The creation of an environment for *minimum personal loss* is a third form of motivating force. Taking different actions in order to achieve a very much improved degree of value means doing things differently and hence brings about the ever-present risk of personal loss. To the extent that the chances of personal loss due to value action are not eliminated from the manager-boss relationship and the manager environment, important negative motivation exists. It is therefore imperative, in creating a maximum of positive motivation, to give much attention to reducing the personal-loss factor.

COMPANY RECOGNITION OF ACCOMPLISHMENTS: Managers have traditionally been recognized for their accomplishments in areas other than that of product value. They need to be assured that, as a reward for their efforts and for the risks they take in the value area, they will receive appropriate recognition for accomplishments.

Value Consultants and Others Using Value Analysis Techniques

In developing reasonable motivation for people who are doing value work, five important methods should be kept in mind.

EMPHASIS: Enough emphasis must be placed by management on the importance of high-grade value work so that the endeavor and the time of the men engaged in it are not constantly encroached upon by ever-demanding performance problems, delivery problems, etc. That management does indeed place as much emphasis on good value as on these other, more short-range factors in the business needs underscoring.

SUPPORT: Good value work is not accomplished without a great amount of "doing." This means men going places, studying new things, encountering problems, and being misunderstood by their coworkers in other company activities. The extent to which their new type of work gets support from management in these situations adds a very significant plus or minus factor to the motivation of the "doers."

STATUS: Anyone engaged in value work requires a status corresponding to that of others in the organization whose work is better known and hence receive more consideration from management. The man must be able to go home at the end of the day and say proudly, and with conviction, "I am in the value activity." Again, the degree to which management provides appropriate status for the people doing this new type of work accounts for a significant plus or minus factor in motivation.

FAIR MEASUREMENT: Fair methods of measurement of performance must be established. Traditional methods of measurement, which do not fit but which are familiar to others in the environment, must not be improperly used. If the man does a good job in his work of identifying unnecessary cost, will managers say, "Good work, Joe"? Or, if he does a poor job, will the managers be able to say, "I think you can do better, Joe"? Fair effective measurement is a strong motivator.

RECOGNITION: Proper and appropriate recognition before their peers in relation to the effectiveness of the work of value consultants becomes a vital plus factor in motivation.

Decision Makers

Each decision maker has specific measured responsibilities; for instance, he may sell the product, design the product, manufacture certain quantities of specification-grade product, provide metered quantities of materials of appropriate grade to the factory, or reach certain inventory-investment objectives.

EMPHASIS: In all cases, emphasis is very real and measurement is very direct. If these people are to invest important segments of their time in working out value alternatives, "debugging" them, testing them, and taking the necessary chances which always come with any change, they must interpret the emphasis on these tasks to mean that accomplishment therein is as important a part of their work as the measured part.

MINIMUM-PERSONAL-LOSS ENVIRONMENT: The reader was alerted in an earlier chapter to the importance of eliminating the personal-loss factor if decisions to produce better value are to be expected. Experience would indicate that the motivation to produce effective results in the improvement of value by decision makers is affected by extremely large plus or minus factors according to the effectiveness with which management handles this phase.

MEASUREMENT OF ACTION AND LACK OF ACTION: Nearly every phase of human nature promotes a negative decision on the part of the decision maker. If the value alternative can be rather promptly ruled out on plausible grounds, the decision maker is then at liberty to return to his major measured field of activity without having suffered personal loss. To provide reasonable motivation for action, measurements are needed which will clearly highlight lack of action. As soon as a fair and supportable measurement of lack of action is provided and accepted, the personal-loss factor is increased by negative rather than positive actions and significant increases in motivation result.

UNDERSTANDING OF FAILURE: In normal activity, success does not result 100 per cent of the time. In some of the projects of studying value alternatives, making models, testing, developing new vendors, and proving new processes, results will be found to be negative. Meanwhile, an important amount of time and of money may have been spent upon the project. It is never known before this work is done whether the result will be an important accomplishment or not. It is important, therefore, that management clearly show itself ready to stand back of, support, and understand the effort when it judges alternatives that had a fair trial but did not work out.

RECOGNITION OF SUCCESS: The earnings position of the company will be greatly benefited from time to time by specific activities in the area of value improvement. Important motivation will be provided and future results will be greatly enhanced if clear recognition of successes is given.

16-2   *Measurement*

Measurement of Organizations

The following Value Analysis Organization Study and Measurement Guide illustrates a good approach to the important problem of measuring organizations. It is meant not only to cover measurement questions but also to contain some of the significant answers for the indoctrination of management people who are performing the study and measurement.

> VALUE ANALYSIS ORGANIZATION STUDY AND MEASUREMENT GUIDE
> (*Mark on scale of 5, 4, 3, 2, 1: 5 indicates highest merit, 1 lowest*)

Areas of study:
1. How well is value analysis understood?
2. How well is the value analysis organization suited to the business involved?
3. How correctly is the value analysis operation set up?
4. How effectively are the value analysts operating?
5. Do miscellaneous factors aid the value analysis operation?

1. *How Well Is Value Analysis Understood?*

How well is it understood by:
Top management?
Intermediate management?
Engineers?
Manufacturing and methods staffs?
Buyers?
Sales people?
Others?

> Value analysis is a creative study of every item of cost in every service or part or material. It considers other possible materials, newer processes, abilities of specialized suppliers, and possibilities for engineering reevaluation. It focuses engineering, manufacturing, and purchasing attention on one objective—equivalent performance for lower cost.

Is value analysis well understood to comprise special techniques, a special system, and special knowledge, not to be just a substitute for cost reduction, by:
Management?
Engineers?
Manufacturing people?

> It is not a substitute for present engineering, manufacturing, and purchasing cost-reduction work; it is a supplement. It improves the effectiveness of the work being done in those areas and, in addition, fills a blind spot. It is accomplished by carefully selected, trained full-time specialists using established techniques and following an established plan which results in eliminating all types of

unnecessary costs not normally identified and eliminated by other methods.

2. *How Well Is the Value Analysis Organization Suited to the Business Involved?*

Does it include the proper number of specialists?

Do they work full time?

> Normally, value analysis specialists return from $10 to $25 to the manager for each dollar they cost.

How well are value analysts qualified by ability, experience, and training?

Do they have (rate each man and average):

a. Engineering or methods and planning experience supported by a general understanding of the properties of materials and their uses?

b. A good creative imagination?

c. Enough initiative, self-organization, and self-drive to start and complete their projects with little if any supervision?

d. A feeling of the importance of value?

e. A mature, stable personality not easily discouraged?

f. The desire to work and deal with others and general knowledge of how to do it?

Have they had sufficient instruction in value analysis techniques?

How well has each learned:

a. To develop the *complete* facts?

b. To use a businessman's judgment?

c. To think and act creatively?

d. To use and bring in help from others?

e. To provide himself with special information?

How well is the value ability developed in each man?

> As other skills are developed, we believe value ability can be developed. Value analysis training aims at that objective. Experience and proper action further develop it.

3. *How Correctly Is the Value Analysis Operation Set Up?*

Do the analysts work individually with one man responsible for one project, instead of by committees?

Do they avoid all discussions or meetings involving more than a total of three at the table at one time?

> Value analysis is not committee work. It is conducted by one man intensively following a project; he may discuss particular phases with others, one or two at a time at most.

Are the value analysts expected to constantly crystallize their suggestions in the value analysis suggestion sheets?

Are the suggestion sheets clear, concise, definite, and tangible, and are they drawn in executive language?

If the value analysts report to materials management, have they established a working relationship based on 100 per cent understanding, confidence, and cooperation with engineering and manufacturing?

If they report to engineering or to manufacturing engineering, have they established a working relationship based on 100 per cent understanding, confidence, and cooperation with the purchasing department and every buyer in it?

Do they report high enough in the organization for their critical problems to be immediately known by sufficiently high authority to at once receive effective action?

To what extent is the business getting a fresh look into each job? (Men with years of experience in the area, who have gone over the same work several times, may be channeled in their thinking.)

> Surprisingly, men who have long worked on a project are often the least capable of eliminating further large quantities of unnecessary cost by value analysis techniques. To eliminate large quantities of unnecessary cost, such men should usually be assigned other work and "new blood" brought into the job.

4. *How Effectively Are the Value Analysts Operating?*

How effectively have the value analysts developed "function" thinking? Is all of their thought on function?

> Value analysts relate costs to the function or service or operation purchased by that cost. They question each specific item of cost to determine what function it really buys. For example: What is it? What does it cost per year? What does it do? What else would do the job and what would that cost? Then, each dollar of cost which does not clearly buy definite function is strongly questioned. Function is simply defined as something that makes the product work better or sell better.

Do they actually get *all* of the available facts before starting work?

Drawings and specifications that are available

Planning cards when they exist

All costs when they exist

Samples of parts when they exist

Assembly in which parts go when such information exists

When starting a job, do they always learn the basic engineering?

Do they always learn the basic manufacturing?

Have they learned to listen and to make absolutely no suggestions at this stage?

Do they avoid going back to engineering and others and making incomplete suggestions?

Are they using the value analysis job plan in all its steps?

Mind setting (Exactly what are we trying to do?)

Information

Analysis

Creativity

Judgment

Development planning

> Value analysis work follows the value analysis job plan in which the analyst intensively seeks out, adapts, evaluates, and applies.

Do the value analysts "blast" in attempting to initiate long-term gain or large-percentage gain of at least 50 to 90 per cent cost reduction in fields of:

Administration?
Engineering?
Manufacturing methods?
Purchasing?

Do they also strive for reductions of 50 per cent down to 10 per cent?
Value analysts both blast and refine. A portion of their time is invested in searching for means of accomplishing the same job for one-tenth or one-fifth or one-half of the cost. The remainder of their study consists of effort to refine, with reductions more nearly in the area of 40, 30, or 20 per cent. It is often easier to remove 50 per cent of the cost than 10 per cent.

Does the managers' representative promptly refer proposals to the proper managers for their assignment?

Do about 80 per cent of suggestions develop into substantial savings?

Do the analysts get right out into the vendors' plants to learn?

Does this activity take analysts out into other plants about one day on the average in each two weeks?

Have any deterring factors which would retard results been avoided, such as the necessity to ask permission of someone who does not understand the details of the need?

Do the analysts use all means of immediate and effective action such as:

Immediate personal contact through trips or planned conferences?
Telephone?
Telegraph?

In searching for methods of value improvement, does the analyst have free reign to initiate studies which take him into the area of:

Administration?
Engineering?
Manufacturing?
Make-it or buy-it?
Proper ordering quantities?
Better inventory control?
All others?
All have a bearing on value. The analyst is free to develop facts in any and all areas.

Does management select about half of the analyst's projects?

Do the value analysts normally select about half of their own projects?
Value analysts should have the initiative to ferret out and identify cases of poor value. They accordingly select 50 per cent of their own jobs and normally handle, in the remainder of their time, jobs referred to them by management. An important reason for this is that, unless they do, shocking cases of poor value which could be readily corrected continue year after year because management in the particular area involved happens to be overlooking them.

Do value analysts regularly consult others—specialists in engineering, in methods, in procurement—in preplanned interviews of one or two hours' duration?

Do the managers assign the suggestion sheets to their appropriate subordinates, supervise them, and secure progress reports on them exactly as they do with other job assignments?

> It is recognized that the managers will supervise their own men and that the men will report back *only* to their own bosses on the status of accomplishment or lack of it.

Is it well understood that the value analysts make no decisions?

> Value analysts make no decisions but develop facts for management decisions; accordingly, while they are a large factor in such matters as "make-it or buy-it," they develop the facts and management decides.

Are the men provided with suitable physical and clerical assistance so that they can invest their time effectively at their highest potential?

> Adequate and suitable space for interviews, for study, etc.
> Clerical assistance
> Stenographic assistance

5. *Do Miscellaneous Factors Aid the Value Analysis Operation?*

Are all buyers trained in the value analysis techniques that pertain to buying?

Have the value analysts arranged for equipping themselves with the specific information they will constantly need to do their job well?

Has the value analysis group assumed a position of real leadership in the department by constantly increasing the knowledge, understanding, and use of value skills through regularly planned courses or study groups?

Are the habits and attitudes which allow significant value improvement in the department progressively improving?

> In management
> In engineering
> In manufacturing methods
> In purchasing
>> Value analysis requires serious thought, hard study, and immediate action. In cases of doubt, it is necessary to err on the side of doing something rather than on the side of stable conservatism. Value analysis performs as an engineering and a manufacturing tool and reaches out of the company into the limitless supply of technical information.

Have the analysts learned how to work with and through the buyers, the engineers, and the manufacturing methods men, never around them? Do they always, in the long pull, strengthen each in his own field?

Do others always cooperate fully with the analyst?

> In management

In engineering

In manufacturing methods

In purchasing

The job of value analysts is to get today's and tomorrow's materials, ideas, methods, and processes into use today. If they operate properly, they will use all of the resources in the entire country in this program.

Measurement of Value Work

Each of the four types of work comprising the value analyst's work should be measured separately, and in general, measurement should be both of the amount done and of the amount not done. The four types of work, the reader will recall, are integration, value appraisal, consultation, and training.

INTEGRATION: The manager to whom value consultants or analysts report should set up with them listings of all persons on the organization who have certain important information about the plans of operation of the value analysts. In large organizations, these lists may best show the name of the activity rather than the name of the individual, together with the number of people involved in each case. At the end of report periods, which might each be ninety days, the work done and the work still to be done should be shown in order to provide the various men or the various groups of men with proper understanding. The quality of the understanding which is being secured by typical men of the various groups indoctrinated should be evaluated. On this basis, replanning to provide the additional understanding can be done.

VALUE APPRAISAL: Wrong measurement is a worse deterrent than no measurement to the establishment of any sound activity. It often happened in earlier value work that a traditional form of measurement, which provided definitely deceptive results, had been used. More recently, the shortcomings of this type of measurement are being realized, and it is being ended. It is definitely incorrect to measure value consultants or value analysts, who use the value analysis techniques and special knowledge for the purpose of identifying unnecessary cost, by the amount of savings which result from their value alternatives. The reader will be quick to recognize that savings are the result of good value alternatives plus effective decisions and actions by entirely different people. First, the value men act to provide value alternatives; then the decision makers act to either implement the suggestions or not implement them. True, the tangible benefit to the business is the result of the actions of these two groups in series, namely, the decrease in cost and the added earnings which actually result. However, it is fallacious to use this outcome as an indication of the quality of the value alternatives or of the effectiveness of the work of the value consultants. Changes in the value group based on such measurements may bring disaster to the business.

When the nature of the personnel in the decision group and the degree of their motivation are such that good action normally results, very poor value alternatives indeed may seem to produce large improvements in earnings. A management that gives credence to such measurements would be inclined to believe that they had indeed learned the proper type and operation for value personnel and would take action accordingly. Exactly the opposite is true; the decision group is so effective that with a very small input it produces large results.

In businesses hardest pressed for good results in value work, experience has shown that the controlling practices of the decision makers are the reverse of the above. Now, even though the effectiveness of the value group in producing value alternatives is very high indeed, very little if anything "comes out" in the increased earnings column. A management judging by this result would be inclined to decide that its value group was inefficient or improperly staffed or organized and would tend to make changes which would destroy any possibility of improving the situation.

It should be very clear that the quality of value alternatives must be measured as such and that, as time progresses, business must learn also to measure the quality, as such, of the decision makers in matters affecting value. Only then can an enlightened management make appropriate decisions and take appropriate action to restore and enhance the value of its products.

An important measurement, then, in value appraisal will be based on an evaluation of the alternatives covered by the suggestion sheets, which, as the reader will recall, constitute the output of value consultants. This must be an objective evaluation of the likelihood that the suggestion will prove practical and of the probable amount of reduction in cost which will be accomplished. Care should be taken in making these evaluations that men who have vested interests, i.e., who will later have the responsibility for either taking action to implement the alternatives or taking action to kill them, are excluded from the evaluation team. A suitable amount of product evaluation should be planned in discussions by the value consultants and the manager to whom they report. In this planning, the various products and product lines should be brought into view, discussed briefly, and either bypassed or scheduled for study. Measurement then follows the system of matching results with plans. Plans will, of course, be constantly subject to change to take into account new information learned from the results of the studies.

CONSULTATION: Important guidance on consultation is obtained from a clear review of both the consultation which has been done during the measurement period and the consultation which has not been done. In other words, these questions should be raised:

On what jobs was consultation done?
On what jobs was consultation not done?
For what men, or groups of men, was consultation done?
For what men, or groups of men, was consultation not done?

A progressive study of this type for each of a few report periods provides vital information to show where more consultation is required and also where more integration knowledge and understanding must be provided to men in other work areas.

Reports of consultation work should contain memorandum statements of activities involved in consultation, such as, "assisted engineer Smith by locating for him a double-range thermocouple of smaller size, greater accuracy, and lower cost than the product previously used."

The report will show the number of times the consultants were invited into each area and the activities resulting.

TRAINING: In regard to training, it is again most significant to have clear-cut information showing what training has been done and what training has not been done. Plans will be prepared to include all the people who should have training, either by name or, in large organizations, by groups and numbers in each group. A suitable rate will be established, and a suitable schedule for training will be prepared. This, then, will allow measuring the actual training against the plan. When desirable, the plan should be adjusted at each measurement period to account for changes in emphasis, shifts in business, or new information of diverse types.

16-3 *Tests*

It is important to know whether the men being taught are learning. If the men are not learning, the trainer is not teaching. For this purpose, tests should be provided to ascertain whether those purported to be receiving training are indeed learning the fundamentals which they will require to effectively carry out their value work.

Periodically, perhaps once each year, a study should be made of the value analysis work content in each of the main areas of the business, such as sales, engineering, manufacturing, purchasing, and management. In studying each area, it is important to examine separately the actions on the four different types of work; for example:

Has suitable integration been completed? If not, what is the status and what plans should now be made?

Is the appropriate amount of product evaluation work being done for these people?

Is the appropriate amount of value consultation work being done for these people?

Are the appropriate numbers of personnel being properly instructed in training classes?

Such a separate study of the four types of value work in each area of the business often brings larger than anticipated benefits. It may show that a tendency has developed for value consultants to work quite efficiently on a few of the work elements, or in some of the needed areas, and to be working very superficially otherwise. With this knowledge at hand, emphasis can be placed where it belongs to the end that a more balanced and profitable program can be reestablished.

Tests of Men

It is desirable, if not necessary, to have a test which can be given to the value consultant or value analyst to show, in reality, how well he is really doing in the work situations which make up the four types of value analysis work. To the writer's knowledge, no such comprehensive test exists today. Some work has been started on the preparation of such a test, and it is expected that tests will become available.

It should be well recognized that in the testing and selection of men, the qualifications required are governed to an important extent by the number of people in the particular value group. For example, if one man has outstanding abilities as a teacher, plus the other essential knowledge and traits, so that he does indeed teach the subject matter, he need not have similarly high excellence in product evaluation or in value consultation. Conversely, if competence is provided to take care of teaching work, then others in that particular value analysis group may do an outstanding job in product evaluation, consultation, and integration without, in fact, having professional-grade skills in teaching, and there will be balanced competence for the overall operation.

It has been found that great care should be taken to guard against assuming that technical people who are highly competent in searching out and generating sound value alternatives are also capable of communicating and teaching. This is not necessarily true. High-grade and skilled value analysts may entirely fail at the task of teaching and training.

While a dearth of overall tests exists at the present time, the reader will find, by reexamining the chapter on qualifications for value work, that there are important opportunities for using available tests to help in the selection of men. For example, such essential qualifications as creativity, emotional stability, and technical knowledge have been sufficiently well established so that measurements and tests exist for these traits and qualifications.

Tests of Work Being Done

CONDENSED QUESTIONAIRE FOR DETERMINING IF THE SYSTEM
OF VALUE ANALYSIS IS BEING USED

1. Have use function and aesthetic function been separated?
2. Has "value"—appropriate cost—been determined for each function by comparisons that are totally separate from "past practice"?
3. In determining the "value," is the definition *value is the lowest cost that will reliably accomplish the function* used?
4. Is this "value" then used for a temporary measurement, with a determination to succeed in the "search" and "thinking" required to actually achieve near this "value"?
5. Has the present or expected cost been determined for each function, separating the use from the asthetic function cost?
6. Is our thinking, in preparing evidence for our decision making, all on the basis of cost per year or per total order, rather than a cost per piece or per single function basis?
7. Have we dropped the name of the material, part, or process out of our thinking, tabulations, and considerations, using, instead, a statement of the function it does for the customer?
8. When the term *function* is used in all of the above considerations, do we always mean and often say, "Function the customer wants"?
9. Has the single function or function group being studied been named very specifically in about six different ways, most of which consist of a verb and a noun?
10. Has the particular name that propels the mind toward solutions been selected for use in all considerations?
11. Has all of the cost of the product, system, organization, or service been assigned function names?
12. Have total functions been divided and redivided into subfunctions so that cost, value, comparison, and other considerations are all based upon a function group the proper size for effective *alternative method* considerations?
13. Are single functions sometimes grouped for the same purpose?
14. Examine some specific items and determine how many of the thirteen results-accelerating techniques have been used. These techniques are for the purpose of preventing the end of the effort before the planned economic benefits have been achieved.
15. Are the assigned scope, capabilities, and operations such that penetrating "look" into each of the following areas, which may be responsible

for enormous amounts of unnecessary cost, is being effectively accomplished?

    a. Marketing

    b. Engineering concept

    c. Engineering design and detail

    d. Manufacturing concept

    e. Manufacturing operation

    f. Purchasing and materials

    g. Management practices

16. Is the five-step problem-solving "job plan" being aggressively used sufficiently to get the results required on the hard ones?

17. Is each step penetrating completed before mixing up the "partly done" thinking process with succeeding steps?

18. Is the job plan *always* used in its thorough and complete form unless the economic objectives have already been reached?

19. At the start of the information step, is there an adequate penetrating thought session on the subject of "What are we really trying to do?"

20. Is all information aggressively gathered? Does it result in more information being related to the situation than has heretofore been collected? Are the assumptions also listed? Is the "information" searchingly screened to eliminate assumptions and false beliefs. Are the assumptions tightly studied to determine which might now been seen to be wrong and which other assumptions are more nearly true and useful? Is all of this *completely* done before proceeding to analysis thinking?

21. Now is analysis thorough, separate, and distinct. What are the meanings from this information? What does it seem to make good sense to now do? How much effort in which directions? Are functions and groups of functions evaluated by comparison in this step? Is it seen that more information is required? Are more assumptions required? Are specific problems now jelled and taken into the creative step? Has a "feel" for the project now been developed? Is this completed before any mental energies or time go into creativity?

22. Creativity can be worthless, or it can unlock the future. Have carefully worded problems, developed in the analysis step, received periods of intense well-directed, free-thinking creativity in an environment relatively free from creativity "blocks"? Have three to five effective people in groups helped in this? Has the thinking been intense and usually not over a half hour at a time? Has creativity followed to minimize disadvantages of promising alternatives?

23. Is the work of the creativity step then judged by *one* person alone? Does he uninterruptedly first search for the good in suggestions listed? Does he search out those bringing the most benefit, even though they have a serious disadvantage, and then set up creativity to minimize the bad factors? Does he include, usually one at a time, other functional people in his discussions and thinking, which are directed at selecting and developing further the most beneficial alternatives?

24. Does the result of all of this search, accumulation of information, accumulation of thinking, creative work, and preliminary judgment now go to the man who is responsible, for his decision, follow-through, further study, test, and implementation?

25. In any step, is the project scheduled back, as often as may be required to accomplish the objective, into an earlier step, such as back for more information, more analysis, more creativity, etc.?

SUMMARY

To allow profit-making results to the business, essential motivation must exist for the managers, the men using the value analysis system, and those making decisions. Negative factors and demotivators for this group must also be made minimal.

The searching, thinking, and communicating work essential to successful value work is well spelled out. A very valid means for determining the success that may be expected from value analysis people on the difficult tasks is to review their activities. Are they doing it?

Means for determining the effectiveness of the decision makers, when dealing with decisions that mean change for the purpose of reducing costs, are needed. This is essential work of top management dealing in products or services in a highly competitive field.

Sometimes, alas, people who have not learned the value analysis system apply the name *value analysis* or *value engineering* to the cost-reduction-oriented work they are doing. A twenty-five-question review schedule is provided in this chapter to assist all people under all conditions in determining whether the value analysis system is, in fact, being used.

Advanced Techniques

The techniques in this chapter can improve the thinking process, communication with involved persons, and ultimate decision making. They can accelerate and increase results when properly used on "hard," perhaps involved, situations where a high order of results is essential. They were developed by professional value analysis and engineering men to meet the needs of tasks they were performing. To develop skill in using these techniques, it may be essential to spend at least a few hours of personal involvement with men who have mastered them.

17-1 Function Analysis System Technique (FAST)[1]

This system was developed and is being extensively used by Charles W. Bytheway, value engineering seminar director of UNIVAC Salt Lake City, Defense Systems Division, Sperry Rand Corp. Others are progressively learning and using it.

[1] The author expresses appreciation to Theodore C. Fowler, value engineer, Rochester, N.Y., for bringing this effective technique to his attention.

The approach to this system for intense study of functions and function interactions lies in asking three questions and then diagramming the results. The questions asked about each function that is performed by the product or service are: "Why?" "How?" and "When?"

Answers to the question "Why?" lead back to what is called the higher-level function. They answer the question "Why is this function being performed anyhow?" Answers to the question "How?" lead ahead to the specific functions that must be performed in order to accomplish this one.

All functions so identified are charted from left to right, with the highest-level functions, which were identified by the question "Why?" on the left and the functions identified by the question "How?" on the right. When this has been properly done, each function in the entire series is illuminated on the left by "Why it is done?" and on the right by "How it is done?"

Next the question "When?" is asked of each function, and it is diagramed in time sequence in relation to the other functions so that examination of the diagram vertically illuminates the matter of which functions are to be accomplished at the same time and the sequential relationships of all others.

How to Use FAST [2]

This technique is useful in determining the function interrelation in analyzing an entire system or a major portion of a system and gives a better understanding of the interaction of function and cost.

Function Determination Logic

This system provides us with the determination logic to determine the basic function and the higher- and lower-level functions, as well as the supporting systems or equipment. The use of this system requires the construction of a FAST diagram utilizing the determination logic questions "How?", "Why?", and "When?"

The steps necessary to construct the FAST diagram are as follows:

1. Prepare a list of all the functions by assembly or system using the verb and noun technique of identification of function.
2. Write each function on a small card. Select a card with the function that you consider to be the basic function. Determine the position of the

[2] Appreciation is expressed to the Xerox Corp., Rochester, N.Y., for permission to use this "How to Use" material, and to Francis Xavier Wojciechowski, value engineer for Xerox Corp., who prepared it.

next higher and lower function cards by specifically answering the following logic questions:

"How?": How is this function accomplished?
"Why?": Why is this function performed?
"When?": When is this function performed?

Using one of the functions selected, apply the logic questions to determine the functions to the right and left of it, as shown in Figure 17-1.

ASK WHY ? ◄———— FUNCTION SELECTED ————► ASK HOW ?   **Fig. 17-1** The "Why" and "How" logic.

Let us look at the example of an overhead transparency projector. The function selected was to "show diagram." By asking the logic questions "Why do we show diagram?" we answer, "Teach students." How do we "show diagram"? "By reflecting image." How do you "reflect image"? "By projecting image," as shown in Figure 17-2. At the same time, the

TEACH STUDENT — SHOW DIAGRAM — REFLECT IMAGE — PROJECT IMAGE   **Fig. 17-2** "Why" and "How" function diagram.

question "Why?" must be answered. Why do we "project image"? "To reflect image." Why "reflect image"? To "show diagram," etc. By this method we can check the proper order of the functions in the diagram and also determine the completeness of the diagram by assuring that all functions are accounted for.

In the next step, we ask, "How is the project image function performed?" The reply is, "Illuminating transparency." The next question, "How do we illuminate transparency?" gives two answers: (1) by providing a light source and (2) by supporting the transparency in a suitable fashion. Therefore, both "provide light" and "support transparency" are needed to answer the question "How?" What about the question "Why?" The answer to both questions, "Why do we support transparency?" and "Why do we provide light?" is "To illuminate transparency." The logic questions are satisfied, and we have the blocks on the FAST diagram shown in Figure 17-3.

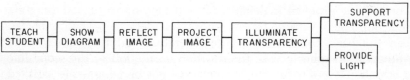

TEACH STUDENT — SHOW DIAGRAM — REFLECT IMAGE — PROJECT IMAGE — ILLUMINATE TRANSPARENCY — SUPPORT TRANSPARENCY / PROVIDE LIGHT

Fig. 17-3 Basic FAST diagram.

The determination logic questions are then applied to each function and the FAST diagram continued until we arrive at a function that is an accepted interface function for the scope of the problem. This will be discussed in more detail under Determination of Scope.

Critical Path Determination

When all the determination logic questions "How?" and "Why?" are answered for each function, we have established the relation between the functions at higher and lower levels that are required to perform the highest-level basic function. The arrangement of these functions, as shown by the FAST diagram, establishes the critical path. The critical path identifies the functions that are the result of other functions to be performed.

Supporting Function Determination

After the critical path functions have been selected and positioned on the FAST diagram, the remaining functions from the list in step 1 are placed on the diagram by applying the question "When?"

On the accompanying complete FAST diagram for the overhead projector, the function of "cool lens" is performed when?—At the same time as the "illuminate transparency" function is performed, and therefore it is placed in the same vertical line. Note, also, that there is a dotted line connecting the "cool lens" function with the "project image" function. The dotted line indicates a secondary or supporting path. The secondary function paths are usually the result of specific methods chosen to implement the function. In this particular case, the "cool lens" function resulted from a light source, which "produces heat" (an unwanted function), and a Fresnel lens, which requires cooling.

If hardware details have been or are being designed, the parts that perform a function can also be added to the FAST diagram and are placed directly below the function that they perform.

Determination of Scope

In order to limit the FAST diagram to a specifically determined problem, the scope of the problem is defined and outlined on the FAST diagram by the scope lines (vertical broken lines). The left scope line is placed between the basic function under consideration and the highest-order basic function. In other words, the function on the left of the scope line is the next higher-order function, which will not be completely satisfied by the solution of this problem. The function on the right is the basic

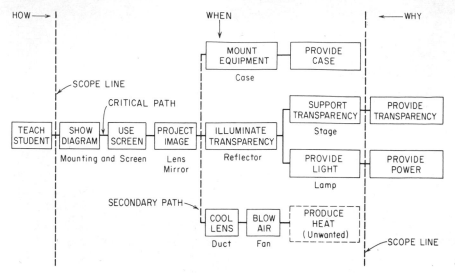

Fig. 17-4   FAST diagram of overhead transparency projector.

function, which must be satisfied by this product or service. In the example considered here, the overhead projector must satisfactorily "show diagram," but it will only partially perform the "teach student" function. The right scope line is drawn to the left of a function that is an acceptable interface to the product or service under consideration—a suitable input to the system.

In our example, the "provide power" interface function is the lowest-level function we wish to consider in discussing the overhead projector. The manufacturer of the overhead projector will expect the user to provide an ac outlet and the transparencies. The choice of the scope is arbitrary, and it is often necessary to reevaluate the scope at the completion of the FAST diagram.

This completes the mechanics of constructing the FAST diagram. A careful analysis of the details of the diagram will reveal interesting and useful relations. The function to the right of a selected function tells *how* the function is performed. The function to the left indicates *why* the function is performed. The functions above and below show which functions are happening at the same time. Finally, if parts are available, the diagram shows what functions are performed by which parts. See Figure 17-4.

In the innovation phase, we generate alternate ways to perform functions. By examining those functions on the FAST diagram that are adjacent to each other or are performed at the same time, many ways to combine, modify, or otherwise perform these functions can be developed. This often leads to innovations or better ways to do the required task.

FAST Diagram Cost Allocation

If the function classification has been performed by the construction of the FAST diagram, the evaluation may be performed utilizing the diagram. To perform this cost allocation, the function blocks on the FAST diagram are numbered. These functions are used as column headings under the appropriate number of the function-cost breakdown sheet. The individual part names and total costs are placed in the two left-hand columns. The functions of the part are analyzed and the cost allocated actually or proportionately to each of the functions performed by the part. The totals at the bottom of the page provide the visibility of cost for each function as well as the total costs for basic and secondary functions. It is sometimes desirable to transfer these totals to the blocks on the FAST diagram to give added visibility to the lateral buildup of costs that provide the basic function. This method makes immediately apparent where the costs are distributed and the total costs involved in performing the functions on the critical path.

Case Study

**FAST DIAGRAM USED; PARTS REDUCED FROM
NINETEEN TO FOUR**

The "How?", "Why?", and "When?" were diagramed covering each of the functions (and parts) of a timing mechanism. The developmental design, shown in Figure 17-5, contained nineteen parts, eighteen of which are shown in Figure 17-6.

Fig. 17-5 Developmental design, timing mechanism.

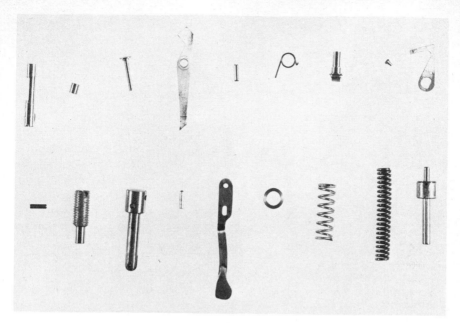

Fig. 17-6   Eighteen of the nineteen mechanism parts studied.

The FAST diagram shown in Figure 17-7 organized the logic and formed the basis for developing improvement thinking. The diagram was then rearranged somewhat, and the names of the parts that accomplish each function were added. See Figure 17-8.

Functions were evaluated, function constraints were clearly understood, and the creative problem setting and solving of the job plan were used, with the result that it was determined that the functions of sixteen parts could be performed by one, as shown in Figure 17-9. The resulting production design is shown in rear view in Figure 17-10. Of course, production costs were correspondingly reduced to less than one-fourth of what they would have been had the original developmental design been manufactured in quantity.

17-2   *Quantitative Evaluation of Ideas*[3]

As value analysis and engineering progresses it has become clear that the original method of evaluating ideas by using the good/bad T chart has serious limitations. For one thing, it precludes the use of value analysis and engineering for such things as marketing trends or feasibility studies. If the problem is putting men on the moon or building sophisticated radar equipment for a strategic strike aircraft, cost may be a secondary factor, the dominant factor being the possibility of being able to satisfy the re-

[3] Written by Arthur Garratt, M.B.E., B.Sc., F. Inst. P., FRSA. Mr. Garratt and Sonia Withers, M.A. of Value Engineering Ltd., London, England, devised the system.

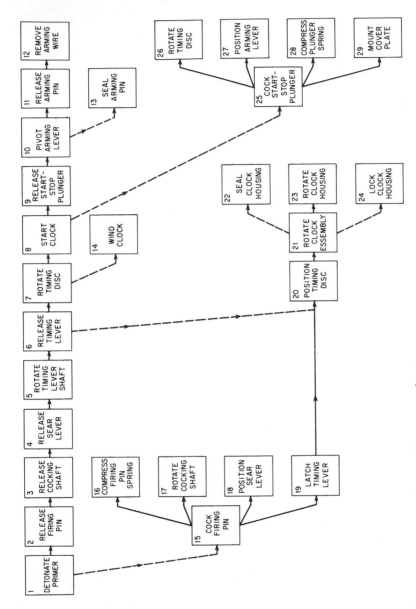

Fig. 17-7 FAST diagram of timing mechanism.

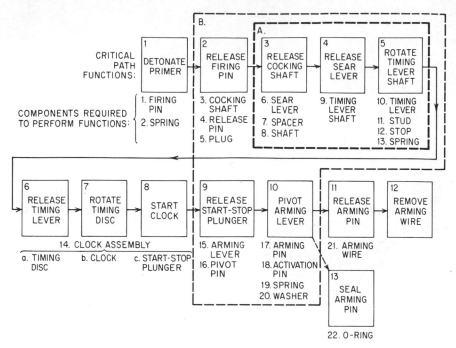

Fig. 17-8   FAST diagram associating names of parts with the various functions.

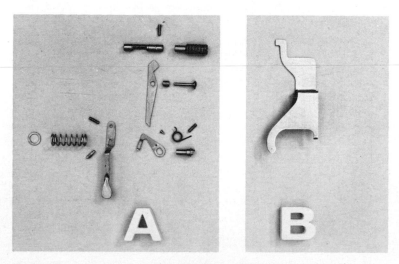

Fig. 17-9   Sixteen parts (*A*) replaced by one (*B*).

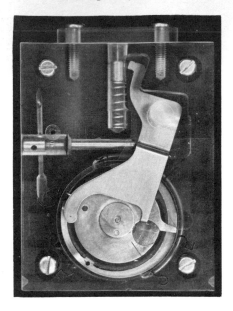

Fig. 17-10   Underside view of resulting production product.

quirement. Of course, once satisfaction has been accomplished, value analysis and engineering comes into its own to reduce costs and improve performance. Another disadvantage of the simple evaluation system is that at a value analysis and engineering seminar the ideas that are not developed are lost, and it often happens that a team has not enough knowledge of company policy to choose the optimum solution, which may not always be the lowest-cost solution. A further disadvantage is that there may be two possible solutions, one costing, say, $25 and the other $26. The second may be much superior from the performance point of view, and yet if the first can be made to satisfy the functional requirements partially, the second will be lost.

It was with these considerations in mind that a more sophisticated method of evaluation was devised. It was decided that it was necessary to find a numerical method of rating performance and other features that would also allow the users to separate their variables and judge how well an idea satisfied each function separately. This led to a form of matrix evaluation. The idea of matrix analysis is not new and has been used before for decision making. It has the advantage that numerical scores can be worked out, with due weight factors, thus providing a figure of merit for each possible decision. Perhaps of even greater importance is the separation of variables. Many psychologists have shown that man has serious limitations in his ability to combine factors in subjective decision problems.[4]

---

[4] See, for example, G. A. Miller, "The Magical Number Seven, Plus or Minus Two," *Psychol. Rev,* 63:81–97, 1956; and R. N. Shepard, "On Subjectively Optimum Selections Among Multi-attribute Alternatives," in M. W. Shelley and G. L. Bryan (eds.), *Human Judgments and Optimality,* John Wiley & Sons, Inc., New York, 1964, pp. 257–81.

The conventional method of matrix analysis is to set up a grid so that different decisions can be evaluated against the factors that have to be satisfied, with suitable weighting factors inserted. Such matrices have certain disadvantages when applied to value analysis and engineering evaluation. The particular objection is in the application of weighting factors to the various functions. It was found that users generally considered three or four functions essential and gave them equal weight and then degraded other functions out of all proportion to their importance. Various modifications were tried until a method was found that is very satisfactory in practice. The modified matrix is set up in the following way.

The first step is to write down all the functions *and characteristics* that must be satisfied. These are put in a positive form; e.g., for an electric motor one writes down "low noise" as being desirable not "high noise" as being undesirable. It is possible to write the latter and then give it a negative sign in the evaluation process, but it has been found that this leads to some confusion and using the positive form throughout is better.

The functions and characteristics must now be arranged in order of importance. Often this can be done by inspection. If not, a preliminary scale matrix is used to sort out the order of importance of each function. This checks against all the others in turn. The process is simple. On a matrix sheet similar to that shown in Figure 17-11 all the functions and characteristics are written down the left-hand side in random order and numbered A to Z. Across the top of the matrix the same letters are also written. A diagonal is drawn across the dead squares where a function is compared with itself.

Starting with function A, go to the second square in the top row and ask the question, "Is function A more important than function B?" If so, fill in 1 in this square; if not, fill in 0. At the same time fill in the opposite sign in the second square down, which is the complementary square and shows that function B is less or more important than function A. Going on step by step, the matrix is filled in. Then sum the numbers across the matrix line by line and write the totals in the extreme right-hand column. The function with the highest score is the most important; the rest are graded accordingly. The one with a score of zero comes last and is the least important. If the scores are not all different, a mistake in logic has been made somewhere; this provides a check on the use of the system.

Let us take as an example Figure 17-12. Having put the functions and characteristics into order, the main matrix can be started. This is written

FUNCTION	1	2	3	4	5	6	7	8	9	RATING
1. DISTRIBUTE AIR	X	I	I	I	I	I	I	I	I	9
2. CONTROL FLOW	0	X	0	I	I	I	I	I	I	7
3. DIRECT AIR	0	I	X	I	I	I	I	I	I	8
4. RESIST HEAT	0	0	0	X	I	I	I	I	I	6
5. RESIST CORROSION	0	0	0	0	X	I	I	I	I	5
6. LOOK GOOD	0	0	0	0	0	X	I	I	I	4
7. RESIST DAMAGE	0	0	0	0	0	0	X	I	I	3
8. EASY TO ASSEMBLE	0	0	0	0	0	0	0	X	I	2
9. PROVIDE RIGIDITY	0	0	0	0	0	0	0	0	X	1

Fig. 17-11 Function rating grid.

MATRIX EVALUATION CHART

Project: MULTIDIRECTIONAL AIR PROJECTOR Criterion: PERFORMANCE	K. PROVIDE RIGIDITY	J. EASY ASSEMBLY	G. RESIST DAMAGE	F. LOOK GOOD	E. RESIST CORROSION	D. RESIST HEAT	C. CONTROL FLOW	B. DIRECT AIR	A. DISTRIBUTE AIR	Date: 4-30	
Function Rank No.(n)	1	2	3	4	5	6	7	8	9		
Function Rating No.(φ)	1	1	2	4	5	6	7	8	9		
IDEA	*SATISFACTION FACTOR(s)*									Σφs	EST. COST
a. ORIGINAL PRODUCT PARTS HZWXY	10	7	3	9	8	9	6	8	10	349	$55
b.											
c. ELIMINATE PARTS X & Y	10	8	4	10	8	9	6	8	10	356	$47
d. MANUFACTURE FROM PLASTIC-COATED OR PRE-PAINTED MATERIAL	10	8	4	10	8	9	6	8	10	356	NOT PRACTICAL
e. BUILD IN LOUVRES TO HEAD	10	10	4	6	8	9	6	7	10	334	NO SAVING
f. RIVET LOURVES IN DUCT INSTEAD OF SCREW	10	10	4	10	8	9	6	8	10	358	$54
g. MANUFACTURE IN GALVATITE MAT'L	10	8	8	5	9	9	6	8	10	349	$42
h. PLASTIC GRILLE	10	8	9	10	10	9	6	8	10	376	NO SAVING
j. SET UP INTERIOR PAINTING FACILITY	10	8	7	10	8	9	6	8	10	362	NEEDS INVESTIGATING
k. DESIGN A SINGLE DOUBLE HEAD	10	10	7	10	8	9	7	9	10	379	$43
l. UNIDIRECTIONAL											$34
m.											
n.											
o.											
p.											
q.											
r.											

CONCLUSION: ITEM KL OFFERS GREATEST POTENTIAL SAVINGS

Fig. 17-12   Matrix evaluation chart. (*Colt Heating and Ventilation Ltd.*)

on a prepared sheet. (These can be purchased ready printed.) The functions are written in their correct order across the top, with the most important function at the right-hand side and the functions numbered from 1 to n from left to right in the row marked "Function Rank Number." Below this is another row, marked "Function Rating Number (ϕ)." This enables a weighting differential to be applied to the functions while preserving their overall order. Weighting is already built in by the rank number, so that the most important function has the highest number, and so on downward. But often a device may have, say, seven functions of which four are very important and the other three, like "looks good," may be much less important. The function rating number enhances the importance of the really significant functions by suitably degrading the importance of the minor functions. The rules of the game are that the function rating number may be less than or equal to but may never exceed the rank number, and so positive weighting is applied automatically. The function rating number also allows two or more functions to be given equal weight where their difference of importance is marginal.

All this may sound complicated, but in practice it is a straightforward operation that sets out clearly criteria that must be satisfied. Now one can proceed to the next stage, and the ideas that have been generated in the creative session are filled in on the left-hand side of the matrix sheet. Against each idea fill in an estimated cost in the extreme right-hand column in the same way as done in the good/bad T chart.

Next, examine each idea on the basis of how well it satisfies each and every function or characteristic listed across the top. These satisfaction factors (s) scored 0 to 10 are filled in under each function. If any s factor is low, creative ability can be used to try and improve it, but remember that this may well alter the cost, which must be modified appropriately. In this way the ideas are under protracted scrutiny on both performance and a cost basis. If any s factor is zero and cannot be raised, the idea is rejected forthwith as being unworkable because it fails to satisfy one function and no further time is spent on it. When all the figures have been filled in, $s \times \phi$ is worked out for all functions and summed across for each idea; it is filled in on the right-hand side under $\Sigma\phi s$. This gives a numerical value for the performance of each idea, duly weighted for the importance of each function or characteristic and alongside an estimated cost.

From the last two columns, an intelligent appraisal of each idea can easily be made. If the problem is performance at any price, the idea with the largest performance score can be selected. Any idea that has a lower score and higher price than another idea can be jettisoned. Then appraisal can be made on the basis of the market. It could be the supply of Christmas novelties, where price is more important than performance. In this case, the lowest cost idea is taken, providing that no s factor is zero. On the other hand, if the target is a medium-quality market, one can select the idea that is the best compromise between performance and price.

The matrix that has been described is a typical value analysis and engineering exercise on a product or part of a product. But it is equally valid for *any management decision* once the functions and characteristics have been established.

It is obvious that performance is not the only criterion that can be applied. A second matrix might be filled in, after a value analysis and engineering session attended by designers and production men, by marketing, using a new set of s factors on the basis of marketing. A third matrix can be prepared on the basis of quality and reliability, and so on, as required. Then an intelligent management decision can be reached to give an optimum answer to several mutually conflicting needs.

A particular feature of the matrix is that a team can prepare one during a value analysis and engineering session, and this can later by analyzed by, for example, a company executive who has before him all the ideas that were generated, costed, and rated.

This system of matrix evaluation has been tried out at many seminars in Europe, with outstanding success. At first, as a control, both systems were used side by side, but it was soon found that the old good/bad T chart led to confusion and teams using the matrix system performed better evaluation much faster. Latest work has combined the matrix with the good/bad T chart in reverse order: initial assessment is done on the matrix, and problems of detail are then tackled on the T chart. The marriage of the two techniques is then a happy one, with lusty offspring in the form of new concepts. A lot of the sting can be taken out of the summation of the product of ϕ and s by using a desk calculating machine on which the products are calculated without zeroing the total so that the final total is $\Sigma \phi \times s$.

Readers are strongly recommended to try the system for themselves. "Like capital punishment, it clears the mind wonderfully."

chapter 18

Using the System
to Reduce Construction Costs

Construction in the 1970s is a 100-billion-dollar industry. Reducing the amount of unnecessary costs, i.e., costs that do not bring either use or aesthetic functions to the user, provides enormous opportunity for benefits to the architect, engineer, contractor, owner, and society.

18-1 Definition for
Construction Industry

George Begg,[1] while opening the symposium on Value Engineering in Federal Construction Agencies for the Federal Construction Agency, stated:

> Value Engineering is hereby defined as an engineering and architectural discipline that (1) focuses attention on the essential function in a chosen design or construction objective, and (2) emphasizes meeting the essential function at the lowest total cost.

[1] Public Buildings Service, General Services Administration, Washington, D.C.

A. J. Dell'isola[2] defines total costs as "construction, operation, maintenance, and replacement."

18-2   Why So Much Unfunctioning Cost in the Construction Industry?

The industry is bound by obsolete codes and by differing codes in differing jurisdictions. Examples of codes that have remained unchanged through twenty to thirty years despite enormously changed conditions are far too common.

Obsolete design details are repeated from job to job.

Materials that bring no user function (either use or aesthetic) are often used.

New functional materials are not used.

Practices from the past are followed.

Habits from the past enter the design, contracting, and construction.

Most construction jobs involve three businesses: architects and engineers, contractors, and owners.

The Architects and Engineers

The objective of the architect and engineer is to produce a good competitive design from available materials and skills without uncertainties and at minimum design cost. Most of the time, using newer materials and/or approaches means time and expense searching and testing. In addition, there is the time, expense, and uncertainty involved in attempting to communicate with and convince the owner. Lastly, the contractor may have problems in finding the equipment and skills needed to utilize the new approach in the construction phase.

Changing from past practice means uncertainties in prices. Also, because the fee is usually a percentage of the project costs, the architect, for all of his extra work and expense, ends up with a lower fee. More work, more uncertainty, and a lower fee are the outlook for the architect. Why should he search for, test, and promote the new, spend much effort in getting approvals of the contractor and owner, or use valuable energies in long drawn-out processes with governing bodies to get codes changed?

Present methods of material selection involve the architect-engineer,

[2] Construction consultant, McKee-Berger-Mansueto Inc., Washington, D.C. Also, pioneer in the use of the value engineering system in the architectural, contractor, and construction phases of the construction industry and the source of much material and all examples in this chapter.

who selects materials that conform to the design criteria of the owner. The architect-engineer is responsible for determining which materials are most suitable from the point of view of economy, function, and maintenance. Generally the selection of the bulk of the material is done by the architect or engineer working on a particular aspect of a design. For example, the electrical engineer selects such items as conductors, conduits, and panel boxes. The architect selects the material for such items as windows, doors, hardware, and exterior finish.

In certain major areas, economic studies are conducted, for example, in fuel selection and structural system. However, in most instances, any selection of material or any studies are made by an individual or group within the same discipline. Normally no formal overall plan is followed, no interdiscipline benefits are developed, and no full-time employee is available to coordinate activities or follow through the development of new ideas.

The Contractors

To the contractor, uncertainty is "poison in the soup." He relies on his experience in quoting prices. He knows the ease or difficulty in getting various skills, equipment, and coordination and mutual assistance between groups in overlap areas. He also knows the probabilities of making mistakes or incurring delays due to error or misunderstanding. He wants to do his work in the manner that he has always done it, with the skills that he knows he can get, with each man doing a task that he knows "forward and backward," and with the interfaces between the various tasks predicted and proved by the involved work groups.

Different materials mean different fabricating methods, unpredicted problems, and perhaps costly delays and repairs. The contractor naturally is reluctant to bid in areas of change without adding contingency costs, which may nullify the benefits of the change on that job. Understandably, the contractor, in general, is not the promoter of change.

The Owners

The owner relies upon the architects and engineers to design for him the building that most economically will meet his needs and wants for use and aesthetic functions. He can and often does, in general terms, encourage the use of new functional products and processes, but he must leave the actions and responsibilities in the hands of the architects and engineers.

18-3 *How the Value Engineering System Is Being Used*

EXAMPLE (FIGURE 18-1):   Place the source of the hot water and compressed air where it is needed. Reduce initial costs $46,000 and life cycle (twenty-year) costs an additional $57,000. Eliminate a low-water-table problem.

EXAMPLE (FIGURE 18-2): Simplify the design of door canopies. Reduce costs from $400 to $150 each. Make unnecessary the involvement of seven trades.

EXAMPLE (FIGURE 18-3):   Change parking-area pavement from 12-inch compacted subbase and crushed-rock base to 8 inches of lime stabilized subgrade and 4 inches of subbase and crushed-rock base. Secure change of government specifications. Reduce construction cost $8,000.

Use the Functional Approach

The following six questions may be used as a guide to the work, which sets the problems and solves them.

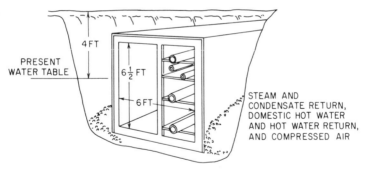

PLANNED WALK-THROUGH TUNNEL

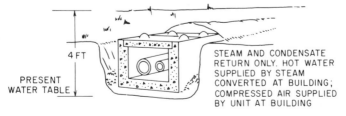

CHANGED, SIMPLIFIED TUNNEL

Fig. 18-1 Planned walk-through tunnel and simplified tunnel; $46,000, lower initial cost; $103,000, lower life-cycle cost.

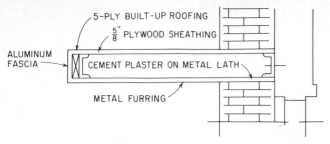

PLANNED DOOR CANOPIES

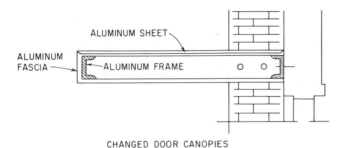

CHANGED DOOR CANOPIES

Fig. 18-2 Planned and changed door canopies. Costs reduced from $400 to $150 each.

1. What is the item, project, or service?
2. What does it do (define the function)?
3. What is the (dollar) value of the function?
4. What does the item, project, or service cost?
5. What else will perform the function?
6. What will that cost?

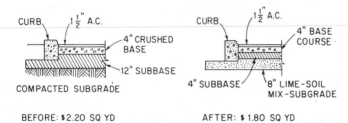

BEFORE: $2.20 SQ YD   AFTER: $1.80 SQ YD

Fig. 18-3 Parking-area pavement.

Name and Evaluate Functions—
Compare with Present or Planned
Costs and Proceed with the Job Plan

Figure 18-4 shows the naming of the functions, the assigning of planned costs, and the meaningful comparisons that are at once made visible.

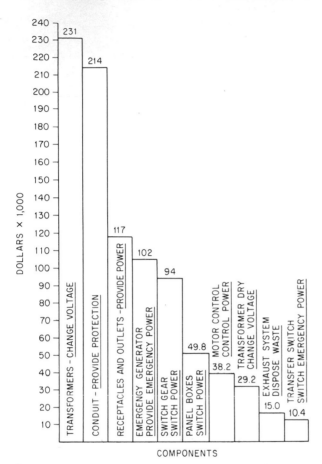

Fig. 18-4 Functional analysis of power distribution system. Transformers performing a secondary function—change voltage, cost twice as much as conductors performing a basic function —transmit power. Conduit cost twice as much for a secondary function—provide protection. A different type of distribution system was recommended, which made it possible to eliminate some transformers, and it was recommended to use lower-cost plastic conduit encased in concrete.

The following examples are illustrative of conductors that perform the basic function and their protection, a secondary function.

EXAMPLE (FIGURE 18-5): *Embedded conductors*
In the planned design the armoured shield, which performs only a secondary function (protects conductors), costs more than three times as much as the conductor itself. The problem-solving plan with its disciplined thinking brought forth two good alternatives, as shown in Figure 18-5.

Considering the function required and the function-producing capability of some less traditional materials brought forth the potential of lower costs for equivalent performance, in the examples of Figure 18-6. Lower costs were obtained using newer functional materials.

18-4 How to Locate Areas Having Potential for Cost Improvement

The following guidelines are often helpful:

Bulk of costs area or item.
Repetitive item.

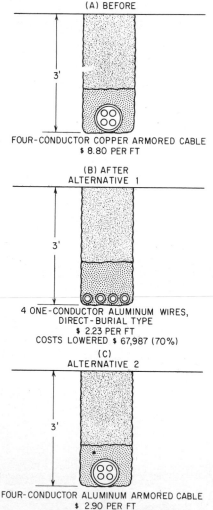

(A) BEFORE

3'

FOUR-CONDUCTOR COPPER ARMORED CABLE
$ 8.80 PER FT

(B) AFTER
ALTERNATIVE 1

3'

4 ONE-CONDUCTOR ALUMINUM WIRES,
DIRECT-BURIAL TYPE
$ 2.23 PER FT
COSTS LOWERED $ 67,987 (70%)

(C)
ALTERNATIVE 2

3'

FOUR-CONDUCTOR ALUMINUM ARMORED CABLE
$ 2.90 PER FT
COSTS LOWERED $ 56,173 (58%)

Fig. 18-5 Buried conductors and their protection.

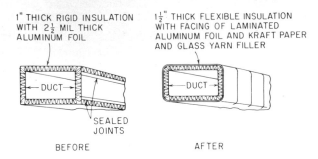

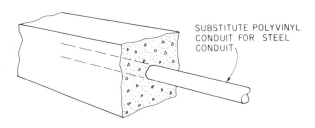

VE CHANGE	SAVINGS
SUBSTITUTE 1½" THICK FLEXIBLE DUCT INSULATION WITH FACING OF LAMINATED ALUMINUM FOIL AND KRAFT PAPER AND GLASS YARN FOR SPECIFIED 1" THICK RIGID INSULATION WITH 2½" MIL THICK ALUMINUM FOIL FOR DUCTS IN CRAWL SPACE	$ 7,710

(A) CRAWL SPACE DUCTS

VE CHANGE	SAVINGS
SUBSTITUTE 4" RIGID POLYVINYL CHLORIDE CONDUIT FOR STEEL CONDUIT	$ 5,000

CHANGE OF GOVERNMENT CRITERIA WAS REQUIRED

(B) CONDUIT

Fig. 18-6   Lower costs using newer functional materials.

Item is an expensive component.
Materials are critical.
Maintenance costs are high.
Operation costs are high.
Total cost appears out of line by experience.
Other similar items are lower cost.
Previous value engineering study areas.
Outdated criteria or standards.

These guidelines brought forth the following examples.

EXAMPLE (FIGURE 18-7):   *Aircraft parking apron*
A value engineering functional study resulted in the recommendation to use vibroflotation instead of removing underlying material. As a result, unsuitable subgrade was properly compacted and did not have to be removed. Costs on the job were lowered $54,000.

EXAMPLE (FIGURE 18-8):   *Foundation plan*
Understanding the function, knowing the technology, and creatively applying the job plan saved another $40,000.

EXAMPLE (FIGURE 18-9):   *Area for value work determined by cost/ value ratio*
In this example, the use of a wooden deck was temporarily assumed, which resulted in an estimated value of $2,500 for each basic function. After the costs for the original design were listed from the estimate, the cost/value ratios were determined. They were $11,150: $2,500 or 4:5 for the timber section and $6,160:$2,500 or 2:5 for the concrete section. This identified the timber section as the area most in need of work.

18-5   *When in the Life Cycle Is Value Engineering Most Productive?*

The phases in the life cycle of the typical construction item may be listed as follows:

Conceptual
Developmental
Preliminary design
Final design
Construction
Operation and maintenance
Replacement

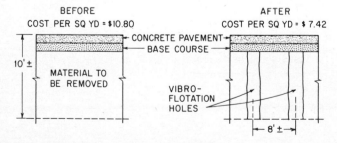

Fig. 18-7   The aircraft parking apron.

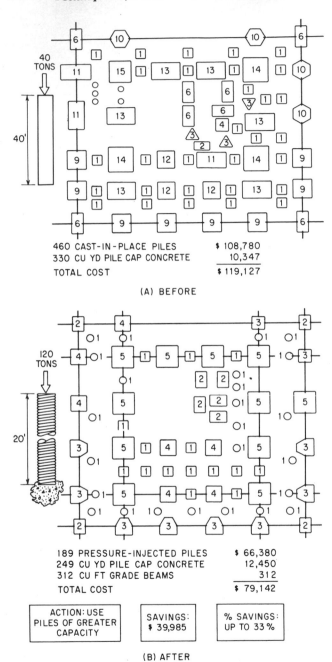

460 CAST-IN-PLACE PILES $ 108,780
330 CU YD PILE CAP CONCRETE   10,347
TOTAL COST $ 119,127

(A) BEFORE

189 PRESSURE-INJECTED PILES $ 66,380
249 CU YD PILE CAP CONCRETE   12,450
312 CU FT GRADE BEAMS   312
TOTAL COST $ 79,142

| ACTION: USE PILES OF GREATER CAPACITY | SAVINGS: $ 39,985 | % SAVINGS: UP TO 33 % |

(B) AFTER

Fig. 18-8   The foundation plan.

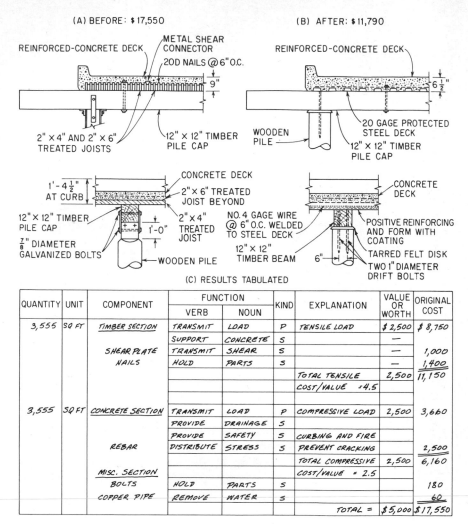

Fig. 18-9 Pier deck. Cost/value ratio used to determine value work needed.

Earlier work was done in the construction phase because of definite results measurement, as was true in the earliest phases of value analysis use. Here were the costs as planned and the costs as changed for uncontestable direct comparison.

Started in Construction—Now Moving Back

Figure 18-10 shows the higher potential earlier in the cycle and the higher cost to change later. It shows that most early work started in the construction phase and is now working back into the earlier phases.

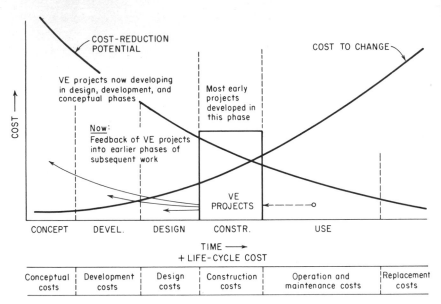

Fig. 18-10   Relation of costs and benefits to phases in cycle of construction work.

18-6   *Ending Nonproductive Nonproduction Costs*

Each cost is changed into the terms of the function it provides.
Each function is classified as to basic or second degree.
The contribution of each function to the real objectives is examined.
Functions are evaluated by comparison.

Through the disciplined thinking of the job plan and the practical knowledge of the architects and engineers, better, lower cost methods are established. Figure 18-11 shows how $80,000 of nonproductive cost was stopped on one construction project.

18-7   *How Basic Obstacles Are Being Overcome*

Certain truths seem self-evident:

1. To effectively and continuously move out large amounts of uncontributing costs, as a matter of routine operation, extensive value analysis and engineering work will have to be done in the offices of the architects and engineers in their work on the final design phase, the preliminary design phase, the development phase, and sometimes the conceptual phase.

2. Architects and engineers are in the position under traditional in-

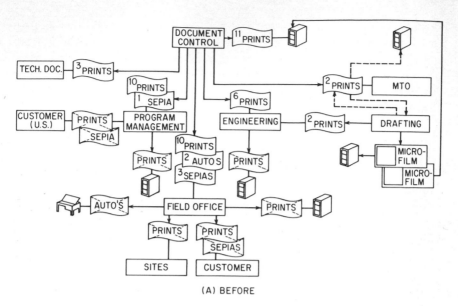

(A) BEFORE

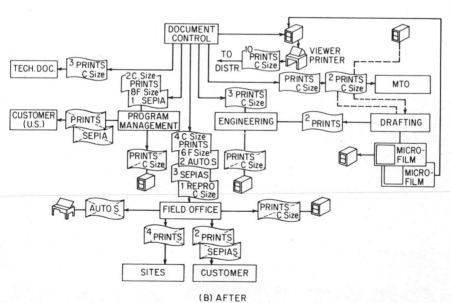

(B) AFTER

Fig. 18-11 Ending nonproductive costs (handling and reproduction of drawings). (A) Before: From the functional analysis sheet it was determined that the cost of the required number of full-size (F-size) prints represented the greatest area of unnecessary costs and that too much storage space for drawings was being used at the home office. (B) After: $80,000 reduction of costs. More microfilm and half-size (C-size) drawings were used. The number of full-size prints was greatly reduced. Making, shipping, and storing the half-size prints all contributed substantially to reduction of costs. Additional equipment required was factored into costs before determining the reduction amount.

dustry service and fee patterns of being required to expand their services to save large unnecessary costs to owners. Some of this reduction of costs must be paid to cover the cost of the new service and the proper profit on the service. As illustrated in this chapter, the lowered costs are a "something for something" matter. Extra people were given extra training and worked extra time to "dig out" the unobvious, which normally saves the owner from five to twenty-five times this extra cost. Business arrangements are being developed that properly pay for this essential added work.

3. Because this extra contribution has not and could not be made in the offices of the architect and engineer in the past, large amounts of unnecessary costs are mandated by the final drawings and specifications. Some of these costs can be retrieved in the construction stage if the extra talent, know-how, and cost are provided. Again, the return is often from five to twenty-five or more times the cost. Therefore, means must be and are being provided to deduct from savings the proper expense and profit for this extra contribution.

4. Taking steps to change outmoded building codes and standards takes effort, time, and money, but the use of today's materials and practices yields so much benefit to builders, owners, and society that we will see better programs reaching essential objectives sooner.

18-8 *Where Effective Work Must Be Done*

Work must be done in the decision-making area, which is responsible for the choice of shapes, materials, methods, and processes used in construction.

Figure 18-12 shows the breakdown of costs under the life-cycle cost concept and the distribution of total costs for a typical facility. Note that only approximately 5 per cent goes for engineering yet the decisions made in engineering will either cause or prevent large expenditures made later in the construction work (expenditures much greater than the total 5 per cent fee).

18-9 *Some Factors That Require Search, Inputs, and Investigation*

In regard to factors needing further study, Professional Engineer Alphonse J. Dell'isola has stated:

> Using VE methods, this optimization of costs is attempted by the systematic development of alternate proposals covering isolated high cost

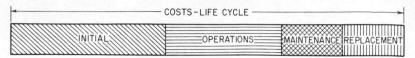

(A) TOTAL COST CONCEPT

(B) TOTAL COST DISTRIBUTION

Fig. 18-12   Total cost concept and total cost distribution of a typical facility. (A) Total cost concept: Typical cost breakdown for a facilities construction. (B) Typical cost distribution for a facilities construction.

areas. During these efforts a number of factors are involved. A listing of some of the principal factors indicates the complexity of the problem and the amount of effort required to arrive at meaningful decision. Each factor requires investigation and evaluation, and input from various sources.

1. Availability of required design data.

2. Initial and installation costs.

3. Maintenance requirements.

4. Source of required material and availability.

5. Prime and/or sub-contractors' reaction and know-how.

6. Conformance to a standard.

7. If standards are not applicable, existence of sufficient data to develop standards.

8. Impact on design. For example, marginal subgrade conditions requiring special treatment.

9. Impact on other necessary requirements, e.g., safety, land use, etc.

... Teams seek to arrive at decisions by using creative problem solving techniques on a formal, organized basis. A group of multi-disciplined trained, personnel are gathered together, and an organized effort made to bring out their latent creative ability. Various high cost areas of a design are challenged by the group and many ideas are generated for alternate solutions. More and better ideas are generated by this approach than by any single individual or by a group not trained in creative problem solving techniques. In addition, one of the principal causes of unnecessary costs, lack of communication amongst specialists, is overcome. The use of a multi-disciplined team approach to decision making is the real core of the VE approach.

Lastly, incentive contracting principles are being used to inspire better, more economical decisions by designers and to enlist the support of contractors—and, to reward them with extra profit for worthwhile proposals.[3]

18-10   *Some Typical Changes*

Component	Original concept	Proposed change	Estimated savings
Structural system foundation and 1st floor	Concrete beam and girder with 4 in. concrete floor slab poured in place	1. Use composite steel deck forms—thicken slab to 6½ in.; eliminate every other beam	$ 34,600
		2. Use reinforced CMU foundation walls around crawl space	39,200
Mechanical system (heating, ventilating, and air-conditioning)	Specified 5-multizone air handling units, with 47 mixing boxes	3. Use 50 Zone Fan coil units with FA and steam coils	128,700
	Hot and cold over and under ducts same size	4. Redesign ducts in accordance with actual loads approx. ratio 4 to 1	25,600
	Use 800 fm for design air velocity in ducts	5. Changed design to use 1,200 fm max. velocity of design criteria	16,900
	Rounded off air exhaust requirements to high side of each room	6. Used exact calculation to determine air-conditioning load (7 tons less)	6,000
Roofing system	Use of an elastomeric system over metal deck with insulation slope 1 in. to the foot (no guarantee available)	7. Use of conventional built-up roofing with nailers as required by initial criteria	26,300
		8. Request waiver on use of nailers—new revised criteria do not require nailers for 1 in. slope. (Use steep slope asphalt)	3,500
Total..........	....	....	$280,800

[3]*Roads and Streets*, January, 1970.

18-11   *Typical Summary Sheet—*
Work Based upon Final Design

The initial cost estimate of the total project was $3,300,000.

Description	Potential contract savings based on team recommendations	Additional life-cycle cost savings
Architectural, civil, and structural:		
Foundations...................................	$ 39,985	
Precast stone, fixed glass filler wall...............	184,661	$414,960
Concrete strength and column sizes...............	14,470	
Floor system..................................	59,649	
Vibration isolation............................	25,000	
Mechanical:		
Utility tunnel................................	46,330	57,880
Heating, ventilating, and air-conditioning systems...	219,970	161,300
Mechanical room relocation.....................	75,219	
Plumbing and domestic water supply.............	3,674	12,040
Vertical transportation (elevators)...............	21,000	
Electrical:		
Feeder cables.................................	9,416	
Branch circuit wiring and elimination of separate neutral.......................................	13,340	
Underfloor duct and related cost.................	55,000	
Total.....................................	$767,714	$646,180

chapter 19

Problems for Assignment

In order to help the reader supplement his acquisition of value analysis knowledge a number of problems from actual practice are offered in the following "do-it-yourself" exercises. It should be noted that these problems are all limited to individual parts or components rather than to inclusive assemblies. This is intentional because students can hardly be expected to devote as much time to problem solving as exercises on a series of complete products would require.

19-1 Procedure for Using the Problems

1. Make your plan for the problem.
2. Follow through each of the steps of the job plan.
3. Fill in some typical information that you have learned or have developed in each phase of the plan.
4. Fill in some typical information that you might learn or have developed by using each of the techniques.
5. Arrive at one or two suggested value alternatives that you believe may be quite good.
6. Prepare an appropriate suggestion sheet.

There are no "pat" solutions to these problems; however, one answer for each problem which met the need at the time is included in the Appendix. *Do not necessarily duplicate the part, but achieve the desired function more economically.*

19-2 *Problems*

Fig. 19-1

1. Special brass nut. Double thread, ½ inch square; made on automatic screw machine; 1 million per year; 3 cents each. Nut receives hand adjustment screw on electric blanket thermostat.

Fig. 19-2

2. Steel control shaft. ¼ inch in diameter, 1¼ inches long; made on automatic screw machine; 1 million per year; 6 cents each. One end screws into brass nut above, other end mounts plastic knob. Center groove provides adjustment for the thermostat.

Fig. 19-3

3. Stainless-steel fastening screw. 1¼ inches long; made from ½-inch diameter stainless steel on automatic screw machine; contains shoulder and undercut section; 40,000 per year; 90 cents each. Used on panels of electronic equipment.

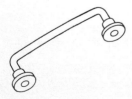

Fig. 19-4

4. Handle. Made from ¼-inch aluminum; 4-inch centers; threaded aluminum collars at each end form method of mounting; 4,000 per year; $1.40 each. Used for convenient handling of electronic equipment when it is out of master panel.

Fig. 19-5

5. *Toggle link.* 1½ inches long; other dimensions in proportion; made as steel forging with later machining; 25,000 per year; 50 cents each. Used in electronic equipment mounted in cabinet.

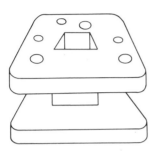

Fig. 19-6

6. *Plastic coil form.* About 1 inch square by ½ inch long; molded, then finish-machined; 15,000 per year; 40 cents each. Mounts coil in electronic control equipment.

Fig. 19-7

7. *Control gear.* Turned, machined, and hobbed from bar steel; approximately 4 inches in diameter, ¼ inch thick; hub ½ inch thick; 600 per year; $8 each. Slow-speed gear used in adjustment of electrical equipment; mounted inside enclosure.

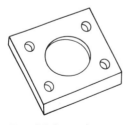

Fig. 19-8

8. *Hydraulic cylinder cap.* Made from ⅜-inch-thick steel; 3 inches square; 1-inch blind hole drilled ¼ inch deep in center and four small mounting holes drilled in corners; 2,000 per year; 53 cents each. Used inside machine.

Fig. 19-9

9. *Adjustment screw.* ¼ inch in diameter; made from brass bar by automatic screw machine; 200,000 per year; 1 cent each. Used in electronic control equipment.

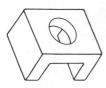

Fig. 19-10

10. Brass terminal clamp. Made by fabrication from brass extrusion, approximately ½ inch long, ¼ inch wide, ¼ inch high; is mechanical part that does not conduct current; 400,000 per year; 7 cents each. Used inside electrical control box.

Fig. 19-11

11. Strain bolt assembly. 1 foot long; consists of machined iron casting threaded with suitable bushings and nuts; made of steel; 5,000 per year; $3.50 each. Used out of doors to support wires and cables.

Fig. 19-12

12. Counterweight balance. Steel; cut from ring of ⅛-inch steel, 1 inch across; each segment mounts on two studs; pieces approximately 3 inches long; 5,000 per year; 40 cents each. Mounts on large ring for counterbalance purposes.

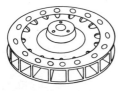

Fig. 19-13

13. Fan. 15 inches in diameter; cast and machined from malleable iron; punched steel ring riveted to one side of blades; blade about 2 inches thick, hub about 3 inches thick; 1,600 per year; $17 each. Used for cooling air inside large electric motor.

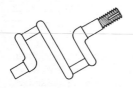

Fig. 19-14

14. Small crankshaft for air compressor. 7 inches long for two connecting rods; forged and machined; 9,000 per year; $5 each.

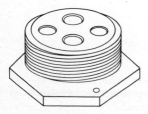

Fig. 19-15

15. Brass heater plug. Machined from hex bar 1½ inches across flats; approximately ½ inch thick; 10,000 per year; 80 cents each. Mounts Calrod heaters into furnace equipment.

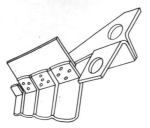

Fig. 19-16

16. Fan-blade assembly. Approximately 1 × 2-foot composite of three pieces of metal and one of plastic; 3,000 per year; $7 each. Function is to clamp on large revolving ring in electric generator and deflect air.

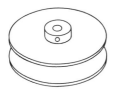

Fig. 19-17

17. Steel pulley. Machined from 6-inch steel rod; 150 per year; $30 each. Used on machines in factory.

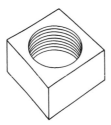

Fig. 19-18

18. Plastic nut. Machined from ½-inch-thick plastic sheet; 1½ inches square, ½-inch hole drilled and tapped; 25,000 per year; 13 cents each. Used in electrical equipment.

Fig. 19-19

19. Bronze arcing horn. 15 inches long by 2 inches wide; fabricated from formed sheet brass by brazing; other dimensions approximately as illustrated; 3,000 per year; $6.50 each. Function is to cool an arc so it will extinguish.

Fig. 19-20

20. Cover fastener. Steel, 4-inch shank mounted in steel U strap; 4,000 per year; 45 cents each. Function is to secure cover on industrial equipment.

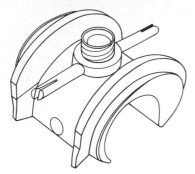

Fig. 19-21

21. Insert for coil-making machine. Machined from steel block about 3 inches long by 2½ inches wide by 2 inches deep; 500 per year; $80 each.

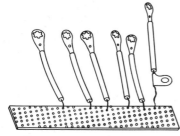

Fig. 19-22

22. Tapped resistor assembly. Made in factory assembly department; 300 per year; $7.50 each. Used in electrical instrument.

Fig. 19-23

23. Porcelain cap. 3-inch inside diameter, 2-inch inside height; 150,000 per year; 40 cents each. For weather protection, outdoor switch gear.

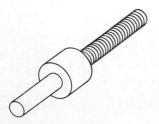

Fig. 19-24

24. Stud pin. Galvanized-steel screw with stainless-steel insert pin; over-all length, 3 inches; 50,000 per year; 25 cents each. For outdoor use on electrical equipment.

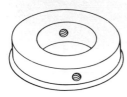

Fig. 19-25

25. Flange. Made from steel bar by machining and turning flange, drilling and tapping two mounting holes; 1,500 per year; $1 each. Function is to hold a Calrod heater loosely through a 2-inch diameter hole in the side of an electric furnace.

Appendix

A-1   *Problem Solutions*

Solutions of the student that provide all of the use and aesthetic functions that the customer wants and are lower in cost than those that follow are better solutions. The following are provided as a guide and to add a variety of realistic approaches from experience.

Fig. 19-1   Supplier, using his specialized nylon casting process, made the nut ready to use for 0.7 cents. In use it was a little better than the brass nut because it tended to grip the screw and hold adjustment. Annual cost dropped from $30,000 to $7,000.

Fig. A-1

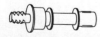

Fig. 19-2   Supplier, using his specialized Zinc casting process with high-speed single-cavity molds, cast the part ready to use for 2 cents. Mold and tooling costs were less than $1,000. Annual cost dropped from $60,000 to $20,000.

Fig. A-2

Fig. 19-3   Specialty supplier with cold-heading equipment made a part of stainless steel that was both equally useful and attractive for 15 cents. The supplier rolled the threads. Tooling costs were negligible. Annual costs were reduced from $36,000 to $6,000.

Fig. A-3

Fig. 19-4   Design was changed to eliminate hubs, which made it a three-piece assembly. Still made of ¼-inch aluminium wire, ends were bent out, flattened, and hole-punched. A supplier specializing in parts that could be made from wire assisted. Costs were reduced from $1.40 to 40 cents. Tooling from the vendor was no separate charge. Reduced annual costs were $4,000.

Fig. 19-5   Change was made from machined forging to casting. It was found that the specified costly heat treatment made no contribution to function, and so it was ended. Cost became 25 cents; $6,000 per year of cost was saved.

Fig. 19-6   Specialty supplier made injection-molded nylon-coil form ready to use. Cost became 3 cents. All use and aesthetic functions were fully provided. A yearly cost of $6,000 became $450.

Fig. 19-7   Change was made to powdered metal. The gear was bought from a specialty vendor ready to use. Tooling cost $900; gear cost 80 cents. Unnecessary cost removed approximately $4,000 per year.

Fig. 19-8   Instead of starting with ⅜-inch-thick steel and then cutting a blind ¼ inch deep partway through the hole, ⅛-inch steel was used and formed to provide the clearance space (instead of drilling). Tooling cost $600. Parts cost 18 cents each, reducing costs 35 cents each on 2,000 per year.

Fig. 19-9   Specialty supplier submitted a proposal to make this on his cold-heading and roll-threading equipment at a cost of 3 cents. No tool cost was necessary. Use and aesthetic functions were suitable, and the change was made, reducing cost 7 cents each on 200,000 screws.

Fig. 19-10   A change was made to miniature zinc die casting by a specialty supplier of miniature items. Tools cost $400. Cost became 2 cents each, $20,000 annual cost reduction.

Fig. A-4

Fig. 19-11   A change was made to fabrication, ending much machine work. It provided all of the same functions. Cost was $1.25 each, reducing costs by $11,000 per year.

Fig. 19-12   Checking into the need for the function as specified, it was found that the function of counterweight was as well performed by rectangular metal pieces as by the specified segments of the circular flange. The function then was served by shearing and piercing a straight piece of bar stock. Cost became 4 cents. Costs were lowered 90 per cent, or $1,800 per year.

Fig 19-13   Aluminium-casting supplier examined the functions required and said he could provide them in a one-piece aluminium sand casting. He did so, and costs were lowered to $10.50 each, totaling $10,000 per year.

Fig. 19-14 Using the results accelerator "Would I spend my money this way?" the analyst reasoned that millions of crankshafts are made each year in all sizes and descriptions for diverse large-volume equipment. Inquiries into the purchasing area of the automobile industry brought information about some suppliers with highly specialized equipment for making crankshafts. Cost from them became $2, meaning a $27,000 annual reduction in costs with no other changes.

Fig. 19-15 Interchangeable part with identical functioning properties was provided by a specialty supplier from his equipment for shell-molding brass. Cost became 25 cents, providing lowered costs of $5,000 per year.

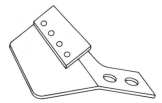

Fig. 19-16 Function of the air deflector and its parts was studied. An alternative design was provided, which was two pieces with four rivets instead of three pieces with thirteen rivets. In tests performance proved to be identical. Cost became $2. Annual cost was lowered by $15,000.

Fig. A-5

Fig. 19-17 Pulley was self-made in the factory because a finer adjustment and more holding power were needed, as compared with the commercially available pulleys. Instead of machining from bar stock, the available pulley of a pulley supplier was bought for $1.90. More tapped holes and an extra setscrew were added. Cost became $4, providing a reduction of $26 each on 150 pulleys per year.

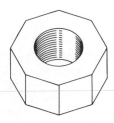

Fig. 19-18 Although the method of making 25,000 of the plastic nuts seemed simple and efficient, suppliers of specialty products were searched. It was found that a standard molded nut from the identical plastics material was available at cost of 7 cents. Costs were reduced $1,500 per year.

Fig. A-6

Fig. 19-19 Specialty-process supplier submitted a proposition to shell-mold this arcing horn in bronze. He would make an identical, interchangeable part at a cost of $2,000 for tools and then $2.25 each. This reduced costs $10,000 to $12,000 per year.

Fig. 19-20 Total function was achieved with a simpler construction. Two parts were used instead of four. A simple eyebolt and U-bolt assembly were welded to the equipment. Costs became 10 cents, with $1,400 per year lowered costs.

Fig. A-7

Fig. 19-21 Specialty-process supplier provided investment casting for $12. Machining work cost $14, reducing costs from $80 to $26 for 500 per year.

Fig. 19-22 Specialty-product vendor in the resistor business was asked to suggest and quote on this special need. For the identical specification, tolerances, etc., he quoted 90 cents, reducing costs by $1,900 per year for the quantity of 300.

Fig. A-8

Fig. 19-23 Functions were totally supplied by a vendor of glass-reinforced plastics who provided a molded cap. By providing a lip to cover the lead wire, he was able to accomplish the complete function with a smaller part. Costs became 25 cents, reducing annual costs by $22,000.

Fig. 19-24 Improved design was made by using the cold-headed process, making it all out of one piece of stainless steel. It was an interchangeable but better-quality part. Cost became 12 cents, reducing the annual cost by $6,500.

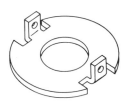

Fig. A-9

Fig. 19-25 The flange was judged to be an overheavy, overcostly construction to loosely secure a light part in the furnace. The flange used would perform the function "hold heavy weight," but the part held (Calrod heater) was light. Also, it would perform the function "tightly enclose," but other parts were "loose." Neither of these functions contributed to customer needs or wants. The part was fabricated from thin steel, basically a circle with two drilled and tapped ears, at a cost of 10 cents. Reduction was 90 cents each, 90 per cent.

A-2 Bibliography

Annual Proceedings of Society of American Value Engineers, 2550 Hargrove Drive, L-205, Smyrna, Ga. 30080. Beginning with vol. I in 1966, these are superior.

Annual Value Analysis/Engineering issue of *Purchasing Magazine* (usually June or July) by Conover-Mast Div. of Cahners Publishing Co. Inc., 205 East 42d St., New York, N.Y. 10017. Beginning in the 1950s these bear upon the use of the system in purchasing work quite effectively.

Bibliography of Value Analysis and Engineering, issued by the Society of American Value Engineers (listed above) and edited by Robert L. Crouse, former president This listing is very complete and very good. It would therefore seem redundant to make extensive listings here.

Dell'Isola, A. J., *Guide for the Application of Value Engineering to the Construction Industry,* 1971, in loose-leaf form available from McKee-Berger-Mansueto, Inc., Construction Consultants, 2 Park Avenue, New York, N.Y. 10007.

Fallon, Carlos: *Value Analysis to Increase Productivity,* John Wiley & Sons, Inc., New York, 1971.

Gage, W. L.: *Value Analysis,* The Polytechnic School of Management Studies, McGraw-Hill Publishing Company, Ltd., London, 1968.

Heller, Edward D.: *Value Management: Value Engineering and Cost Reduction,* Addison-Wesley Publishing Company, Inc., Reading, Mass., 1971.

Mudge, Arthur: *Value Engineering*, McGraw-Hill Book Company, New York, 1971.
Ollner, Jan: *Funktions Kostnads Analys*, Sveriges Mekanförbund, Stockholm, 1967 (in Swedish).
Olsson, Erik, and Ulf Perning: *Värdeanalysis*, Bokförlaget Prisma, Stockholm, 1970.

A-3   Good "Make-or-Buy" Criteria—"Creep"

The following article by Accountant Robert L. Dixon sets forth vital and too-often unassessed truths, which are as pertinent in the 1970s as in the 1950s. In fact, they are essential to earnings-producing decisions in the "make-or-buy" area.

CREEP[1]

Robert L. Dixon, Ph.D., CPA
PROFESSOR OF ACCOUNTING
UNIVERSITY OF MICHIGAN

Creep occurs when a business moves, slowly or speedily, into areas not fully explored. When this happens, a lot of problems arise. Do you want the enterprise to creep away from its original purpose or size? Have you set up your organization, control facilities, records, to enable you to deal with the spontaneous new creature your company can come to be? Creep is almost always found in successful companies, though it is sometimes the cause of failure. The accountant is the best, often the only, person able to detect creep; he may be the person to deal with the problems created.

A business enterprise, typically, is established for a limited purpose, such as the production of a single product or product group, the production of services, or the marketing of certain products. Usually this newly-established enterprise is simple in form, with specialized objectives. The profit motive leads to its creation, and it is expected that profit will be realized through pursuit of this specialized activity.

The case histories of some of the larger corporations, on the other hand, would undoubtedly show that a considerable proliferation of activities accompanies the aging process.

The addition of new activities to the one of initial specialization appears in various ways. Commonly it will appear in the form of integration through taking on the production of component parts formerly delegated to outsiders, or through extending back to the production of raw materials for use in the plant. The sales organization may be expanded to include wholesaling activities and may even be extended forward to include ownership and operation of retail outlets. This process may at the same time be accompanied by a horizontal expansion of activities in which an array of new products is added to the original specialty. In fact, the expansion, diversification, and proliferation may reach the stage where the original

[1] *The Journal of Accountancy*, July, 1953.

objective, through the multiplication of side activities, has become an obscure element in the total activity of the corporation.

Going along with this expansion process one is likely to find another, less spectacular but none the less significant, factor leading to the variegation of enterprise activity. This is the piecemeal attachment of relatively minor activities of service and supply. Examples of this are the establishment of a department for the production of tools; a department for the maintenance of machinery and electrical equipment; a department to service company-owned trucks and automobiles; an engineering department; a legal department; a carpentry and upholstering shop; a printing shop, and so on.

In many instances these accouterments are not added full grown as the result of a formal analysis and decision, but rather they edge into the picture, starting with the incidental, part-time activity of one or more employees, but ending up later as full-fledged departments of the plant.

In other instances these added activities are undertaken because *they seem to offer cost-saving opportunities*. The reasoning is somewhat as follows: because we have an established plant and organization an important portion of our costs is pretty well fixed; these costs will go on at approximately the same level whether our plant is fully or only partially used; it follows then that we can add odd jobs here and there, call them sideline or self-service activities, *without causing increases in these fixed costs*. In fact, in order to determine whether we should provide our own services and supplies in a particular case, we need consider only the *variable* costs of our existing organization, the variable costs of the added activity and, in cases where new equipment and new permanent personnel are required, certain added fixed costs. But the bulk of the fixed costs can be ignored since they will not be affected by the attachment of the additional operation. In many cases when the addition of a new activity is being considered, the management may go as far as to exclude overhead costs altogether in the computation of the costs to be added. They reason that addition of new activity should not relieve the old activities of any overhead costs.

Under the circumstances of this kind of cost calculation few vendor bids may hope to be successful, since by the self-service activity not only are the middlemen's profits and the distribution costs eliminated, but also the outside producer's profits, and even, in a sense, the producer's fixed costs. In fact, the situation practically offers a bonanza for the manufacturer. The added activities appear to be real bargains.

We are all aware of the advertising slogan, "Direct from the factory to you," but here we are able to go one step farther, in effect bringing the factory right into the home.

In some cases the opportunity for cost saving is so obvious that the self-service activity is allowed to develop, or is taken over in toto, without any preliminary, formal cost studies.

But in other cases the margin of saving may not be so obvious, and the cost accountant may prepare detailed cost studies. In these, if he follows the more orthodox theory, his report will be based on the estimated *incremental* costs, rather than the total costs, of the added activity.

Creep Factors

It was noted above that minor side activities tend in some cases to edge into the operations of a business firm where no special thought has been given to their short-run or long-run effects upon costs and efficiency; it is also true, however, that such activities are frequently added by positive action on the basis of cost studies.

Attention is directed to the proposed exclusion of fixed costs in the decision-making process. Certain observations with respect to this exclusion appear to be in order.

First, if the company is in a position to make permanent additions to its side activities without adding to its fixed costs, something must be out of order. Fixed costs reflect *capacity* to operate, and they appear throughout the entire business organization. Evidently if the fixed costs can be ignored in such a calculation, the company is overequipped and overstaffed for its regular work.

Second, although it is probably impossible to have a condition of absolute balance of staff and equipment throughout the organization, the situation would be rare in which the added activity can be imposed upon the below-capacity segments of the company without in any way impinging on the fully active segments.

Third, equipment to some extent, and human beings to a considerable extent, are capable of being pressed beyond capacity limits for periods of time, but beyond these time limits something must be done to relieve them.

Finally, if idle capacity does temporarily exist throughout the company, the addition of *extracurricular* activities may so pre-empt that available time that it will be difficult to re-establish full-time regular operations when business conditions come back to normal.

All of this means that the fixed costs simply cannot be ignored in making the produce-or-purchase decision, unless one is to be satisfied with a very short-sighted analysis. Fixed costs commensurate with the added activity will inevitably "creep" into the total cost picture, because even though there may be no *immediate* addition to the fixed costs, the added activity will encroach upon the available capacity, and sooner or later this will lead to an actual, though unanticipated and perhaps unrecognized, increase in fixed costs.

The creep effect upon fixed costs can develop in three general ways.

First, if the added activity is allowed to get out of hand in its growth it is obvious that more building space, more equipment, and more salaried personnel must eventually be added. This will be true even though the regular activity of the enterprise is maintained at a fairly fixed level. The question then is, would we have added this activity had we anticipated the fixed cost addition?

Second, even if the added activity is kept at a moderate level, when the main activity is increased fixed-cost increases will again be encountered.

Thus, suppose a dozen men and some equipment are added in order that the company can repair its own transportation equipment. This may lead to no immediate addition of employees in the personnel department, the accounting department, or in the other administrative segments of the company; however, the later addition of one person to regular activities can bring into operation a chain of reactions in the form of salaried employee increases, salary increases, and fixed asset additions. The probabilities are that no one will recognize that the factor which really caused the fixed cost increases was the apparently bargain-price addition of the repair operations sometime earlier.

Finally, if the added activity is either kept level, or increased, it will be all the more difficult to cut down on fixed costs should subsequent reductions in the regular operations be necessary.

Side Effects of Creep

The principal aim in the section just concluded was to point out that the exclusion of fixed costs in the contemplation of a produce-versus-purchase decision constitutes a dangerously shortsighted treatment of the problem; that a full quota of fixed costs will almost inevitably creep into the picture regardless of the subsequent activity trends of the regular and added operations.

What might be called a side effect of creep, although it is actually a direct evidence of creep, is a tendency for the company to compensate unconsciously for overloads resulting from piecemeal additions of "bargain" activities. If, for example, an officer is hired to perform an administrative task under a particular set of conditions, and if then one by one a number of minor, peripheral activities are taken on by the company, the accumulation of these activities may more and more infringe upon the officer's time until through sheer necessity he is forced drastically to neglect his primary responsibilities.

Although no poll of managements has been taken on this point, it is suspected that they are not immune from creep, and one may well wonder if business efficiency and competitive vigor are not often impaired through the accumulation of these barnacles which appear to be bargain activities; in other words, activities which *apparently* do not add to the fixed costs.

Arguments Against Bargain Activities

At this point it may be well, again, to make clear just what sort of activity is being examined. This article does not pretend to weigh the wisdom of a decision to produce rather than purchase where the decision rests primarily (1) upon a question of public relations, or (2) on the basis of guaranteeing adequate supply when needed, or (3) on safeguarding quality, or (4) even decisions to produce rather than purchase during periods of depressed business conditions where the aim is to keep the working-force intact and to minimize idle capacity losses. Also it is recognized that new lines of production may properly be undertaken, and old ones dropped, in order to keep pace with changing market conditions. Rather, this is an appraisal of the wisdom of adding an activity, formerly provided by an outsider, on the basis of cost studies which appear to justify the added activity on the ground that fixed costs can be ignored.

The theme of this article is that a major danger in the addition of bargain activities is the creep danger. And this danger is likely to be overlooked in the case of any added activity, whether or not cost saving is the prime motive. In fact it is all the more likely to be overlooked where factors other than cost saving guide the decision.

Another type of danger lies in the fact that the company is not a specialist in the added activity, and that after it has become tied to it, with added personnel and equipment, the discontinued vendor may through research develop cost and sales price reductions which make the decision to produce completely untenable when looked upon with hindsight. Then it may be too late. Reversion to the purchase status is then blocked by prospective sacrifices in the disposal of equipment and the need for discharging personnel.

Public relations may constitute an argument on each side of the question. For instance, an entirely unsupportable contention may be made, particularly in the smaller community, that the local manufacturer should make himself as nearly autonomous as possible, since this means that he will thereby provide more jobs for local labor. Needless to say this is pure bunk. It is a form of disguised charity without the slightest scientific justification.

From the opposite point of view, it is evident that the maintenance of good public relations may actually dictate the avoidance of certain productive activities simply because the good will of the community compels the patronizing of small business firm suppliers.

From the economist's point of view, and unfortunately this argument is not likely to be very compelling with individual businessmen, it may be argued quite conclusively that a decision to produce, when based on a partial cost compilation (that is, with fixed costs excluded), is contrary to the public economic interest. In short, it constitutes mismanagement of economic resources. Just realize that the vendor's price, against which is being matched only a partial summation of costs, is high enough for him to cover not only his variable costs, but also fixed costs, and a profit margin on top of it all. If the vendor's offer, under this assumption, comes within gunshot of meeting the purchaser's variable cost computation, we are doing serious injury to our economic system if we make a decision to produce rather than buy from that vendor.

Another observation is this: activities are usually annexed, with cost saving as the reason, only when they are more or less intimately related to the primary functions of the company. Actually, however, it might be more reasonable, from the standpoint of impact on total profits, to take on completely extraneous operations—again with the assumption that the fixed-cost factor need not be a matter of concern. Thus, the automobile company might just as reasonably open a public restaurant, a dance hall, or a bowling alley, confident that the present executives can soak up such minor administrative burdens as would be involved, and that thereby they have an edge over existing recreational establishments which require a full complement of personnel.

Creep Avoidance

As has been mentioned earlier, some activities are added with clear recognition that no cost saving is attainable, simply because certain non-cost factors are of pressing importance. Others, the ones under consideration here, are annexed because, with fixed costs ignored, bargain rates appear to be achieved. Both kinds cause fixed cost pressures, and lead to unanticipated cost increases—although they may not be recognized in some cases until years later. The important question is then, having brought the nature of creep into the open, what can be done to avoid it?

Among a number of defensive measures undoubtedly existing, four will be suggested here.

First, in the company's organization chart make notations of the number of individuals in each department or other subdivision of the company. From these notations calculate a series of ratios which may be called responsibility indexes. Thus, calculate the ratio of productive and non-productive employees to foremen in each of the productive and service departments of the plant; then, the ratio of foremen to plant manager or other personnel at the level above foremen. Similarly compute such ratios of responsibility through to top management, in each case using as the numerator of the ratio the number of persons who *report*, or for whom the person reported to is responsible.

Since the number of reporting persons will fluctuate, particularly at the lower levels of the organization, as productive activity fluctuates some judgment must be exercised in establishing certain of the ratios. Whether to use average ratios or ratios to reflect capacity might be debated; however, for present purposes it would seem that the ratios should be computed on a capacity basis. If, for example, the planned description of a given supervisory job is that it shall involve responsibility for receiving and analyzing reports from five persons, or responsibility for supervising the productive activities of twenty-five persons, any contemplation of additional activities should include recognition of probable immediate as well as long-run effects on the responsibility ratios. So far as possible this change should be taken into consideration in arriving at a decision.

A second safeguard in the insurance against creep consists of the exercise of caution that the comparative statement of costs is complete and correct. The costs of purchased supplies, services, etc., are likely to be compiled fairly completely, including an allowance for freight, handling, purchasing, and other incidents of the purchase. Certainly there is no justification for excluding, or overlooking, similar costs which will be incurred if the decision goes in favor of production rather than purchase. Interest on the additional investment should not be overlooked. If the question is one of production of component parts, the acquisition of raw materials is likely to cause a set of costs similar to those incurred in the purchasing of finished parts. A real risk is the likelihood of understanding even the immediate costs of production.

A third factor to be considered in determining the advisability of adding a new activity is the relative merit of that particular activity as compared with alternatives. It would obviously be illogical to devote available equipment and energies to an operation which would provide a cost saving of a few hundred dollars when the same facilities, otherwise used, could accomplish savings of thousands. Even more foolish would be the addition of an activity of the minor cost-saving variety which might interfere with, or preclude, the later expansion of the company's main operations at a profit in excess of the expected cost-saving. Mistaken decisions of this sort constitute a principal creep danger, leading to a condition of overcrowded facilities and neglected responsibilities.

Creep, as has been emphasized, is not a short-run problem. It consists of the more or less gradual, unrecognized, cluttering up of business activity, accompanied by a parallel deterioration of company efficiency, a building up of fixed costs, and the undermining of profit potential. A fourth factor in the protection against creep is that of flexibility. New activities which are clearly temporary, which can be added and discarded on short notice without significant disruption, are much less likely to cause future trouble than are those which are less flexible. It is pretty well agreed that it is more difficult to dislodge an activity than it is to add one. For the classic object lesson on this point, consider the bureaus of our federal and state governments. But, if an addition is to be made, at least as between two alternative activities which are otherwise equally attractive, the one which can later be abandoned the more easily is certainly the one to be chosen. It is therefore suggested that, among other things, serious consideration be given to the degree of permanence of any new plant, equipment, and, especially, personnel, which may be required in undertaking an added activity.

If careful analysis indicates that the proposed activity meets the test of flexibility—that is, if it can be dropped on short notice without serious sacrifice of personnel or of investment in inventories and fixed assets—and if the contemplated addition is purely and unquestionably for a short-run period, then a "partial costs" schedule is appropriate. In other words, under these circumstances it *is proper* to prepare a schedule which is limited to the incremental costs, *the costs which would be added,* and to ignore prorations of existing fixed overhead items. Because of the importance of situations of this class, the point will be considered further under the next section heading.

If, on the other hand, it is contemplated that the new activity may be more or less permanently attached, as where the company will take on its own full-scale printing operations, its own engineering, or toolmaking, or component parts supply, a partial costs schedule is entirely inappropriate. In fact, this point is the crux of the whole situation. For purposes of making the decision to add an activity which may be fairly permanent, the schedule of estimated costs of production should include not only an exhaustive list of the probable added costs, but also a complete assignment of all of the overhead charges, even including administrative overhead, which through regular cost accounting techniques are properly prorated against any regular segment of the enterprise.

Add Allowance for Profit

But this is not all. In addition to the full charge for prorated and added costs, an allowance should be added for profit. That is, in order to justify the addition of a permanent new activity on the grounds of cost savings, the best available supplier's price must be shown not only to exceed the estimated full cost of production, with no apportionable costs omitted, but it should be higher *by an amount at least equal to the rate of profit which the company is able to make through its principal operations.*

The reasons for this fairly extreme view have been expressed earlier in this article, and it should be repeated that the requirement that full costs plus profit be included is, in fact, no more than a minimum protection against creep. Clearly the relationship between today's costs and today's purchase prices may be only a temporary one, and it is altogether too probable that the nonspecialist producer will lag behind the specialist supplier whom he has discarded in the hope of achieving production economies. Thus, the decision can easily turn sour in spite of all of the measures which have been suggested by way of protection.

Justifiable Bargain Activities

It was stated above that where the added activity is clearly intended to be temporary it is proper to base the decision on a partial list of costs. The point here is that the nonpermanence of the activity tends to insure against the creeping up of fixed costs and managerial overloads. However, resolutions are too often forgotten, and unless positive plans are made in advance for the early abandonment of the activity, it will turn out to be a "sticky," if not permanent, activity, and the fixed costs will flow in to fill up the gaps in the cost analysis.

One form of added activity which, for example, may well be justifiable is that which can be started and stopped repeatedly to serve as fill-in work during periods of temporary lull in the principal activity of the company. Such fill-in work may even extend as long as the depression period of a business cycle, provided it can be stopped conveniently at the time of resumption of normal operations. Under such circumstances the presumption is that the regular working-force should be maintained and, from the cost point of view, the recovery of any portion of costs in excess of variable costs is preferable to their nonrecovery.

One may also justify the addition of activities on a partial cost, or bargain basis, when it is evident that substantial cost reductions will be achieved after a period of experience. In fact, costs during the initial period may be so unrepresentative of the future that they may in effect be disregarded.

Also, where a company is chronically operating below capacity, and has found itself absolutely unable to expand its market, there is justification for taking over certain activities of its suppliers, provided that an already unfavorable position is not further weakened, and provided that existing fixed costs cannot be cut down to a level commensurate with existing activity. Again, however, it should be emphasized that the company should not take over "just any old activity" in which its variable costs will be less than the best outside price. A very careful survey of all opportunities for cost saving should be made before any is chosen.

Elimination of Creep

Assuming that one has already suffered a good case of creep, what steps can be taken to cure the situation? Can we apply the same tests in deciding upon the elimination of activities that we use when consideration is being given to the addition of such activities? Are the same tests applicable in reverse?

Obviously a fringe activity should not be eliminated if the potential cost of acquiring the supplies, services, etc., from outsiders is so far in excess of the costs of self-service that over-all profits would thereby be diminished. But, in exploring this possibility, what costs of production should be included?

It was pointed out above that perhaps the most potent defense against creep is a requirement that outside suppliers be used, in the case of any relatively permanent program, unless it can be proved that their offering prices are higher than the buyer's total costs plus a margin of profit. Does this mean that an existing activity should be dropped in favor of outside supply if it is found that the existing activity when charged with full costs would not show profit if it were given credit for its output at regular market prices?

In general the answer would appear to be *yes,* although subject to one exception. The rule may be expressed somewhat as follows: A company should divest itself of any activity which has been undertaken because of its cost-saving potential if such activity would not be added under the suggested rules for the prevention of creep. The only exception is this: If specialized machinery, equipment, housing, or other specialized fixed assets have been purchased, and are of such nature that they have no alternative full use, the depreciation and other non-separable costs of such assets can be eliminated from the calculation except to the extent that the assets have a significant present market value. In other words, the cost of such assets is "sunk"; to the extent that such cost cannot be retrieved by sale or through other employment in the business, the cost may be said already to be invested in future production of the related product, and the sacrifice cannot, therefore, be avoided by the discontinuance of the activity. If, with depreciation of specialized assets modified or eliminated, it is found that a given activity, when charged with all costs usually prorated to a routine operation and "loaded" with a profit margin, is not able to compete with the price of comparable service as offered by outside suppliers, the activity should be abandoned.

The term "activity audit" might be adopted to describe a more or less continuous study of the ancillary activities of the business firm for purposes of detecting existing or potential creep.

Summary

A business firm, as it matures, is likely to accumulate an array of productive activities which were never contemplated when the company was founded. Many of these activities are added on a self-service basis as a matter of convenience, or they are added during periods of short supply, or to assure reliable quality, and for other reasons; such activities may well be continued provided that their full costs are adequately recognized and provided that management realizes what cost sacrifices are being made to achieve such convenience, etc. Many other activities, however, may have been taken on solely because of apparent cost savings, and additional activities may from time to time be contemplated. All such activities should be subjected to frequent activity audits to determine whether or not real cost advantages exist. Unless these activities are purely temporary, idle-time fillers, their continuance or addition cannot be justified on the grounds that they need be charged with only a part of the list of costs normally charged to regular, principal operations. This is true because fixed costs commensurate with the activity will inevitably creep into the operating costs structure.

Equally important, though not examined in detail in this article, are the additions of new lines of products which can be demonstrated *to show a profit* only because they are charged with costs on a partial, or incremental, basis. In course of time they too will cause creep.

Added activities, ranging all the way from minor service items to the production and sale of new product lines, not only create fixed costs but also tend to distract operating management from its principal objectives, and it may be no exaggeration to state that many business firms owe to creep not only the decline in their profit rates but also their ultimate failure.

Index

Index